FEASTA *review*

NUMBER 1

edited by RICHARD DOUTHWAITE
and JOHN JOPLING

FEASTA
*the foundation for the
economics of sustainability*

DUBLIN
MMI

First published in Dublin (May 2001) by
FEASTA
the foundation for the economics of sustainability
159, LOWER RATHMINES ROAD, DUBLIN 6
Tel (01) 4912773
e-mail feasta@anu.ie
website www.feasta.org

Distributed in the UK by Green Books Ltd, Foxhole, Dartington, Totnes, Devon TQ9 6EB
Tel (01803) 863 843
e-mail john@greenbooks.co.uk

Feasta is registered as an educational charity Nº13052
(registered office: Crolly's Cottage, Kilcroney, Readypenny, Co. Louth)
It gratefully acknowledges support from the R.H. Southern Trust
and the Polden Puckham Trust.

A CIP record for this
title is available from
The British Library

FEASTA review issn 1649-0568

issue number 1 isbn 0-9540510-0-9

Cover photographs, cover and book design by mermaid turbulence
Set in Garamond Three with Futura titling display and panels
printed in Dublin by Colour Books

contents

FUTURE ENERGY USE

introduction

Two and a half years after its launch in October 1998, it's becoming a little clearer what Feasta is about. At the launch we set ourselves the task of answering a number of questions. Among these were: 'What is it about the existing economic system that causes it to undermine itself? Why, for example, is it widening the gap between rich and poor, both within nations and between them? Why would it collapse if it failed to grow? And what compels it to progressively destroy the natural world on which human life depends?'

Once we can answer questions like these, we can move on to second-stage questions such as : 'What changes do we need to make to the economic system if we are to remove its undesirable characteristics? And, given that most governments are dominated by powerful forces committed to defending, and, indeed, accelerating, the present self-destructive arrangements, what steps can we take to bring the changes we identify as desirable about? And, once the system has been changed, what would the world that resulted be like to live in?'

We're a lot surer than we were about some of the answers to the first stage questions, as we hope this, the first *Feasta*

Review, makes clear. As we suspected, the problems are concerned with the design of the economic system itself. If the design of any system is flawed, it is going to be difficult to make it work properly, no matter how hard people try. And if some folk have their own motives for not trying very hard, then it may function very badly indeed, just as the Irish economy is doing in some important respects now.

For example, while the total income accruing to Irish residents and businesses registered here will probably be seen to have grown by over 8 per cent in 2000 when the figures are published later this year, the National Economic and Social Forum reports that the distribution of this income is one of the most inequitable in Europe and that, despite the unprecedented rate at which it has been growing recently, more than 20 per cent of the population are still living in households below the poverty line. So, has this country's rapid economic growth come about because low wages make us more internationally competitive? And is the growth our competitiveness brings making the inequality worse? And is the government unwilling to approve national wage agreements which would

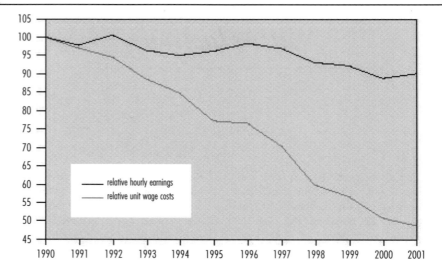

This graph, taken from the Winter 2000 **Bulletin** of the Central Bank of Ireland, demonstrates that Irish wage costs per unit of output in the manufacturing sector have fallen sharply in relation to those in the country's main trading partners. Actual wages are now among the lowest in the EU. Only Portugal, Greece and Spain are cheaper.

reduce inequality for fear this would damage our competitiveness and thus kill the goose which is laying so many golden eggs for the rest of the population? In other words, is Ireland in a Catch-22 situation because of the way its economy works? Feasta believes that the answer to all four questions is 'Yes'.

Most of the changes we have identified as necessary so far are structural—and therefore radical—rather than superficial and administrative. We've satisfied ourselves, for example, that far-reaching reforms are needed to the way that money is created and put into circulation. And that scarce rights—such as the right to emit a greenhouse gas—belong to us all equally and need to be allocated on a basis that benefits everyone. They must not be kept as the preserve of those who

have held them historically and the very rich. We're convinced, too that sustainability will be very hard to achieve within the context of an ever-more integrated world economy, and that it has to be sought by creating thousands of largely self-sufficient and probably very different local economies in which everyone living in each area has a say.

The second-stage questions are much tougher. How to bring about radical change, other than by bloody revolution, is among the most intractable questions human societies have ever faced. In an ideal world, mainstream politics would offer the option of radical change but the evidence of recent decades in Western democracies is that governments of all colours discover that the pressure to operate within the existing system is irresistible. Even if a Green party was able to form a majority government by itself, it would almost certainly succumb to the same pressures.

This democratic deficit drives many of those wanting change to organise protests and campaigns outside politics. Their work is immensely valuable in alerting the public to vital issues but, overall, its effect is to soften the edges of the system and thus make it more acceptable, rather than to change the way it works. To put this another way, campaigns can alleviate symptoms—an activity which can be extremely important when you are ill—but not cure the disease. And that's where Feasta comes in. Feasta is not a campaigning organisation but a network of activists of all kinds who have joined together to identify the changes needed to create a just and sustainable world. Our aim is to assemble these into a coherent whole to be introduced together, as a package, rather than piecemeal, as soon as circumstances develop which make this politically possible.

We may not have long to wait for such a crisis and a lot of thinking is required before then. And a lot of practical work too, if we are to do any road-testing on the solutions we are developing. Accordingly, Feasta has joined with other organisations in setting up some of the systems—like community currencies and an interest-free bank—required for the strong local economies on which, we think, a globally sustainable future will depend. On another level, we are working with other NGOs to devise structural reforms to the international financial system within a framework to limit climate change. And we've made good progress in assembling study courses that explore what true sustainability really means.

However, while we are pleased with the progress made in our first two and a half years, what excites us is the belief that, as more doers and thinkers join the Feasta network to contribute to it, its influence, scope and effectiveness will improve significantly. It better had, too, because radical yet carefully considered alternatives are urgently required.

Irish economists'
attitudes on sustainability

A FEASTA SURVEY

When people look back on the 1990s a generation or so in the future, one of the things they are going to find it almost impossible to understand is why, with pressing environmental and monetary problems all around them, a majority of the economists working at the time expressed not the slightest concern about the instability and unsustainability of the global economy. Why did the profession responsible for advising on how best to run the world system of production and distribution fail to explore the ways in which its defects might be rectified? our successors will ask, shaking their heads in bewilderment.

It's hard to answer this question convincingly today, even though the economists concerned are our contemporaries. Accordingly, before Feasta's launch in October 1998, the steering committee felt it would be a good idea to see what Irish economists actually thought about sustainability. How would they define it? Did they think that the present system was sustainable? And, if not, did they think that its instability mattered? We invited a cross-section of economists to take part in a three-round e-mail survey. In week one, the invitation said, they would be sent three questions to answer quickly, without too much thought. In the following two weeks, we added, they would be sent summaries of the replies we had received together with a further three questions which arose from their answers. Confidentiality would be maintained. As we were not looking for considered responses, their names would never be put to their answers.

Ten people agreed to take part but, in the event, replies were received from only six of them, five men and a woman. Two of these taught development studies, the third worked for the Central Bank, the fourth for a trades union, and two taught economics, one at Trinity College, Dublin, the other at an institute of technology outside the capital. Politically, they ranged from moderate right to marxist left. None was known to be involved in the Green Party.

Well, what did they say? Did any of them think that the present system was sustainable? The answer is no. Not one. But we'll come to that later.

First Round

QUESTION ONE asked our panellists how they defined sustainability. Were they happy with the Feasta definition that a sustainable system is one which is 'capable of being continued unchanged for hundreds of years without causing a progressive deterioration in any of the factors which make it up'? If not, would they advance a better one?

Four respondents were broadly happy with the Feasta definition, although only one gave the actual form of words unqualified approval. Two had problems with the time period it specifies. One would have liked the phrase 'hundreds of years' replaced by 'for the foreseeable future' while the other wanted an infinite time horizon. Both these options were, in fact, considered when the definition was being developed and were rejected, the first because 'the foreseeable future' was thought to be too vague, especially as we can't foresee what will happen tomorrow, while the second was turned down because no system is infinitely sustainable: after all, the Earth will eventually plunge into the Sun, which is itself a dying star. Nevertheless, the time period is obviously an important part of any definition of sustainability. 'Systems are not usually sustainable or unsustainable' someone who did not participate in the survey commented. 'They range from very short term sustainability (jumping off a skyscraper) to very long term (self-regenerating forests).'

The Feasta definition was also criticised because it banned the progressive deterioration in any factor on which the system relied. One respondent thought that this prohibition would rule out running down, say, fossil energy sources while developing renewable energy supplies to replace them. He therefore wanted minimum levels to be set for certain key factors such as air and water quality, and reductions to be allowed in the levels of other factors. Another respondent had similar views: 'I am not a believer in the infinite substitutability of factors,' he wrote, 'but I do think a certain level is allowable.' In fact, the definition would not rule out running down a factor by a certain amount so long as the run-down then stopped. What it does ban is a 'progressive'—that is, a continuous, unlimited—running down. It thus insists that limits have to be set, as the two respondents suggested. All six respondents therefore agreed that a sustainable system has to ensure that no factor on which it relies deteriorates beyond a certain point.

One respondent was unhappy because there was nothing about social justice in the Feasta definition. 'A system based on slave labour could be sustainable for hundreds of years' he pointed out entirely correctly. However, if the conditions for the slaves deteriorated over the years they would eventually become too weak to work and the system would collapse. In other words, because workers, whether slaves or not, are one of the factors on which an economy relies and there are limits to the extent to which they can be exploited, any system which involves a progressive worsening in their conditions cannot be regarded as sustainable. Consequently, the maintenance of a minimum level of social welfare—if not social justice—is implicit in the Feasta definition

Only two respondents offered their own definitions of sustainability. 'A system capable of allowing unchanged, indefinite consumption services' one said, a form of words compatible with the Feasta version but which seems to lack a cutting edge. The other wrote,

A sustainable system: a dynamic process that allows the needs of the present generations to be met without adversely affecting the achievement of wants of future generations... I know that is pretty vague but you did say you wanted an off-the-cuff response. Under my interpretation of the Feasta definition, growth is ruled out. My definition allows for growth.

Not so, said another correspondent:

I do not see that Feasta's approach is necessarily static—after all, technological development and cultural or social innovation could equally be fostered and harnessed to secure greater efficiency and wider social opportunities (instead of securing constant growth) within Feasta's criteria of sustainability. In other words, the possibility of change, of evolution toward greater efficiency and equality is not precluded by the demands for a sustainable system—just the opposite, in fact: these ends might be far more likely than they currently are under a system driven by the central impetus of value-free growth.

QUESTION TWO came in two parts. Part one asked if the present world system could be considered to be sustainable by the respondent's own definition and by the Feasta one. Part two went on to ask if an economic system which required constant growth could be made to operate sustainably. On part one, no-one wrote that the present system was sustainable by any definition and four said explicitly that it was not. Two respondents gave reasons. One of these was that the destruction of the environment was still being counted as a contribution to growth. The other was that the present system could not handle growth in a socially and environmentally friendly way. Interestingly, though, one of those who avoided saying if the present system was sustainable, a development studies lecturer (DSL), thought that the unsustainable nature of the way we live today had not yet been proved.

On part two, four people thought that it was possible for growth to continue indefinitely—in other words, that a growing economy was compatible with a finite world—but they stressed that the growth which took place had to be in terms of quality rather than quantity.

Interestingly, only one of our respondents was absolute in his rejection of growth:

A system based on endless growth would inevitably prove incompatible with... sustainability. In particular, the endless growth that the present system demands is value-free growth, taking no account of the social costs of growth, including increasing inequality and poverty, or of the environmental costs of growth, including pollution, ozone-depletion and so on. The central problem is that the present demand for continuous growth does not arise out of development geared to meet the basic needs of the general population but from the driving logic of the system—constant accumulation and the increasing concentration of capital and resources in fewer hands, increasingly corporate and global in orientation.

The second person who said that a constantly growing economy was not sustainable did so because he thought that the market system as structured at present 'does not control the behaviour of entrepreneurs in their quest for expansion and politicians do not control them either because the entrepreneurs can buy off the politicians. This means that there is no protection afforded for the environment, conservation of natural resources such as marine life or the rain forests.' He did not say whether a growing economy would be sustainable if the market system was changed in some way.

QUESTION THREE asked whether it was wise for humanity to stake its survival 'on the assumption that a dynamic form of sustainability is possible?' 'Yes' said one respondent, with no qualification whatsoever. Another was more anguished about his decision but eventually came to the same conclusion:

I understand and sympathise with some people's concern that while, in theory, dynamic sustainability may be possible, in reality markets don't always work in a sustainable manner, governments have often failed to legislate to combat market failure, and often we don't have enough information to properly model the system. There is much truth in these observations, but if we are talking about dynamic systems we should not fall into the trap of extrapolating from past behaviour, and underestimating the ability of the global system to react in ways that will address many of these problems. At the end of the day, I think it comes down to your faith in human ingenuity, and I hope that my faith is not misplaced.

Only two people rejected outright the idea of attempting to achieve both growth and sustainability simultaneously. In one case, the rejection was because the respondent despaired of attempting to control a perpetually-expanding system sufficiently well to ensure that it remained sustainable. In the second case, the respondent thought that constant expansion was a destructive impulse and so wasn't desirable anyway. A third respondent expressed no opinion on the wisdom of pursuing both goals but thought that a growing capitalist system could 'certainly continue to function in a manner which would be satisfactory to some for the foreseeable future'. Whether this was desirable for much of humankind was 'obviously debatable.' he added.

Second Round

It was apparent from the answers we got to the first-round questions that our sample was divided four to two, the majority belonging to the pro-growth faction. To some extent, this split reflected the differences in values and belief between what the US sociologist Lester Milbrath* refers to as the 'Dominant Social Paradigm' and the 'New Environmental Paradigm'. Some of the differences Milbrath identified are shown in the tables over the page. Broadly, the DSP people believe in markets and human ingenuity;

they focus on the short-term and are prepared to accept risks to eco-systems to achieve economic growth. The NEP adherents on the other hand prefer planning to markets, are sceptical about humanity's ability to foresee and forestall actions which will severely damage the planet and give priority to eco-system viability and long-term sustainability over raising incomes in the short term.

Milbrath's analysis made the answers we got to our second-round questions broadly predictable. Unfortunately, only five people replied this time—one DSP-er, the only woman in our sample, dropped out.

QUESTION ONE asked the panel if they thought that the type of growth being generated in the world today was benefiting more than a minority of the human population. No, said one of the two NEP-ers. 'The type of growth being generated today is primarily of benefit to a small section of society' He went on:

Admittedly, this growth may, for some social groups or geographic areas, mean more general benefits—like employment. However, in equating such 'growth' with progress or development, the disbenefits, like increasing inequality, poverty or environmental 'risk', are blatantly written off as unfortunate but necessary side effects, or else simply ignored. To a large degree, powerful institutions—multinational corporations, the IMF, World Bank, EU, US, etc—are orchestrating this growth through NAFTA, GATT, and other 'globalisation' policies. These institutions are not in the business of creating a fairer society or practising respect for the environment, and their policies favour very narrow interests. The inevitable result is the relentless concentration of capital (and power) in fewer hands and a cavalier attitude to environmental protection, which is rarely allowed to get in the way of profits.

---

* Milbrath did not originate these terms. DSP was coined in 1974 by Dennis Pirages and Paul Ehrlich while NEP was used in 1978 in 'The "New Environmental Paradigm" A Proposed Measuring Instrument and Preliminary Results', by Riley E. Dunlap and Kent D. van Liere, *Journal of Environmental Education* 9: 10-19. Milbrath's own paper can be found in *Building Sustainable Societies*, edited by Dennis Pirages, Sharpe, New York, 1996.

FUNDAMENTAL AND BELIEF DIFFERENCES BETWEEN THE TWO PARADIGMS

DOMINANT SOCIAL PARADIGM (DSP)	NEW ENVIRONMENTAL PARADIGM (NEP)
Priority for economic growth and development. Focus on short-term or immediate prosperity.	Priority for ecosystem viability, focus on long-term sustainability.
Continuation of economic growth justifies dangers of perturbing biogeochemical systems.	Disturbing biogeochemical systems is rarely if ever justifiable.
Perpetual economic growth: unrestricted population growth.	Growth beyond replacement must be halted for sustainability.
Accept risks to ecosystems to maximise wealth.	Avoid risks to the ecosystem and overall societal well-being
Reliance on markets to spur growth and ensure a bright future.	Reliance on foresight and planning to secure a bright future.
Emphasis on immediate, materially oriented gratification.	Emphasis on simplicity and personal growth.
Emphasis on hierarchy and authority.	Emphasis on horizontal structures that maximise interaction and learning.
Centralised decision-making and responsibility.	Greater personal and local responsibility.
Emphasis on private rather than public goods.	Ensure protection and supply of public goods.
Great faith in science and technology.	Sceptical about technology, wants critical evaluation.
Reliance on mechanistic simple cause/effect thinking and narrow expertise.	Recognises the need for holistic/integrative thinking.
Emphasis on competition, domination and patriarchy.	Emphasis on co-operation, partnership and egalitarianism.
Violence needed to maintain society.	Averse to violence—seek order without it.
Subordinate nature to human interests.	Place humans in an ecosystemic context.
Emphasise freedom so long as it serves economic priorities	Emphasise freedom so long as it serves ecological and social imperatives.

CONTRASTING POLICIES/STRATEGIES/APPROACHES
AS A RESULT OF THE DIFFERENT PARADIGMS

(DSP)	(NEP)
Maximise growth even at the cost of polluting.	Reduce waste and avoid pollution even at economic cost.
Encourage conspicuous consumption	Discourage conspicuous consumption.
Emphasise work to fill economic needs	Emphasise fulfilment in work.
Utilise whatever resources are needed to maximise current economic activity for the benefit of the current generation.	Conserve and maintain resource stocks for future generations.
Emphasise the profitable use of non-renewable resources; rely on markets to resolve resource shortages.	Emphasise renewable resources; plan for resource shortages.
Encourage the virtually unrestricted deployment of technology.	Critically evaluate and if needed, restrict the deployment of technology.
Use hard/large-scale technologies.	Use soft/'appropriate' technologies.
Support the development of nuclear energy.	Phase out nuclear energy.
Sacrifice other species for economic gain.	Protect other species, even at economic cost.
Encourage monocultures to maximise output and wealth for humans so as to allow unlimited population growth.	Restore/preserve ecosystem diversity. Observe limits to population growth.
Emphasise high-yield, intrusive agriculture.	Emphasise regenerative/appropriate agriculture.
Rely on markets to determine who gets what. Minimal use of planning.	Plan, but also use subsidies, taxes and prohibitions to ensure that markets give the results that society wants.

The second growth sceptic was just as blunt.

In the past 25 years the developed economies have grown but most of the economies of the south have gone backwards or stagnated. So a minority of the world's population have enjoyed the benefits of growth. Within the developed economies the gap between rich and poor has been widening e.g. in the UK, in the US and in Ireland.

The pro-growthers did not agree that current growth was not benefiting most of the world's human population. 'It is' said the central banker baldly. Both the DSLs thought that more explanation was needed. 'Material goods are now more widespread than ever before. Look at the evidence in terms of TV, radios, bicycles, cars etc., in rural areas in Asia, Africa, Latin America' one wrote. 'Growth is not a homogenous activity/process. The historical records show that some countries and regions are better-off in a material sense now than at any other time in the past. Indeed, looking at global aggregates, there would appear to be improvements in terms of life expectancy, lower infant mortality rates and improved levels of education in many countries.' He failed to stop to ask whether economic growth was responsible for these improvements.

The second DSL was more cautious. 'No one type of growth is being generated today. Some of it is obviously not benefiting the majority but, until recently, much of East Asian growth did just that as, for example, Oxfam's 1997 report, *Growth With Equity* shows. The key question is the type of growth and the structures through which the growth operates. A less equal structure—of land ownership for example—will tend to ensure that growth favours the minority.'

What about the effect of present growth on future generations? Was it beneficial for them too in view of global warming and the loss of soil and biodiver-

sity? 'The jury is still out' the central banker said. Both development studies lecturers were also non-committal: '[It] depends on the type of growth we are talking about and the distribution thereof' one wrote. '[That] depends whether our present use of resources increases or decreases the opportunities [available to] future generations' the other said. The sole growth sceptic who answered this question said that he could not possibly see how the growth being currently generated under 'the capitalist democracies... could possibly be construed as doing more good than harm for the future.'

QUESTION TWO read: 'Given that all respondents seem to agree that the achievement of sustainability requires the acceptance of limits, do you feel that any of the limits you would like to see observed have been exceeded yet? If they have, should priority be given to changing (reducing?) the economic system so it no longer breaks these limits rather than to continuing to expand it to generate further growth? In other words, do you really think that growth and sustainability can be achieved simultaneously? Economics is all about making choices. Shouldn't we chose to give sustainability priority? ' We then made the question more provocative by adding an aside: 'On the question of limits, Paul Ehrlich said to the Royal Netherlands Academy of Arts and Science last month: [September 1998}:

Estimates of the long-term carrying capacity of Earth with relatively optimistic assumptions about consumption, technologies, and equity are in the vicinity of two billion people. [His reference for this was G.C. Daily, A.H. Ehrlich and A. Ehrlich: 'Optimum Human Population Size', *Population and Environment*, 15:469-475, 1994.] Today's [six billion] population cannot be sustained on the 'interest' generated by natural ecosystems, but is consuming its vast supply of natural capital — especially deep, rich agricultural soils, 'fossil' groundwater, and biodiversity — accumulated over centuries to aeons. In some places soils, which are generated on a time scale of centimeters per century are disappearing at rates of centimeters per year. Some aquifers are being depleted at dozens of times their recharge rates, and we have embarked on the greatest extinction episode in 65 million years.

Predictably, both growth sceptics thought that limits had been exceeded and priority should be given to getting back on to the sustainable side of them even if that meant halting economic growth. One wrote:

Without any figures or unshakeable scientific proof to hand, I would just say on the question of limits that living in a fairly large city provides daily evidence that all kinds of desirable limits are already being exceeded. The industrial noise, the filthy rivers, the polluted air, the evening 'glow' in the sky—not to mention whatever is actually living in the Irish Sea at this stage—suggest broken limits all over the place.

I seriously worry about the purely 'reformist' approach to sustainability inherent in the argument that growth and sustainability are compatible. This angle is already being applied by many public and private sector bodies, who are happy to use (or even exploit) the rhetoric of sustainability without ever actually putting in place policies that could even begin the move towards a more sustainable economy. In short, the argument that economic growth and sustainability can both be attained simultaneously sounds, at best, meaningless and, at worst, a handy way of legitimating the current trajectory of economic growth, however damaging it may be. Yes, I think sustainability has to be given priority, otherwise the structural change necessary to actually achieve it will never come about.

The other wrote:

Marine resources—if one looks at the Atlantic it is clear the acceptable limits have been breached but it is difficult to stop the fishermen from Europe who are now moving to the South Atlantic to exploit the resources there at the expense of inshore fishermen in Africa. Similarly in the rainforests in SE Asia and Brazil, thousands of acres of trees that take hundreds of years to grow are being felled and not being replaced. But how do you stop this in a market system where

multinational companies that exploit the resources are larger than governments and these companies may be protected in their exploitation by the government of country of origin e.g. US multinationals operating in South America. Economics is about choices for government, but governments may have agendas which push difficult choices onto other governments. This applies in the pollution area when a process is banned in one country, it is exported to another with less stringent legislation. So even if limits are being exceeded it is difficult to get governments to accept a common agenda to tackle the problem of sustainability.

One of the three pro-growthers, a DSL, also thought that limits had been exceeded:

Many countries have seen increasing erosion of some of their resource base, in terms soil erosion, running down of water tables, chemical pollution of soil and surface water etc., and at an international level there are also concerns in terms of overfishing, levels of airborne pollutants, etc.

However, this did not mean that he thought that becoming sustainable should be given priority over growth as, he seemed to suggest, corrective measures were already in hand:

Many national governments and international agencies are trying to combat these problems already with varying degrees of success, and in some cases, local communities, for example Machakos in Kenya, have responded to resource erosion problems in very innovative and effective ways.

Both the central banker and the other DSL seemed unsure if any limits had been breached so far. 'There are in my limited view only a few basic limits that are critical' the banker wrote. 'How far away [we are] from the[se] limits I can't judge. This counsels caution not stagnation.' The DSL wrote: 'Of course, if I felt that some of the limits I deem critical had been exceeded, I would prioritise correction over growth'. But not, perhaps, if it meant a big fall in the standard of living. 'One could have a "sustainable" situation of appalling poverty and exploitation. Why prioritise that?' he asked. The central banker, on the other hand, thought that there was no absolute reason to give sustainability priority 'Other choices might be desirable if [you are] violating your sustainability criterion.' he said. The mind boggles. Just what might such choices be?

QUESTION THREE pointed out that, in their answers to the first round of questions, most respondents had expressed the view that the economic system needed to be altered or controlled in some way to ensure that it became less unsustainable. 'Do you feel that it is realistic to expect the required changes or controls to be introduced, and to be made to work effectively, within whatever period is left before the carrying capacity of the planet is sharply reduced if (1) free trade and the free movement of capital are preserved and (2) in circumstances in which every firm's survival depends on its ability to find a competitive edge over its rivals, thus putting it under constant pressure to try to cut costs by evading the new controls? ' the question asked. 'No' said one growth critic. He went on:

The issue of sustainability is an externality and the market system is totally guided by short term profits and the current share price. Nothing else is relevant. The free movement of capital has spread this right throughout the world and companies are only interested in getting resources as cheaply as possible to increase profits and if it means depleting resources, so what? Firms will always try to avoid controls. Look at all the financial scandals in Ireland at the moment. An expert in management told me that in business anything goes as long as you do not get caught. So if controls are put on certain aspects of business behaviour, firms will try to circumvent them if it means more profit.

The other critic was equally definite.

The two conditions [in the question] relate to the kind of neoliberal policies that demand far-reaching deregulation (though with massive State intervention in infrastructure, security, social control and so forth). I do not see how any limits or controls can realistically be put in place as long as these 'facts of the market' prevail.

The three pro-growthers all dodged the question. Both DSLs used the old trick of answering one question with another. 'First,' one wrote, 'we need to answer the question: 'Is the carrying capacity of the planet being reduced?' And if it can be shown that it is, then it is up to political will to ensure that appropriate responses are taken.' The second admitted that Feasta's question was a reasonable one. 'But if one answers it in the negative, that leaves you with another question— how feasible it is to expect limits to be imposed on trade, capital and the competitive system? The key issue is a political one—how can we mobilise pressure to reform the system?' he wrote, thus indicating that he thought that reform was required.

Our laconic central banker thought so too. 'Make markets for the environment. Think expansively, act contractionary!' he said.

Third Round

The reform of the current economic system was the subject of our final round of questions. Unfortunately, only two pro-growthers—the DSLs—and one growth sceptic replied.

QUESTION ONE asked our panellists if they thought that, rather than trying to make the existing economic system operate better by imposing additional regulations, it might not be more effective to make fundamental changes to it. If they did, what changes were they inclined to favour?

One of the DSLs seemed broadly happy with the present system while the other thought that the only way to change it was to bring it under 'maximum democratic control' in order to regulate it. One should not run away from it, he advised. The growth sceptic, on the other hand, doubted if regulation would work. ' Business people will always try to buy the regulators' he said. 'The term regulatory capture is well known in the US, where regulation of utilities has occurred over a long period of time.' He went on:

By its nature the capitalist system is difficult to change from the path it is presently pursuing because the nature of a system is one of individuals looking after their own interests with no regard to the greater good of society. To them there is no society, so trying to include other goals such as the quality of life, social justice etc is not on. I must admit that I may be unduly influenced by work I have been doing on the Irish economy since 1987. Governments in the period have acted as pawns to business interests, while they express commitment to social justice, and have reduced taxes and used spending in such a way that the better off in our society are the beneficiaries of growth and that the less well off get the crumbs from the table. Maybe it is different in other European countries.

As for the international agencies, they are subject to the will of the major donor countries and in many cases act in the interest of multinational business. The current banana war between the US and the EU, occurred because Chiquita, the US multinational banana grower in South America, gave a $550,000 donation to the Democrats in the US and the US took up the case with the World Trade Organisation. It is only when catastrophe is approaching that the business people, who have received more and more power over the system in recent years through the liberalising of capital controls, will agree to do anything to save the system.

QUESTION TWO, which asked if neo-liberal economics ought to be resisted and whether we should we attempt to develop an alternative ideology to confront it, produced a near-unanimous response.

'Yes, I believe it does need resisting' one DSL wrote, although he had no idea of what ideology should replace it. Instead, he thought, people who felt as he did could work on a pragmatic basis, opposing such things as the free movement of capital and bio-patenting, and working for the global regulation of multinational corporations. 'There is a theme running through these suggestions' he wrote, 'namely, the desirability of democracy. But that is something that is best worked out in practice, not as an abstract philosophy.'

The other DSL thought that 'certain aspects of neo-liberalism' needed addressing, particularly its theory-based policies which had failed in the real world. He said he found the pandering of governments to 'market/investor confidence' particularly worrying.

We are presently witnessing cases where governments are willing to handcuff themselves in terms of policy response in order to maintain that confidence, or are prepared to surrender sovereignty without looking for complementary restraints.

He had been alarmed, he said, at the secretive way the Multilateral Agreement on Investment had been developed. 'Does that process not conflict with the supposed agenda of a 'greater voice for the people'? he asked. However, he too advised against trying to develop an alternative ideology and recommended pragmatism. 'I would not recommend devoting time to finding an alternative ideology. It too could become dogmatic' he wrote. 'Instead, a more flexible, open-minded and accommodating mindset is needed. As Keynes once remarked 'If the facts change, I change my opinion'.

The growth sceptic was more radical, although even he did not call for a new ideology. 'There is need for a thorough revamp of economics so that the goal of society is the well-being of all society and this includes both the rich and the poor in the developed societies and in the South as well' he wrote. 'Neo liberal economics is a misnomer in the sense that there is nothing liberal or free about the markets [in which it operates] ' he wrote. 'World industry has become concentrated with globalisation. This has led to duopoly, monopoly and oligopoly in the major industrial markets. Moreover, firms rig the markets through advertising and other means. They restrict entry and keep prices high.'

QUESTION THREE asked the panellists what areas they would like to see Feasta investigate and made some suggestions. The two DSLs agreed that a priority area was the extent to which current growth was benefiting or harming future generations and how the present system might be better regulated to ensure that their interests were protected. But both rejected out of hand the study the growth sceptic thought most important—defining the goals of economic progress and the development of alternative indicators to monitor it. This was too abstract, one said, and in any case, it was work already being done by organisations such as the UNDP. 'Not a priority. Done to death' the other said.

Conclusions

It's very hard for someone with a particular worldview to sympathise with the opinions of those working within a different one. However, the overall impression given by the answers of the members of our panel who still adhered to the Dominant Social Paradigm to someone who no longer shares that view was that they were finding their positions increasingly difficult to maintain and were consequently having to resort to 'this has still to be proved' arguments about matters which those within the New Environmental Paradigm had long regarded as cut and dried. The first-round question about whether current growth was proving universally beneficial provided a good example of the diverging views on an outcome over which the statistics show there can be little doubt.

It is not an easy matter for anyone to switch from one paradigm to another as the process involves a complete re-assessment of all the things they thought they knew. Moreover, the switch is particularly difficult for economists because it involves the recognition that incremental changes to the present system—the imposition of tougher regulations perhaps—are unlikely to be enough to correct what is going wrong and that a massive, radical restructuring is required. Any economist who adopted this view would automatically be seen as an extremist and consigned to the fringes of the profession. So, naturally, they resist changing for as long as they can.

PROFESSOR HERMAN DALY

THE FIRST ANNUAL FEASTA LECTURE
TRINITY COLLEGE, DUBLIN
26 APRIL 1999

uneconomic growth in theory and in fact

HERMAN E. DALY

Every economic activity has some impact on the natural world and there is a limit to the total impact nature can withstand without being permanently damaged. As a result, there must come a point beyond which increases in economic activity reduce the level of the benefits humanity derives from nature by more than the benefits the extra activity brings. Such growth is 'uneconomic'—and it is the type of growth being generated in the US today.

What I'd like to talk about this evening is a concept which I think is important, although you don't hear it talked about very much. It is the idea of uneconomic growth. We hear about economic growth more than we want to sometimes, so is uneconomic growth a possibility? I want to argue that it is.

The text for my homily this evening is taken from John Ruskin: 'That which seems to be wealth may in verity be only the gilded index of far-reaching ruin'. That's my theme and I want to develop it in the following way: first I'll discuss the issue of uneconomic growth in theory. Does it make sense theoretically? Does it flow out of standard economics? I will argue that it is highly consistent with micro economic theory but that it conflicts with macro economic theory as currently done.

Then I want to discuss what I could call the paradigm issue, although I'd prefer to use an economic term. Josef Schumpeter, a great economist of the early part of this century, referred to a pre-analytic vision. Whenever we engage in analysis we don't start from scratch—we have to start with some perception of the nature of the thing that we are going to take apart in analysis. That pre-analytic vision is highly determinative of what we end up with in our conclusions. It is not an act of analysis. You don't arrive with a pre-analytic vision by analysis.

Then, if I have convinced you perhaps of the theoretical meaning of uneconomic growth, what about uneconomic growth in fact? Perhaps it is just an empty theoretical box in which nothing really belongs. I want to present some evidence that in the United States and some other countries. aggregate growth is now in fact costing us more than it is worth and, at the margin, it lowers welfare.

I'll talk about the United States, I'm not going to talk about Ireland for the sufficient reason that I don't know anything about Ireland in spite of the fact that my ancestors came from here. So I thank you for sending your ancestors and sharing your genes with me. However, no information about Ireland was transferred genetically, so I have to learn something.

Thirdly, since I will have argued that the ideology of growth forever does not really come out of economic theory, why do we emphasise economic growth to the eclipse of uneconomic growth? I'll suggest that this is to do with fundamental problems associated with the names of Malthus, Marx and Keynes and more recently with the World Bank.

If I have time then I will also say something about globalisation as a major obstacle to recognising the existence of uneconomic growth and particularly to stopping or avoiding it. Then there will be a period for open discussion.

Let me begin then with the question, can growth in GDP—that's usually what we mean by economic growth, growth in GDP—can growth in GDP in fact be uneconomic? Well, I think before answering that we should ask a similar question in micro economics. Can growth in micro-economic activity— that is, an activity in the firm or the household—can that be uneconomic? Of course it can. The whole idea of micro economics is seeking an optimal level of some activity. As the amount of the activity increases, eventually increasing marginal costs will intersect diminishing marginal benefit. If you grow beyond that, it's uneconomic. Optimisation is the essence of micro economics and that implies stopping. So the marginal cost equals marginal revenue rule, which you're all too familiar with if you've had the first course in economics, is aptly called in some textbooks the 'when to stop rule'. I like that term, the 'when to stop' rule.

Well, you've taken your course in micro economics. Here's the next course in macro economics. No more equating

HERMAN E. DALY is currently Professor at the School of Public Affairs, University of Maryland, College Park, MD 20742-1821. From 1988 to 1994 he was Senior Economist in the Environment Department of the World Bank. Prior to 1988 he was Alumni Professor of Economics at Louisiana State University, where he taught economics for twenty years. He is co-founder and associate editor of the journal Ecological Economics. His interest in economic development, population, resources, and environment has resulted in over a hundred articles in professional journals and anthologies, as well as numerous books, including **Toward a Steady-State Economy** (1973); **Steady-State Economics** (1977; 1991); **Valuing the Earth** (1993); **Beyond Growth** (1996); and **Ecological Economics and the Ecology of Economics** (2000). He is co-author with theologian John B. Cobb, Jr of **For the Common Good** (1989; 1994) which received the 1991 Grawemeyer Award for Ideas for Improving World Order. In 1996 he received the Honorary Right Livelihood Award ('alternative Nobel prize'), and the Heineken Prize for Environmental Science awarded by the Royal Netherlands Academy of Arts and Sciences.

of marginal costs to marginal revenue, no more when-to-stop rule, you just aggregate everything into GNP and this is supposed to grow forever. This is a curious thing. At the foundation level of economics, micro economics, the idea of uneconomic growth is fundamental, non-controversial really, but when you get to macro economics you just aggregate everything. Oops, all of a sudden there's no longer a when-to-stop rule, no longer any question of an optimal level of overall economic activity. So, let me try to speculate a little bit on why that's the case and in order to do that, let me go back to that idea of a pre-analytic vision or paradigm that I mentioned.

I'd like first to present the pre-analytic vision of the ecological economist.

I think that this is shared by many other economists but there are various disputes. I have called this the macro view of a macro economy. The important thing about this vision is that the economy is seen as a sub-system of a larger ecosystem. The larger eco-system is finite, non-growing and materially closed. There is an inflow of solar energy into the larger system and an outflow of heat energy radiated from the larger system. As that solar energy is degraded it turns all the biogeochemical cycles that support life, all the light-grey stuff, it makes all those things move. The economy is seen then as an open sub-system. It's open with respect to both matter and energy. It takes in low entropy matter and energy from the eco-system and expels high entropy waste matter and energy back to the eco-system and lives off that gradient. It lives off that degradation of materials and energy. So we start with depletion, we end with pollution. There is no way we can avoid that anymore than we can stop eating and

A MACRO VIEW OF THE MACROECONOMY

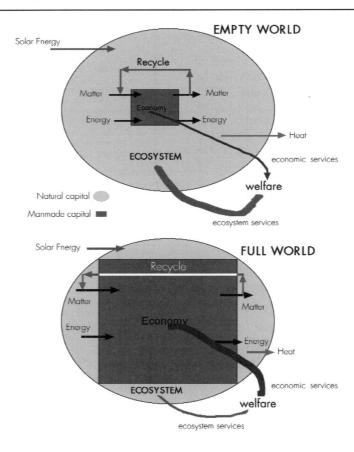

eliminating waste. It is a natural part of the economy. It is the digestive tract and it has to be there.

Matter can be recycled. We can take some of the waste matter and use it again. One might think 'Well, let's recycle energy too' but the physicists tell us you can't do that. More precisely, they say you can do it but it will always take more energy to gather up the waste energy and bring it back and use it again than the amount of energy that you recycle. The energy cost of recycling energy is always greater than the amount of energy recycled. So it's a losing proposition and economists have to understand that. It doesn't matter what the price of energy is, it will just never be possible to recycle energy because there's a physical constraint under which we have to live, the second law of thermodynamics or the entropy law.

One more thing. Everything inside the oval in the diagram representing the ecosystem is in physical units. But we can't just analyse the economy in terms of physical units because, if we do, we reach the conclusion that the ultimate physical product of the economic process is waste matter and waste energy and it doesn't make much sense to have an economy whose ultimate output is waste. It is a kind of idiot machine but that's the ultimate physical product. So, if you want to make sense of the economy you have to escape from the physical dimensions into some area which imposes value or welfare, psychic satisfaction of wants. I have put that outside and just called it Welfare—satisfaction of wants—and indicated two sources of services. The first is the upper line, economic services, which are wants being served by what I've called man-made capital, the dark-grey stuff in the economy, artefacts. The lower line represents eco-system services—the satisfaction of our wants satisfied directly by the eco-system, the light-grey stuff. What we're really interested in as economists is to maximise total welfare, maximise the sum of those two flows of welfare. We don't want to just maximise one, we want the sum of the two to be as great as possible.

Now what happens with economic growth is that as the economy in its physical dimensions grows by transformation of what used to be light-grey stuff, natural capital, into dark-grey stuff, man-made capital. The tree is cut down in the forest and converted into a table, one less tree in the forest, one more table in your house and so on. But as it grows, there's an encroachment on the rest of the ecosystem so there's an opportunity cost. As we expand the economic services flow, we reduce the eco-system services flow and we maybe will keep doing that as long as the additions to the economic services flow are greater than the subtractions from the eco-system services flow in terms of its usefulness to us. But at some point, well before occupying all of the light-grey space and turning it into dark-grey stuff, we will come to an optimum, a point beyond which further growth is going to be uneconomic, it's going to reduce eco-system services by more than it increases economic services. The scale of the economy then will have become optimal relative to the eco-system.

Notice here that I'm only counting human welfare. I take a very anthropocentric approach. Only human beings are counted in welfare. If we were also to count the sentient enjoyment of life by other species as a part of welfare, then that would be all the more reason for maintaining some of the light-grey stuff, which is habitat for other species. This would make the opportunity cost of human expansion even greater, to the extent that we count reduced enjoyment of life of other sentient creatures in the equation.

Kenneth Boulding once presented a very profound theorem. He said that when something grows it gets bigger. I call the top diagram the empty world scenario and the lower one the full world. That's a little misleading because the world is never empty. Previously it was empty of us and our furniture and full of other things. Now it is full of us and our stuff and relatively empty of what used to be there, so it's a little misleading but you know what I mean.

The two pictures are basically the same; both of them show the economy as a subsystem of a larger system that is finite, ongoing and materially closed. The economy depends on a larger eco-system for its maintenance in both cases. One case, the full world; the other case, the empty world. We may disagree on which is the most accurate representation of the world in which we live. I tend to say the full world is more accurate. Other people may say 'No, the empty world. We've still got all those spaces.' We're living with the same analytic vision and can argue back and forth and we can present evidence to each other in an effort to convince.

Empirical work helps to establish one vision, one view, rather than the other and I think that maybe part of the debate among economists is of that nature. Probably among economists there are those with the full world view and those with the empty world view but they share the basic pre-analytic vision. That debate I think is fruitful and continues.

There's another kind of debate. Maybe it's not a debate because it starts with a very different pre-analytic vision. It says 'No, that's not the right way to look at it. You're looking at the problem wrong. The economy is not a sub-system of a larger eco-system that's open and finite and so on, you've got it just backwards. The economy is the total system and the eco-system is a sector and instead of that erroneous picture which you've put up it ought to look like that. What is the eco-system? Well it's the extractive sector of the economy, garbage dumps, stuff like that and we can recycle these materials faster and faster and the economy grows. In this picture the economy is growing into the void. Economic growth in this vision does not entail encroachment on anything else. There is no opportunity cost, nothing has to be sacrificed as the economy expands, so who could be against growth? It doesn't increase the scarcity of anything else. It doesn't encroach on anything. There's no opportunity cost. In fact growth just relaxes scarcity among all parts within the economy so the idea that there is anything problematic with growth is utter nonsense and this is the way the world is.

Now I think it is very difficult to argue across those two paradigms. It's like Ptolemy and Copernicus arguing back and forth. You can present evidence but basically it's just a matter of just how you want to look at it. That's not to say that one way is not better than the other, but it's hard to force the argument.

In an effort to be as fair as I can, let me make a qualification. Recall that in the previous picture I made a clear separation between physical units and welfare units. The dark-grey stuff was totally physical. In this case, to be fair to the economists, they're thinking of dark-grey stuff as GDP rather than tonnes and barrels and so forth. So, as it has a value dimension rather than a purely physical dimension, it's not fair to say that they're thinking physical things will grow forever. What they're really thinking is that value will grow forever. But value, I would argue, while it is not reducible to physical dimensions is not independent of physical dimensions either. It has to have a physical dimension. I'll leave this as an assertion for now. Value in here, in the physical world, has to be incorporated in some way in some physical body. Yes, knowledge has value but it only enters into the functioning of the economy when its embodied in low entropy matter and enters into some useful function.

Well, that then is my view of the difference in the paradigms. My answer to the economists who say 'all we want to do is make value grow forever, we're not trying to make matter and energy grow for ever!' is to say 'Fine. In that case, let's restrict the throughput flow of matter and energy and you get busy with technology and let the value supported by that fixed flow grow forever and I'll applaud you and I'll be happy and you'll be happy.' That's an easy resolution to that one if you can really make that GDP grow and grow forever with a fixed materials throughput. I think there's room for progress in that direction but I think there are also some limits.

With regard to the question of uneconomic growth in theory, we started with a pre-analytic vision. Let's take a first step towards analysis of that vision. The con-

ECOSYSTEM AS SUBSYSTEM OF MACROECONOMY

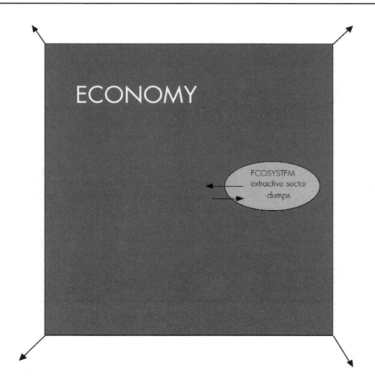

tinuous curve represents welfare or marginal utility or the benefits of growth. Q on the horizontal axis is, let's say, GDP. As we go out along the horizontal axis we have diminishing marginal utility. I think that's a very fundamental law of economics which is well established.

The dotted curve which is the cost of GNP growth—in other words, the social and environmental sacrifices made necessary by that growing encroachment on the eco-system. I've named that a Jevonian view in honour of William Stanley Jevons, a great economist of around 1870 or so, who used that kind of diagram for

a different problem but the logic is very much the same. In this diagram what is uneconomic growth? Well, economic growth is out to point b on the horizontal axis. At point b, line ab is equal to bc. The marginal benefits of further growth are just equal to the marginal costs. Growth beyond point b is uneconomic growth. It is growth for which the distance from the horizontal down to the dotted curve is greater than the distance up to the continuous curve, growth which makes you poorer than richer. And so there's the definition of uneconomic growth, growth beyond point b.

JEVONIAN VIEW OF LIMITS TO GROWTH OF MACROECONOMY

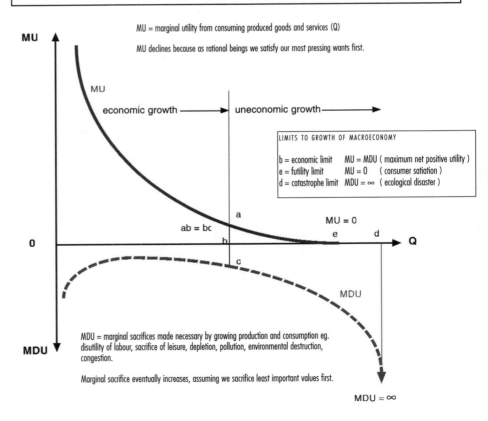

MU = marginal utility from consuming produced goods and services (Q)

MU declines because as rational beings we satisfy our most pressing wants first.

MU

MU

economic growth ⟶ uneconomic growth ⟶

LIMITS TO GROWTH OF MACROECONOMY

b = economic limit   MU = MDU (maximum net positive utility)
e = futility limit   MU = 0   (consumer satiation)
d = catastrophe limit MDU = ∞   (ecological disaster)

a

MU = 0

ab = bc

e   d

0   b   Q

c

MDU

MDU = marginal sacrifices made necessary by growing production and consumption eg. disutility of labour, sacrifice of leisure, depletion, pollution, environmental destruction, congestion.

MDU

Marginal sacrifice eventually increases, assuming we sacrifice least important values first.

MDU = ∞

I've distinguished several different limits to growth. One is Point b, the economic limit where marginal utility equals marginal disutility. Another is Point e, where marginal utility falls to zero. I've called this the futility limit because when you are there you have so many goods to enjoy that you don't have time to enjoy any of them. Consequently, adding more isn't going to do you any good because you can't use all the stuff you've already got. It's just futile no matter how little they cost. The third is Point d, where the dotted curve takes a nose dive straight down to infinity. I call this the catastrophe limit, the ecological catastrophe limit. That's the nice scenario where you invent some marvellous new product which has an unpredicted side effect which absolutely ruins the capacity of all green plants to photosynthesise and suddenly zap! Well, the nice thing about the economic limit is that it is the limit we encounter first.

The other two limits don't necessarily have to happen in the order that I've shown them. I think the catastrophe limit could occur sooner than the futility limit. However, I think the economic limit is going to come first although in the worst case scenario it might coincide with the catastrophe limit.

It seems to me that in our national accounting it would be very nice if we had two sets of accounts instead of just one. If we had one set of accounts which measured the benefits—the continuous line—and one set of accounts that measured the cost—the dotted line—and instead of adding them up, and conflating costs and benefits, we actually compared them at the margin in an effort to seek an optimal level of activity instead of simply assuming that economic activity should grow forever.

OK. I think that's all I'll say about theory. On the question of fact, is there any evidence that some countries may be beyond point b and in an era of uneconomic growth? I'll offer two pieces of evidence.

One. There were two important American economists, William Nordhaus and James Tobin. Tobin won the Nobel prize for other work. Thirty years or so ago they asked the question 'Is growth obsolete?' and by obsolete I think they meant uneconomic. To answer that question they said 'Look, we all know that GNP was never designed to be a measure of welfare. It is a measure of activity. Fair enough. So let's test it. Let's design an index which is a measure of welfare or which we think is a measure of welfare and then we'll correlate GNP with our attempt to measure welfare.' They called their index Measured Economic Welfare, MEW, and they discovered that, yes indeed, low and behold, there was a positive correlation. For the period 1929–65 as a whole, for every six-unit increase in GNP there was on average a four-unit increase in MEW. Not one to one but six to four. Not bad. Breath a sigh of relief. The conclusion they reached was that even though GNP was never intended as a measure of welfare, nevertheless it was sufficiently well correlated with welfare for us to continue to operate on the assumption that it was a reasonable measure of welfare.

Well, some twenty years later John Cobb and Clifford Cobb and I decided to take another look at this. We were developing our index of sustainable economic welfare and we thought that Tobin and Nordhaus's work was the best basis for this we could discover. We broke their time series into two segments, and discovered for the later period, the eighteen years from 1947 to 1965, the correlation was not 6:4 but a six-unit increase in GDP gave you only a one-unit increase in their measured economic welfare. So at a minimum it looked as if increasing GNP was becoming a less and less efficient way of increasing welfare given their own figures, their own definitions and so forth. We then wanted to extend their work and see what happened after 1965 but for various reasons we couldn't do that because the statistical series had changed.

Growth in the United States now is uneconomic because it's increasing costs faster than it's increasing benefits.

We didn't like their measure anyway because it didn't make any correction for changes in the distribution of income, for the depletion of natural capital and so on. So we developed another index we called the Index of Sustainable Economic Welfare. And we did the same thing that Nordhaus and Tobin did. We correlated it with GNP and there was a positive correlation between our index and GNP up to mid to late seventies; then our index flattened out while GNP kept on rising. Eventually our index actually declined slightly and GDP kept on going.

We didn't make all that many changes to MEW. We just subtracted for the depletion of natural capital and made a correction for the distribution of income because we thought the assumption that an extra dollar of income to the very wealthy should be counted the same in welfare terms as an extra dollar to the poor was against economic theory. We did not make any deductions for diminishing marginal utility of income resulting from growth as a whole for countries getting richer. Nor did we deduct anything for the consumption of harmful goods such as tobacco or alcohol and so forth. So we played very conservatively and still found that welfare as measured by this number in the United States declined as GNP kept on going up.

Now measuring welfare is a very difficult and tricky business. I don't want to say that our measure is a great measure of welfare but given the fact that with GDP, they weren't even trying to measure welfare when they designed that, and we were at least trying to do so, we probably got something of a better measure of welfare than GDP. The correlation between the two is very poor

OK. So that's just a bit on uneconomic growth in fact. I think in fact that growth in the United States now, aggregate growth, is uneconomic because it's increasing costs faster than it's increasing benefits. Do I mean by that that there's no way we can improve welfare in the United States? No, of course not. There are plenty of things that should grow and plenty of things that should decline. The problem is aggregate GDP. If you want to talk about those things which should grow you have to get away from the aggregate and talk about the parts, you have to get away from macroeconomics back to microeconomics and identify those individual things for which marginal benefits are still greater than marginal costs. That gets you away from this gross policy of just stimulating aggregate economic growth and that's the big problem.

Let me then move to the question of some historical political reasons for mandating growth. I've argued that the push for growth doesn't really come out of standard economic theory which says that there is such a thing as an optimum and you should stop there. In macroeconomics, though, we don't, we keep on growing. Where did that mandate come from? I want to suggest several places. I think it came from practical political problems faced by economists. For example, the practical problem of over-population associated with the name of Malthus. The standard cure for over-population in today's world is that of the demographic transition. If we just keep on with economic growth there comes a point beyond which, as people keep getting richer and richer, they begin to have cars and refrigerators instead of babies. Economic growth goes up, population tends to go down and the demographic transition happens automatically. So if you are worried about population, yes it's a legitimate worry but don't worry, just devote all of your efforts to economic growth and the population issue will be solved on its own.

Then we move to another big problem, the unjust distribution of income between social classes, associated largely with the name of Karl Marx although many others. What's the solution to this? Do you re-distribute? Oh no, that causes problems. We will grow so that the unjust distribution between classes is at least rendered tolerable. I mean even if the rich get richer faster than the poor get richer, the poor shouldn't complain because they are getting absolutely richer. So the way to do that is to get aggregate growth, to make everyone better off. 'A rising tide lifts all boats' people say, which of course is not true since a rising tide in one part of the world means an ebbing tide somewhere else, but maybe for one part of the world it's true.

What about involuntary unemployment, the great problem recognised by John Maynard Keynes and of course many others. His solution was to cure unemployment by stimulating aggregate demand. How do you stimulate aggregate demand? Well many ways but principally by investment. You stimulate investment and growth and that will cure the unemployment.

Must we grow beyond the optimum scale in pursuit of full employment? It seems that's an important unasked question. Continuing in this time-honoured tradition of Malthus, Marx and Keynes, in 1992 along comes the World Bank's *World Economic Development Report* which was dedicated that year to development and environment. 'Yes,' it said, 'there is a problem of environmental degradation but, hey look, just keep growing. As we grow more we will eventually become rich enough to pay the costs of cleaning up and improving the environment.' So, in time-honoured tradition, they discovered something which they christened an 'Environmental Kuznets Curve' after Simon Kuznets who was a great statistician and economist. The idea is an inverted U-shaped curve. As economic growth continues along a horizontal axis, in Kuznets' case, inequality would increase and then reach a maximum and then inequality would decrease beyond some point. Well, they adapted that and they said we will show the increase of GNP along the horizontal axis. Then they took a number of measures of pollution of various things, very selective measures, and sure enough, they found pollution of certain things increased with GDP up to a maximum and then began to decline. Hurray! The cure to an environmental problem is just to persist in uneconomic growth. Once you get beyond the hump of the U it goes down and you enter the realm of win-win solutions, everything gets better at the same time and so forth.

So, what is the point that I am making? The point is that these problems all have the same solution, more economic growth and the assumption in all cases is that growth truly is economic, that this growth really is making us richer at the margin rather than poorer. If we enter an era of uneconomic growth then uneconomic growth makes us poorer. It is not going to sustain the demographic transition and cure overpopulation. Neither will it help to redress unjust distribution, nor will it help in cleaning up the environment.

So we need more direct and radical solutions to the problems of Malthus, Marx and Keynes. Population control to deal with over-population. Redistribution to deal with excessive inequality. And, as for unemployment, I'm not sure I know the answer to that one, maybe a public sector employer of last resort, ecological tax reform, raising resource prices, job sharing, various things.

This to me is a very sobering conclusion. It seems to me that the reason we have emphasised growth politically, put it in first place, is that it would solve all these really crushing problems: overpopulation, unemployment, unjust distribution without being radical. It gives a win-win solution to all of these totally bone-crushing problems. Take that away, and you have to go back to the really radical solutions and the politicians don't want to do that, the public is not ready to support them in that. If growth really is uneconomic now, then we have to face

| *We have to face very radical kinds of solutions to fundamental problems.* |

very radical kinds of solutions to fundamental problems. All the more temptation to assume 'Well of course growth has to be economic' and so on.

In conclusion, let me just point out that I think these kinds of radical policies that I have alluded to without really defining—policies to deal with overpopulation, unjust distribution and environmental degradation—will have to be carried out by nation states, at the national level. This is the locus of community in today's world, this is the locus of authority to make policy. I know it's changing, I know it's shifting but that's where it exists right now and if we have globalisation then I fear that we are going to undercut the ability of nations, of com-

munities, to carry out the very radical kinds of policies that will be needed to face these difficulties.

I should distinguish in closing, just for clarity, internationalisation from globalisation. I think internationalisation refers to the increasing importance of international trade, international relations, treaties, alliances and so forth. International of course, means between or among nations. The basic unit remains the nation, even though relations among nations become increasingly important and critical and necessary. So that's internationalisation.

Globalisation refers to the economic integration of many formally separate national economies. Globalisation, mainly by free trade and free capital mobility but also to a lesser extent by easing migration, is the effective erasure of national boundaries for economic purposes. What used to be international now becomes inter-regional; what used to be governed by comparative advantage and mutual gain now becomes governed by absolute advantage with no guarantee of mutual gain. What was many becomes one. The very word integration derives from integer of course, integer meaning one, complete or whole. Integration is the act of combining in the one whole. Since there can be only one whole, only one unity with reference to which parts are integrated, it logically follows that global economic integration implies national economic disintegration.

By disintegration I don't mean that productive units disappear, just that they are torn out of the national context and rearranged internationally. As the saying goes, 'to make an omelette, you have to break some eggs'. To integrate the global omelette you have to disintegrate some national eggs. While it sounds nice to say 'world community' we have to face up to its costs at the national level where institutions of community really exist. If you disintegrate real community where it really is at the national level, in the name of a hopeful, ideal, global, attenuated notion of community where it doesn't exist yet, it seems to me very problematic.

By globalising, we take away from nation states their ability to enforce and to enact the polices necessary to internalise external costs, to control population, to do the things that are necessary. We enter into a regime of standards-lowering competition in which trans-national corporations are able to play off one government against another in an attempt to get the lowest possible social and environmental costs internalised into their product and production. The big loser in this process is going to be, as I see it, the labouring class in the countries which in the past, for whatever reason, have managed to maintain high wages, lower population growth, higher standards of environmental internalisation. All of these standards will be competed downward to a world average, which will be, relatively, a low world average. So I

see this globalisation as a major obstacle to enacting the kind of radical polices that are necessary in order to avoid this downward spiral of uneconomic growth.

In fact globalisation is just a way, it seems to me, of undercutting the ability of nations to deal with their own problems of overpopulation, unjust distribution, unemployment and external costs. It tends to convert many difficult but relatively tractable problems into one big intractable global problem. For that reason I think we should be very careful about celebrating and pushing globalisation and should move back towards a model of internationalisation. That's not giving up on global economic community, world community, it's a different model of community. It says that world community should be a community of communities, of nations federated into a community rather than a direct membership community in which there's no intermediation by nations and in which nations basically disappear. Well, with that provocation I think that maybe I should stop.

five policy recommendations for a sustainable economy

HERMAN E. DALY

Two months after his Feasta lecture, Herman Daly returned to Europe to receive the $100,000 Sophie Prize for 1999 which he shared with Fr Thomas Kocherry, a leader of the fisher people in India. The prize was established in 1997 by Jostein Gaarder, the author of **Sophie's World**, a novel about the history of philosophy, to honour individuals and organisations who have pointed to alternatives to the present economic system in a pioneering or a particularly creative way and/or have put such alternatives into practice. This is the text of the speech Professor Daly gave on receiving the award in Oslo on 15 June 1999.

The five following policy suggestions are in sequence, starting with the least controversial and moving to the most controversial. Since even the least controversial proposals have not yet been adopted one might reasonably ask 'Why not just focus on, say, the two or three least controversial proposals and forget for now the more controversial ones?' This would be a reasonable strategy, except for the fact that the three least controversial policies are national policies that would be undercut by global economic integration, and logically require the fourth and more controversial policy of resisting global integration if they are to be effective. The fifth suggestion is a kind of 'meta-policy' of facing up to what A.N. Whitehead called the 'lurking inconsistency'—'This radical inconsistency at the basis of modern thought', he said, 'accounts for much that is half-hearted and wavering in our civilisation.' It enfeebles purpose itself, and consequently policy which necessarily presupposes

purpose. My fifth suggestion is, you might say, like an invitation to Sophie Amundsen's [the Sophie referred to in the title of Gaarder's book] 'philosophical garden party'!

1. Stop counting the consumption of natural capital as income.

Income is by definition the maximum amount that a society can consume this year and still be able to consume the same amount next year. That is, consumption this year, if it is to be called income, must leave intact the capacity to produce and consume the same amount next year. Thus sustainability is built into the very definition of income. But the productive capacity that must be maintained intact has traditionally been thought of as man-made capital only, excluding natural capital. We have habitually counted natural capital as a free good. This might have been justified in yesterday's empty world, but in today's full world it is anti-economic. The error of implicitly counting natural capital consumption as income is customary in three areas: (1) the System of National Accounts; (2) evaluation of projects that deplete natural capital; and (3) international balance of payments accounting.

The first area of error (national accounts) is widely acknowledged and efforts are underway to correct it— indeed, the World Bank played a pioneering role in this important initiative, and then seems to have lost interest.

The second (project evaluation) is well recognised by standard economics which has long taught the need to count 'user cost' (depletion charges) as part of the opportunity cost of projects that deplete natural capital. Bank best practice counts user costs, but average Bank practice ignores it. Uncounted user costs show up in inflated net benefits and an overstated rate of return for depleting projects. This biases investment allocation toward projects that deplete natural capital, and away from more sustainable projects. Correcting this bias is the logical first step toward a policy of sustainable development. User cost must be counted not only for depletion of nonrenewables, but also for projects that divest renewable natural capital by exploiting it beyond sustainable yield. The sink or absorptive services of natural capital, as well as its source or regenerative services, can also be depleted if used beyond sustainable capacity. Therefore a user cost must be charged to projects that deplete sink capacity, such as the atmosphere's ability to absorb CO_2, or the capacity of a river to carry off wastes. It is admittedly difficult to measure user cost, but attempting to avoid the issue simply means that we assign to depleted natural capital the precise default value of zero, which is frequently not the best estimate. Even when zero is the best estimate it should be arrived at not by default, but by reasoned

calculation based on explicit assumptions about backstop technologies, discount rates, and reserve lifetimes.

Third, in balance of payments accounting, the export of depleted natural capital, whether petroleum or timber cut beyond sustainable yield, is entered in the current account, and thus treated entirely as income. This is an accounting error. Some portion of those non-sustainable exports should be treated as the sale of a capital asset, and entered on capital account. If this were properly done, some countries would see their apparent balance of trade surplus converted into a true deficit, one that is being financed by drawdown and transfer abroad of their stock of natural capital. Reclassifying transactions in a way that converts a country's balance of trade from a surplus to a deficit would trigger a whole different set of IMF recommendations and actions. This reform of balance of payments accounting should be the initial focus of the IMF's new interest in environmentally sustainable development. Instead they seem interested only in pushing for liberalisation of the capital account as well as the current account, thereby, as will be argued later, subverting their basic charter.

John Ruskin, back in 1862, must have presciently been thinking of modern GDP when he wrote, 'That which seems to be wealth may in verity be only the gilded index of far-reaching ruin... Growth in GDP, so-called economic growth, has for some countries literally become uneconomic growth because it increases unmeasured costs faster than it increases measured benefits. Consequently, many policies justified mainly by their contribution to GDP growth, such as global economic integration, suddenly lose their rationale. Maybe that is why the World Bank lost interest in correcting the national accounts.

2 Shift the tax base from value added (labour and capital income) and on to resource throughput (that to which value is added).

In the past it has been customary for governments to subsidise resource throughput to stimulate growth. Thus energy, water, fertiliser, and even deforestation, are even now frequently subsidised. To its credit the World Bank has generally opposed these subsidies. But it is necessary to go beyond removal of explicit financial subsidies to the removal of implicit environmental subsidies as well. By 'implicit environmental subsidies' I mean external costs to the community that are not charged to the commodities whose production generates them.

Economists have long advocated internalising external costs either by calculating and charging Pigouvian taxes (taxes which when added to marginal private costs make them equal to marginal social costs), or by Coasian redefinition of property rights (such that values that used to be unowned and thus not valued in markets, become private property whose values are protected by their new owners). These solutions are elegant in theory, but often quite difficult in practice. A blunter, but much more operational instrument would be simply to shift our tax base away from labour and capital income on to throughput. We have to raise public revenue somehow, and the present system is highly distortionary in that by taxing labour and capital in the face of high unemployment in nearly all countries, we are discouraging exactly what we want more of. The present signal to firms is to shed labour, and to develop technologies that increase the throughput of energy and materials. It would be better to economise on throughput because of the high external costs of its associated depletion and pollution, and at the same time to use more labour because of the high social benefits associated with reducing unemployment.

Shifting the tax base on to throughput induces greater throughput efficiency, and internalises, in a gross, blunt manner the externalities from depletion and pollution. True, the exact external costs will not have been precisely calculated and attributed to exactly those activities that caused them, as with a Pigouvian tax that aims to equate marginal social costs and benefits for each activity. But those calculations and attributions are so difficult and uncertain that insisting on them would be equivalent to a full-employment act for econometricians and prolonged unemployment and environmental degradation for everyone else. Politically the shift toward ecological taxes could be sold under the banner of revenue neutrality. However, the income tax structure should be maintained so as to keep progressivity in the overall tax structure by taxing very high incomes and subsidising very low incomes. But the bulk of public revenue would be raised from taxes on throughput either at the depletion or pollution end, though mainly the former. The shift could be carried out gradually by a pre-announced schedule to minimise disruption. This shift should be a key part of structural adjustment, but should be pioneered in the North. Indeed, sustainable development itself must be achieved in the North first. It is absurd to expect any sacrifice for sustainability in the South if similar measures have not first been taken in the North. The major weakness in the World Bank's and IMF's ability to foster environmentally sustainable development is that they only have leverage over the South, not the North. Some way must be found to push the North also. The Nordic countries and the Netherlands have begun to lead the way without being pushed.

While it is true that land and natural resources exist independently of man, and therefore have no cost of production, it does not follow that no price should be charged for their use. The reason is that there is an opportunity cost involved in using a resource for one purpose rather than another, as a result of scarcity of the resource, even if no one produced it. The opportunity cost is the best forgone alternative use. If a price equal to the value of the opportunity cost is not charged to the user, the result will be inefficient allocation and waste of the resource—low priority uses will be satisfied while high priority uses are not. Efficiency requires only that the price be paid by the user of these 'free gifts of nature'—but for efficiency it does not matter to whom the price is paid. For equity it matters a great deal to whom the price is paid, but not for efficiency.

To whom, then, should the price be paid? Since we cannot pay nature directly, we pay the owners of nature. But who is the owner? Ideally ownership of land and resources should be communal since there is no cost of production to justify individual private ownership 'by whomever produced it'. Each citizen has as much right to the 'free gifts of nature' as any other citizen. By capturing for public revenue the necessary payment to nature, one serves both efficiency and equity. We minimise the need to take away from people by taxation the fruits of their own labour and investment. We minimise the ability of a fortunate few private land and resource owners to reap a part of the fruits of the labour and enterprise of others. Land and resource rents (unearned income) are ideal sources of public revenue. In economic theory 'rent' is defined as payment in excess of supply price. Since the supply price for land is zero, any payment for land is rent. If we paid no rent the land would not disappear.

3 Maximise the productivity of natural capital in the short run, and invest in increasing its supply in the long run.

Economic logic requires that we behave in these two ways toward the limiting factor of production—i.e. maximise its productivity and invest in its increase. Those principles are not in dispute. Disagreements do exist about whether natural capital is really the limiting factor. Some argue that man-made and natural capital are such good substitutes that the very idea of a limiting factor, which requires that the factors be complementary, is irrelevant. It is true that without complementarity there is no limiting factor. So the question is, are man-made capital and natural capital basically complements or substitutes? Here again we can provide perpetual full employment for econometricians, and I would welcome more empirical work on this, even though I think it is sufficiently clear to common sense that natural and man-made capital are fundamentally complements and only marginally substitutable. In the past, natural capital has been treated as superabundant and priced at zero, so it did not really matter whether it was a complement or a substitute for man-made capital. Now remaining natural capital appears to be both scarce and complementary, and therefore limiting. For example, the fish catch is limited not by the number of fishing boats, but by the remaining populations of fish in the sea. Cut timber is limited not by the number of sawmills, but by the remaining standing forests. Pumped crude oil is limited not by man-made pumping capacity, but by remaining stocks of petroleum in the ground. The natural capital of the atmosphere's capacity to serve as a sink for CO_2 is likely to be even more limiting to the rate at which petroleum can be burned than is the source limit of remaining oil in the ground.

In the short run, raising the price of natural capital by taxing throughput, as advocated above, will give the incentive to maximise natural capital productivity. Investing in natural capital over the long run is also needed. But how do we invest in something which by definition we cannot make? If we could make it, it would be man-made capital! For renewable resources we have the possibility of fallowing investments, or more generally 'waiting' in the Marshallian sense—allowing this year's growth increment to be added to next year's growing stock rather than consuming it. For nonrenewables we do not have this option. We can only liquidate them. So the question is how fast do we liquidate, and how much of the proceeds can we count as income if we invest the rest in the best available renewable substitute? And of course how much of the correctly counted income do we then consume and how much do we invest?

One renewable substitute for natural capital is the mixture of natural and man-made capital represented by plantations, fish farms, etc., which we may call 'cultivated natural capital'. But even within this important hybrid category we have a complementary combination of natural and man-made capital components—e.g. a plantation forest may use man-made capital to plant trees, control pests, and choose the proper rotation—but the complementary natural capital services of rainfall, sunlight, soil, etc. are still there, and eventually still become limiting. Also, cultivated natural capital usually requires a reduction in biodiversity relative to natural capital proper.

For both renewable and nonrenewable resources, investments in enhancing throughput productivity are needed. Increasing resource productivity is indeed a good substitute for finding more of the resource. But the main point is that investment should be in the limiting factor, and to the extent that natural capital has replaced man-made capital as the limiting factor, our investment focus should shift correspondingly. I do not believe that it has. In fact, the World Bank's failure to charge user cost on natural capital depletion, noted earlier, surely biases investment away from replenishing projects.

4 Move away from the ideology of global economic integration by free trade, free capital mobility, and export-led growth—and toward a more nationalist orientation that seeks to develop domestic production for internal markets as the first option, having recourse to international trade only when clearly much more efficient.

At the present time, global interdependence is celebrated as a self-evident good. The royal road to development, peace, and harmony is thought to be the unrelenting conquest of each nation's market by all other nations. The word 'globalist' has politically correct connotations, while the word 'nationalist' has come to be pejorative. This is so much the case that it is necessary to remind ourselves that the World Bank and the IMF exist to serve the interests of their members, which are nation states, national communities—not individuals, not corporations, not even NGOs. The Bretton Woods institutions have no charter to serve the one-world without borders cosmopolitan vision of global integration— of converting many relatively independent national economies, loosely dependent on international trade, into one tightly integrated world economic network upon which everyone depends for even basic survival. If the World Bank and the IMF are no longer committed to serving the interests of their members, then whose interests are they serving? Globalisation, considered by many to be the inevitable wave of the future, is frequently confused with internationalisation, but is in fact something totally different. Internationalisation refers to the increasing importance of international trade, international relations, treaties, alliances, etc. Inter-national, of course, means between or among nations. The basic unit remains the nation, even as relations among nations become increasingly necessary and important. Globalisation refers to global economic integration of many formerly national economies into one global economy, mainly by free trade and free capital mobility, but also by easy or uncontrolled migration. It is the effective erasure of national boundaries for economic purposes. International trade (governed by comparative advantage) becomes, with the introduction of free capital mobility, interregional trade (governed by absolute advantage). What was many becomes one. Where there had been a guarantee of gain from trade to each nation, now there is only a gain to the world as a whole, with the possibility that some nations may lose as others gain.

The very word 'integration' derives from 'integer', meaning one, complete, or whole. Integration is the act of combining into one whole. Since there can be only one whole, only one unity with reference to which parts are integrated, it follows that global economic integration logically implies national economic disintegration. By disintegration I do not mean that the productive plant of each country is annihilated, but rather that its parts are torn out of their national context (dis-integrated), in order to be re-integrated into the new whole, the globalise economy. As the saying goes, to make an omelette you have to break some eggs. The disintegration of the national egg is necessary to integrate the global omelette.

The model of international community upon which the Bretton Woods institutions rests is that of a 'community of communities', an international federation of national communities co-operating to solve global problems under the principle of subsidiarity. The model is not the cosmopolitan one of direct global citizenship in a single, integrated world community without intermediation by nation states. Who conferred upon these institutions the right to unilaterally change the very reason for which they were created?

To globalise the economy by erasure of national economic boundaries through free trade, free capital mobility, and free, or, at least, uncontrolled migration, is to wound fatally the major unit of community capable of carrying out any policies for the common good. That includes not only national policies for purely domestic ends, but also international agreements required to deal with those environmental problems that are irreducibly global (CO_2, ozone depletion). International agreements presuppose the ability of national governments to carry out policies in their support. If nations have no control over their borders they are in a poor position to enforce national laws, including those necessary to secure compliance with international treaties.

Cosmopolitan globalism weakens national boundaries and the power of national and sub-national communities, while strengthening the relative power of transnational corporations. Since there is no world government capable of regulating global capital in the global interest, and since the desirability and possibility of a world government are both highly doubtful, it will be necessary to make capital less global and more national. I know that is an unthinkable thought right now, but take it as a prediction— ten years from now the buzz words will be 'denationalisation of capital' and the 'community rooting of capital for the development of national and local economies', 'minimum residence times of foreign investments', 'Tobin taxes', etc., not the current shibboleths of export-led growth stimulated by whatever adjustments are necessary to increase global competitiveness. 'Global competitiveness' (frequently a thought-substituting slogan) often reflects not even a real increase in resource productivity, but rather a standards-lowering competition to reduce wages, externalise environmental and social costs, and export natural capital at low prices while calling it income.

5 Facing the Lurking Inconsistency.

To serve the purposes of ending poverty and conserving the biosphere (sustainable development) we must first rescue the idea of purpose itself from the nether world of illusion and epiphenomena to which it has been banished by mechanist philosophers and neo-darwinist biologists. If purpose is not causative in the real world, then all policy is nonsense, and all theory on which policy is based is useless.

The term 'lurking inconsistency', as well as its meaning, is taken from Alfred North Whitehead (*Science and the Modern World*, 1925) : A scientific realism, based on mechanism, is conjoined with an unwavering belief in the world of men and of the higher animals as being composed of self-determining organisms. This radical inconsistency at the basis of modern thought accounts for much that is half-hearted and wavering in our civilisation. It enfeebles [thought], by reason of the inconsistency lurking in the background. For instance, the enterprises produced by the individualistic energy of the European peoples presuppose physical actions directed to final causes. But the science which is employed in their development is based on a philosophy which asserts that physical causation is supreme, and which disjoins the physical cause from the final end. It is not popular to dwell on the absolute contradiction here involved.

The directly experienced reality of purpose and final cause must, in the view of mechanism, be an 'epiphenomenon'— an illusion which itself was selected because of the reproductive advantage that it chanced to confer on those under its influence. It is odd that the illusion of purpose should be thought to confer a selective advantage while purpose itself is held to be non causative—but that is the neo-darwinist's problem, not mine. The policy implication of the mechanistic dogma that purpose is not causative is laissez faire beyond the most libertarian economist's wildest model. The only 'policy' consistent with this view is, 'let it happen as it will anyway'. Is it too much to ask the neo-darwinist to speculate about the possibility that the survival value of neo-darwinism itself has become negative for the species that really believes it? Could this lurking inconsistency have lethal consequences?

Teleology has its limits, of course, and from the Enlightenment onward it is evident that mechanism has constituted an enormously powerful research paradigm for biology. The temptation to elevate a successful research paradigm to the level of a complete world view is perhaps irresistible. But mechanism too has its limits. To deny the reality of our most immediate and universal experience (that of purpose) because it doesn't fit the research paradigm is profoundly anti-empirical. To refuse to recognise the devastating logical consequences that result from the denial of purpose is anti-rational. That people already unembarrassed by the fact that their major intellectual purpose is the denial of the reality of purpose itself should now want to concern themselves deeply with the relative valuation of accidental pieces of their purposeless world is incoherence compounded.

If purpose does not exist then it is hard to imagine how we could experience the lure of value. To have a purpose means to serve an end, and value is imputed to whatever furthers attainment of that end. Alternatively, if there is objective value then surely the attainment of that value should become a purpose. Neo-darwinist biologists and ecologists, who do not accept the reality of purpose, owe it to the rest of us to remain silent about valuation—and conservation as well.

Economists, unlike biologists, do not usually go to the extreme of denying the existence of purpose. They recognise purpose under the rubric of individual preferences and do not generally consider them to be illusory. However, preferences are thought to be purely subjective, so that one person's preferences are as good as another's. Unlike public facts, private preferences cannot be right or wrong— there is, by assumption, no objective standard of value by which preferences can be judged. Nevertheless, according to economists, preferences are the ultimate standard of value. Witness economists' attempts to value species by asking consumers how much they would be willing to pay to save a threatened species, or how much they would accept in compensation for the species' disappearance. The fact that the two methods of this 'contingent valuation' give quite different answers only adds comic relief to the underlying tragedy which is the reduction of value to taste.

Economics too suffers from the lurking inconsistency, but not to the extent that biology does. Purpose has not been excluded, just reduced to the level of tastes. But even an unexamined and unworthy purpose, such as unconstrained aggregate satisfaction of uninstructed private tastes—GDP growth forever— will dominate the absence of purpose. So, in the public policy forum, economists with their attenuated, subjective concept of purpose (which at least is thought to be causative) will dominate the neo-darwinist ecologists who are still crippled by the self-inflicted purpose of proving that they are purposeless. Consequently GDP growth will continue to dominate conservation, as long as the lurking inconsistency remains unchallenged.

Whitehead's observation that, 'it is not popular to dwell on the absolute contradiction here involved', remains true 75 years later. This wilful neglect has allowed the lurking inconsistency to metastasise into the marrow of modernity. The Enlightenment, with its rejection of teleology, certainly illuminated some hidden recesses of superstition in the so-called Dark Ages. But the angle of its cold light has also cast a deep shadow forward into the modern world, obscuring the reality of purpose. To conserve the biosphere we will first have to reclaim purpose from that darkness. What do you think about that, Sophie?

the irrationality of
homo œkonomicus

HERMAN E. DALY

As his two preceding lectures have indicated, Herman Daly is sharply critical of attitudes in the economics profession. In this interview with an American journalist, Karl Hansen, in 1995, he spells out his criticisms in some detail.

Karl Hansen *Is the intellectual higher ground in economics increasingly up for grabs?*

Herman Daly Good question. My hope is the answer's 'yes'. And in the long run I think the answer is yes. But currently academic economics is quite dismal. University departments of economics are just wasting everyone's time. That's harsh but I think there are some interesting problems, that might otherwise have been dealt with by economics, that don't go away just because economists say, 'Well, that's not economics … that's … economic policy or environment or something else.' So they keep themselves exceedingly pure just working out the logical implications of what they have taken to calling the 'canonical assumptions', which is a revealing phrase.

There are certain canonical assumptions which define what it all is, and then you play games and [make] logical derivations on those assumptions. And the world and its real problems are just sort of left to one side. And if you try to apply any of that to the real world it's a

real problem because you've abstracted from what are the most important things. The first thing the canonical assumptions abstract from is any notion of community—nothing but isolated individuals, *Homo œkonomicus*. Community both in the social sense of our identities being made up of interrelationships, and community in the ecological sense of mutual dependence of species in the natural world. So in the core of economics, those things are abstracted from.

When you say that, economists sometimes get mad. They say, 'Oh well, look here at this area of environmental economics, it's been developing here. We're talking about those problems.' Okay, they're beginning to. Problems are being forced on them, and so they're making whatever ad hoc adjustments are necessary to try to deal with the problem. But it's not a satisfactory situation. And I think it [the intellectual higher ground] is up for grabs in the sense that it's beginning to be challenged and I think that some of the popes of the profession are getting rather defensive. But it's still the ant versus the elephant. They're still pretty much totally in control of all the major journals and the major university positions, etcetera, etcetera. So it's maybe a little wishful thinking on my part to say it's up for grabs, but I think it will be.

Who are the 'popes of the profession'?

Oh my. Well, people like Lawrence Summers and all the Nobel laureates. Robert Solow, Milton Friedman, folks like that. All the faculty of the major universities.

I think a lot of people would say you're a pope or upcoming pope of the profession...

Well, that's interesting. I suppose that whatever influence I have is much more directly on the general public and not so much through the profession. So that the people who would look favourably on me... Well, I don't know ... It just remains to be seen how it plays out because they're not the people in the positions of power.

Okay, if the intellectual higher ground is up for grabs, what is the answer? Is it ecological economics? Economic anthropology...?

Well that's what John Cobb and I tried to deal with in *For the Common Good*—what if economics is to move away from being a self-centred academic discipline interested only in working out the consequences of its own assumptions and if it's to engage itself more in the world. And we argued that you have to shift from *homo œkonomicus* as the isolated individual to the idea of person in community, whose identity is largely a function of his relationships in community with others and with the ecosystem. So that this community perspective of social and ecological interdependence is critical—and

for the future. Economists say 'Oh yeah, well we dealt with that.' But you go and you look at the basic textbooks and you get the standard isolated circular flow of firms to households, of exchange value going around and around. There's no environment. The theorems of underlying supply and demand are purely individualistic. There's no social element in any of it. And so some people will say, 'Oh you're just criticising bad elementary textbooks. I mean, the profession has gone way beyond that.' Well, wait a minute. Where do people learn their economics? All our congressmen, whatever they know they got out of some basic elementary textbook, and what good is it ... Should the elementary textbook be consistent with more advanced economics? And if advanced economics discovers something is wrong, shouldn't that be reflected in the next edition of the textbook? So I don't accept that. I think the textbooks really show you what are the most fundamental positions that the public accepts so that it is quite fair to... I would say that we have to work into economic theory not only the circular flow of exchange value which is important but also this one-way throughput of matter and energy—the digestive tract as well as the circulatory system—because it's that that ties us to the environment. The sources of low-entropy matter-energy, and the sinks for absorption of high-entropy matter-energy. And that has to be built into the very foundation of Economics, Chapter 1. Not tacked on at the end of a chapter on Depletion and Pollution as Externalities like 'Oh gee, we never expected this to happen but it did so now we have to say something about it.' It's built into the very functioning of the economic process that we have to deplete, we have to pollute, that we have to keep those two activities within some sort of ecological constraint and what those constraints are affects the optimal scale or size of the total economy relative to the environment. And that big question has been completely left out. There's no concept of an optimal scale of a total macro-economic system relative to the larger ecosystem. And that fundamentally we have to bring into economics along with the standard questions of allocation and distribution. Some people are beginning to see that, others are really resisting it. So it's strange. The International Society for Ecological Economics— although there are a lot of different opinions there, I think it tends to cluster around the vision which I just stated. There's another group in Sweden, the Beijer Institute for Ecological Economics, which much more leans toward standard economics. They are recognising that there are real problems of dealing with the environment and that maybe standard economics hasn't done enough in that direction, but they have a great deal of faith that the same basic paradigm will function in that direction. So that's a tension. On the one hand, you have people who are fundamentally standard economists but they say 'Oh here's a set of problems we do need to think about a little more.' And then another group of people who say you really need to change your whole way of looking at things in order to adequately deal with those problems. So there's that tension, and it's a very difficult tension. Because on the one hand you don't want to alienate people, you want to talk to economists, you want to build bridges with economists, you want to bring their talents to bear on important questions. On the other hand, you don't want to be co-opted and swallowed up and have the basic important issue reduced to something that's not so important and fails to see the point and doesn't really engage the issue and sort of co-opts things. So it's a difficult tension.

Why is free trade necessarily bad for the environment? ...

My problem with free trade is partly due to the environment—but it's larger than that. I think it's a bad social policy and bad environmental policy. By free trade, what I mean is deregulated international commerce. So the opposite of free trade is not autarky or no trade. The opposite is not state trade or total monopolisation of trade. The opposite of free trade, which is deregulatory, is regulated trade. Trade which is regulated in the national interest by governments involved. And the notion that there should be no national interest [in] this trade across national boundaries, that the state has no interest in this, that this should be left entirely to the mutual benefit of the trading parties ... I mean imagine if this logic were applied say to corporations—individuals within corporations just trade with each for their own mutual advantage—nonsense! ... Every deal that corporation people make has to be vetted up through higher authorities to make sure that it's really in the interest of the larger entity. And so I think the same thing is the case with trade across national boundaries. The reason again goes back to community because if you have the free flow of goods and capital and, increasingly, labour across national boundaries, then you really lose any possibility of policy at the national level. You can't have an interest rate policy that's different from your neighbour because capital is mobile. You can't have environmental cost internalisation standards that are different from other people because if you have higher standards that'll raise your prices higher than your trading partners', and you put your own people at a disadvantage. So you have to have some equalising kind of tariff. So the argument is not that there should be no trade. Trade can be very beneficial. But the argument is that trade should not be based on standards-lowering competition. You have to maintain certain standards. And standards-lowering competition can be weakening the environmental standards to give cheapness, weakening social insurance standards and safety standards to get cheapness. Weakening standards of child labour ... throwing in prison labour even, [about] which even GATT says, 'Prison labour is too much, we'll retaliate against that.' So I think maintaining these social standards which have been actually hard-won over many years—I mean the length of working day, that's been limited; child labour, these sorts of things. You can make products cheaper if you lengthen the working day, if you employ children ... and so I think there has to be this national community protection of basic standards. We can't allow that to be competed away in the name of free trade. Interestingly, the classical doctrine of free trade as it came from David Ricardo is much more in line with what I've just been saying because in that system, capital did not cross national boundaries. Capital stayed at home and labour stayed at home. The only things that were traded were goods. So you really did have a much more community/national orientation. You have national capital co-operated with national labour—albeit with class conflict, the national community was able to contain that class conflict. You had national labour and national capital co-operating to make national goods, and those goods that competed internationally with other countries and their teams. Nowadays that's all gone, nowadays you have free capital mobility and so you have a capitalist of one nation [saying] to the labourers of that nation, 'Sorry guys, we live in a global economy, I can employ

labour at one-fifth of what you want and I can bring the product right back here and sell it, so you guys are out of line, too bad.' And the labour comes back and says, 'Well gee you know, there are bonds of national community.' 'I just told you we live in a global community. All that stuff is over with. All that old national stuff that caused wars. We live in a global economy. Everything is going to be peace now. Don't you want the Chinese labourer to be as rich as you are—are you a racist?', and on and on. So this idea of

There is no global community. Where community really exists is at the national and subnational level where people take on mutual responsibilities for each other.

mutual responsibilities in a national community [is] being dissolved by this idea of the global world economy. We have a global community now superseding the national community—that's passé, now it's global community. That sounds good if you say it fast enough and don't stop to think about. But it's empty. There is no global community. Where community really exists is at the national and subnational level where people take on mutual responsibilities for each other. Not at the global. Now maybe someday there will be a global community. But our view—of John Cobb and I—is we're all in favour of global community, but it would have to be a federation of strong national communities—a community of national communities. And the present vision is not of a federated community of communities, the present vision is of a cosmopolitan world without borders in which you erase national community and replace it with this globalised single sort of tightly integrated world community. So the vision of a globally integrated economy is really a single system. You have one tightly integrated system that's mutually dependent across the globe. That's a very dangerous

To the degree possible, strive for self-sufficency.

kind of system—something goes wrong, you're in big trouble. We prefer nations to be much more fundamentally self-sufficient, not totally self-sufficient, that's too expensive. But to the degree possible, strive for self-sufficiency and maintain loose international trading relations to make up for where it's hard to be self-sufficient. I mean everyone can make their own aspirin and matches, you don't need to trade multinationally for that. But there are some things that you do need to trade for. That's the kind of vision that we put forward, and you maintain more local control over your economic life. If you don't, then control is shifted far away and the foreigners who control the capital investment in your country may be lovely decent people, they may even be nicer than the local people, but they're far away and they don't really know or have an interest and a feel for what happens there. This is a vision that John Maynard Keynes expressed very similar kinds of notions [to] when he wrote on national self-sufficiency, and his views along with others have kind of been swept aside in this globalisation mania, which really serves the interests of the global multinational corporations because what holds them in check is the nation state—the rules of the nation. So if they can sort of weaken the nation and play off one against the other, then they don't have any real restraints. ... The other way of controlling international capital would be to have international

government and some people advocate that. I see that as frightening. International government. Some things have to be international, for example, we have to deal with global CO_2 and things [like that] at a global level. But again that has to be a federation of national governments because once you have a treaty for global CO_2 or something, who's going to enforce it? It has to be the national governments who signed the treaties. They have to be strong enough to enforce within their own boundaries the conditions that they agreed to in the international treaty. And if capital, labour and goods flow freely across their borders they don't have any basis for exercising the control that they agreed to. Long-winded answer, I'm sorry.

Regarding World Bank leadership ... should economists continue to dominate affairs at the Bank ...?

... I think economists exercise too large an influence at the World Bank. ... You might think of the Bank as kind of the functioning church in the world out there trying to do good in the world. And the economists at the World Bank all went to seminary and learned their theology and they're trying to apply that theology in the world to do good. Well I think they learned bad theology. I think the seminaries were teaching bad theology and that takes us back to the first point about the intellectual high ground in economics. All economists who work at the World Bank, whether they're from Africa or California, I mean they got their degrees from Harvard, MIT, Oxford, McGill, you know all these top-rate universities across the world, which all teach pretty much the same thing. And so that's their view of the world. And, give 'em credit, they're very often wonderful people trying to do good in the world on the basis of what they know and what they've been taught. So I think the real problem goes back to the academic departments of economics which are supplying the World Bank economists and which are still directly supplying advice to the World Bank. And of course since the World Bank is populated by the products of these places, they're eager to receive the advice from them, and I think that's a fundamental problem. Now, since I pick on economists so much I should say though that when you look around, is there some other discipline that's better? … for development decision-making. That tends to make me a little more appreciative of economists because the problems that I've been criticising economists for are problems of the disciplinary structure of knowledge. And that's not just limited to economists. All universities have this disciplinary structure in which the discipline is defined in its own terms, in an inward-looking way. So while I would like to see more influence of sociologists and anthropologists and certainly ecologists and environmentalists at the Bank, I wouldn't want to turn it all over to them. I wouldn't want any of those disciplines to be as dominant as economists are. So I guess my argument would be for a more diverse set [of] disciplinary backgrounds. I wouldn't want to replace economists with sociologists. I don't think that would do the job. On the other hand, I think a greater influence of sociologists and especially ecologists and environmentalists at the Bank would be absolutely needed.

If economics has been so successful because of the tools it has given people to make decisions, what new tools do you think should be added to the development decision-maker's tool kit?

I like your questions. I think economics has been very successful in one very

important area: allocative efficiency. So that [regarding] the efficiency of allocation of scarce resources among competing ends, economists have preached the importance of decentralised decision-making co-ordinated by markets and the price system. This has historically dramatically proven to be much better than central planning—collapse of the former Soviet Union and so forth—[and] is something that needs to be recognised and taken seriously. As far as market control of allocation of resources [goes], I think economics has provided a whole lot. And good reasons were given for why this is so. Now, my problem is that allocation is only one fundamental economic problem. It's important, but it's only one. There are two others, which I mentioned briefly before: there's distribution and scale. So allocation is about how resources get divided up among different users— how much goes to produce bicycles, how much to cars, how much to houses. You know, is that efficient given what people want and their ability to pay? You end up giving people the most that you can get of what they want with the resources available. That's a question of efficiency—are allocations efficient or inefficient? The distribution question is a question of justice. Who gets all the stuff that was produced. Does it go to you or me. And that's a question of justice—is it fair, is it a fair distribution? And then the third question of scale—the total amount that gets produced in all of the resources and the depletion and pollution generated by the use of those resources. Is that at a total scale which is within the absorptive and regenerative capacity of the ecosystem? Or are you destroying natural capital at a rate which is too great? The welfare effects of destroying natural capital may be greater than the welfare benefits of what you produced. And whose products required the destruction of that national capital? So just from a purely anthropocentric view, not giving any value to other species or nature intrinsically, just as an instrument for human betterment, you still run into this limit of scale. So I think those are the two questions which economists have not dealt with. They have logically recognised the necessity of the distribution question and so standard economic theory says that all theorems about allocative efficiency pre-suppose some given distribution, which may be just or unjust. They recognise that, but they don't emphasise it. It's there but it's not front and centre. And the scale question is not

> *Economics has been negligent regarding distributive justice and extremely negligent regarding optimal scale.*

even recognised. That's off the radar screen. And to the extent that it's recognised, well it's just a matter of property rights—'If we just get prices better in property rights, then the problem disappears. It doesn't matter if we grow more as long as we pay the costs of growing more.' So my view is that while economics has done a great deal in the matter of economic efficiency, it has been negligent regarding distributive justice and extremely negligent regarding optimal scale. So those two things are where the effort should go. We've pretty much given good answers to the allocation problem, I don't think we need to spend time and effort proving once again that the market is efficient, investigating every possible variation. I mean okay, there's room for people who are interest-

ed in that, I mean fine, I don't want to tell people what they should do, let people study that. But socially, I don't think that's where the big payoff is right now because past success in that has been impressive, and we need some success in the areas of distribution and scale and that's where we need to devote the effort.

Can you think of any particular tools in those areas which you take a shining to?

I think that yes, there has been an evolution in policy which has forced us to deal with the scale question. And that has been in things like the bubble system* where [there are] marketable licences to deplete or pollute. And these kinds of policies are excellent because they clearly say the first problem you have to solve is the scale problem—what's the total amount of emissions that are acceptable in this watershed or airshed or county or whatever. The second question is, given that there's that total limit, that means it's no longer a free good, that means it's valued: the distribution question—who owns it. You've created a new asset which is now limited—who owns it? Shall we give it equally to all citizens? Shall we give it historically on the basis of who's been using it most? So you have to face the question of fairness of distribution. And then in third place—after you solve the scale question, on ecological grounds presumably, after you solve the distribution question, on equity grounds presumably—only in third place is the market trading allowed to solve the allocation question and efficiency. So I think that [has] provided a way of moving in the policy area ... And since it seems to

---

* An example of the 'bubble system' is the arrangement made by the EU countries in relation to the Kyoto Protocol. Under this, the EU nations undertook to reduce their greenhouse gas emissions as a bloc to 93% of its 1990 level by 2010. They then decided amongst themselves which countries would make what cuts and which countries would be allowed (like Ireland) to increase emissions so that the overall reduction target was met. (eds)

have evolved pragmatically, I think it's way ahead of a lot of standard economic theory. It just sort of pragmatically brought in scale without creating a big fuss about it. ... And of course population issues, we have to deal with population limitation and that's been a long and heated subject but I think we do need to deal with that much more forthrightly. And, well, the scale question—that's part of the scale question of population times per capita resources or total resources. So one way of reducing scale is dealing with population, the other way is per capita consumption. So both of those I think are important. So in the North we have to focus more on limiting our per capita consumption. In the South I think the focus has to be more on limiting numbers. And that might be the basis of a kind of North-South bargain. Because currently it's very difficult for the North to tell the South you should limit your numbers so you save all these resources that we can gobble up in over-consumption. And it's also difficult for the South to say to us, you should limit your per capita consumption and save these resources so we can dissipate them all in population growth down here. So it seems to me there has to be some basis of a global agreement or compact. And that idea of limiting scale, by operating both on population and per capita consumption is to my mind a reasonable possibility. But I don't mean to tell you that's it's not something that popular, it's certainly not popular. The other thing I would mention in addition to this tradable permits notion and that some of us are pushing right now ... given the political climate, probably the best thing that we can pray for is ecological tax reform. Shift the tax base from income, labour, value-added onto that to which value is added—namely the resource flow. So tax throughput, tax depletion and pollution,

tax the resource flow—that to which you are adding value. That is what's causing depletion and pollution. Those are 'bads'. Tax bads, stop taxing goods. That's the basic idea. You don't want to tax what you want more of. You do want to tax what you want less of. This could be sold as a revenue-neutral shift. We're not going to tax more, we're going to tax differently, we're going to tax different things to instil different incentives. And the incentives that result from this would be not to dampen the incentive to work or to accumulate capital or to improve it, but to dampen the incentive to use more resources. So we would then collect money from the resource flow, which is what is tightly associated with depletion and pollution. And that would I think be a move toward efficiency, and standard economists agree with that to a large extent. It's kind of a political movement. In Europe, in Germany, Ernst von Weizsäcker and others have pushed this idea very strongly and I think convincingly. So it seems to be kind of the one policy I can think of now which in a conservative political time might have some political chance of being considered, and yet which could still have some real bite, some real effect. Now, some people would immediately say that it's very optimistic to think that it's politically feasible ... given our recent experience here [in the US] with an attempt to pass a gasoline tax. So this would be kind of [a] gasoline tax writ large on all resources. Well you know, maybe so. It wouldn't be politically easy, but it does seem to me that it's in the realm of feasibility. There's so much logic to it, and I think your neo-classical economist [and] your ecological economist pretty much are in agreement that this would be a good sort of thing.

Re revenue neutrality—not within a sector?
Absolutely. It would be revenue-neutral only in an aggregate sense that the government raises the same amount of revenue. By raising it differently it would impinge on different groups differently so that you might say that everyone would benefit by a reduction in income tax and everyone would pay more in resource taxes. However the next balance in each case is going to be different. Some people or some interests may consume a whole lot of resources, and so there would [be] a shifting incidence—the incidence would fall differently, so I think that probably initially to gain political acceptance there would have to be some compensation for the differing incidence. So maybe corporations who are adversely affected by the shift would ... maybe they would get a little greater forgiveness

on income taxes or something. But those are important questions that have to be worked out, it's pretty hard to know exactly what this incidence would be. And one would have to move towards it gradually, a certain amount each year. We couldn't just do an abrupt, all-at-once shift. It would have to be a gradual thing which would give people a chance to see what's coming and adapt to it before it hits, and make their adjustments.

Thank you very much.

Thank you.

[This interview was conducted at College Park, Maryland, on 8 February 1995. It first appeared in *Developing Ideas,* a magazine published until 1999 by the International Institute for Sustainable Development in Canada, and is reprinted with the IISD's consent.]

DR DAVID KORTEN

the civilising of global society

DAVID C. KORTEN

We live at one of the most critical and exciting moments in all of human history.
We face both the necessity and the opportunity to reinvent society.

It is a substantial privilege to present the annual FEASTA lecture and to be part of your effort here in Ireland to challenge the destructive forces of corporate globalisation and global capitalism. And I want to thank my good friend and colleague Richard Douthwaite from whose work I have learned so much for his role in arranging this presentation. Since you have already had lectures from Herman Daly, Richard Douthwaite, and Vandana Shiva, you are already fully familiar with the limits of corporate globalisation and the ideology of economic growth. So I'm going to concentrate on sharing some of my most current thinking on understanding the deeper roots of our crisis and the nature of the global citizen movement that is emerging to counter the destructive forces of global capitalism.

The citizen protests in Seattle the end of last year brought the World Trade Organisation meeting to a stand-still and focused world attention on an increasingly visible tension between two extraordinarily powerful social forces.

One is the force of corporate globalisation driven by a once seemingly invincible alliance between the world's largest mega-corporations and its most powerful governments. In the eyes of its propo-

nents, the integration of national economies into a seamless global economy is spurring economic growth through the expansion of trade to bring material prosperity to all the world, spread democracy, and create the financial resources and new technologies needed to protect the global environment. But, most of all, it is making many of these proponents very rich and powerful, which may have something to do with their enthusiasm.

The second force is the global democracy movement being advanced by a planetary citizen alliance known as global civil society. Before Seattle '99, this force found expression in the national democracy movements that played a critical role in the break-up of the Soviet empire and the fall of apartheid in South Africa—and in other great progressive social movements of our time, such as the civil rights, environmental, peace, and women's movements.

The corporate force is centrally planned by a well-organised and well-funded corporate élite and, PR rhetoric notwithstanding, the driving motive is a competitive drive for profits. The citizen force depends largely on voluntary energy, is self-organising, and is grounded in a deep

46

value commitment to democracy, community, equity, and the web of planetary life. Although it has no identifiable organisational or institutional form, it is taking on a striking sense of coherence and acquiring the power to at least make the corporate élites very nervous. Its impetus comes from the awakening of millions of people of every nationality, race, and religious affiliation to the contradictions of corporate globalisation, which, contrary to its claims, is enriching the few at the expense of the many, replacing democracy with an élitist and authoritarian corporate rule, destroying the environment, and eroding the relationships of trust and caring that are the essential foundation of a civilised society—all in the mindless pursuit of money to further enrich those who already have more money than they could possibly use.

Let's look more closely at the story of the Seattle WTO protests that the corporate media pretty much missed. My home is on Bainbridge Island, a 35-minute ferry ride from Seattle, so Seattle is rather like my home town. The media portrayed the demonstrators as anti-trade. In fact the issue that brought 70,000 people from all around the world to Seattle's streets was democracy. They were protesting corporate rule—of which the WTO is a powerful symbol. The violent response of the police with plastic bullets, tear gas, and pepper spray dramatically confirmed the demonstrator's worst fears about the state of democracy in America and the openness of the WTO process to citizen input.

The Seattle protests also signalled a historic shift in progressive politics in America from the politics of identity and special interests to a politics of the whole. It gave expression to a grand convergence of social movements that is giving birth to the global democracy movement. Union workers, environmentalists, mem-

DAVID C. KORTEN holds MBA and PhD degrees from Stanford Business School and taught for five years at Harvard Business School before joining the Harvard Institute for International Development to head a Ford Foundation project to strengthen national family planning programmes. He moved to Southeast Asia in the late 1970s, working first for the Ford Foundation and then as regional advisor on development management to USAID. Eventually, disillusioned with the official aid system, he spent the last five years of his fifteen in Asia working with NGOs identifying why development was failing.

He came to realise that the deepening poverty, growing inequality, environmental devastation, and social disintegration he was observing in Asia were also being experienced in nearly every country in the world. Moreover, the United States was actively promoting policies that made matters worse. For the world to survive, the United States must change, and he returned to the US in 1992 to help bring that change about. He has since written two highly influential books, **When Corporations Rule the World** (1995) and **The Post Corporate World: Life After Capitalism** (1999).

bers of the faith community, feminists, gays, human rights and peace activists and many others acknowledged the reality that either we work together to build true democracy and create a world that works for every person, for every living being, or we will have a world that works for no one.

The churches mobilised around the call of Jubilee 2000—debt forgiveness for low-income countries—giving expression to a growing awareness among people of faith that the call for economic and social justice is a foundation of Christian teaching. Labour unions reached out in solidarity with all the world's workers in a call to guarantee basic rights and living wages for all working people everywhere in a realisation that, in a global economy, unless all workers have rights and living wages, none will have them. Environmentalists and union leaders joined in common alliance out of a realisation that there will be no jobs without a healthy environment. And that without secure jobs and labour rights, the environment will be destroyed in the struggle for survival.

> We are witness to the emergence of an epic struggle between corporate globalisation and popular democracy.

Then there were the real heroes of Seattle, the youth who put their bodies on the line in the face of brutal police violence to bring the WTO meeting to a stand still. Tired of being manipulated and lied to by a system that is stealing their future, they spent months training one another in the principles and methods of non-violent direct action, preparing themselves for a highly decentralised consensus-based mode of organising that modelled the radically democratic societies they intend to build. They proved that radical democracy can be highly effective, even under violent assault by the brutal forces of a police state.

Similar demonstrations against corporate globalisation of comparable or even larger scale have become common place around the world, with notable examples in Geneva, the UK, France, Brazil, India, Thailand, and many others.

We are witness to the emergence of an epic struggle between corporate globalisation and popular democracy. Though it most certainly involves issues of class, it is more than a class struggle. It is a struggle between humanity and its institu-

tions—between life and money—between two cultural belief systems that stand in stark and irreconcilable conflict.

Catholic theologian Thomas Berry traces the underlying problem to the false premise of an obsolete scientific story that has diminished our image of ourselves and deprived our lives of meaning. He makes the case that our survival as a species may depend as much as anything on discovering a new story that gives us a reason to live—a story that helps us ask one of the most basic of questions: why? It is the story of a living cosmos and the human search for our place of service to life's epic journey. The easiest way to demonstrate the significance of Berry's insight is to recite to you a version of the new story grounded in discoveries from the cutting edge of contemporary science that places our current dilemma in its larger context.

This story begins a very, very long time ago—perhaps as much as 15 billion years ago—when a new universe flared into being with a great flash—dispersing tiny energy particles, the stuff of creation, across the vastness of space. With the passing of time these particles self-organised into atoms, which swirled into great clouds that coalesced into galaxies of countless stars that grew, died, and were reborn as new stars, star systems, and planets. The cataclysmic energies unleashed by the births and deaths of billions of suns converted simple atoms into more complex atoms and melded atoms into even more complex molecules—each step opening new possibilities for the growth and evolution of the whole.

Each stage transcended the stage before in order, definition, and capacity as the drama of creation unfolded. It seemed that a great intelligence had embarked on a grand quest to know itself through the discovery and realisation of the possibilities of its being.

More than eleven billion years after the quest began there was an extraordinary breakthrough on a planet later to be known as Earth. Here the cosmos gave birth to the first living beings—microscopic in size, they were the simplest of single-celled bacteria. Inconsequential though they seemed, they embodied an enormous creative potential and, with time, created the building blocks of living knowledge that made possible the incredible accomplishments to follow. They discovered in turn the arts of fermentation, photosynthesis, and respiration fundamental to all life. They learned to exchange genetic material through their cell walls to share their discoveries with one another in a grand co-operative enterprise that created the planet's first global communication system—billions of years before the Internet. And they transformed and stabilised the chemical composition of the entire planet's atmosphere. As the fruits of life's learning multiplied, individual cells evolved to become more complex and diverse.

In due course, individual cells discovered the advantages of joining with one another in clusters to create complex multi-celled organisms—converting the matter of the planet into the splendid web of living plants and animals with capacities far beyond those of any individual cell. Those among the new creatures that found a niche in which they could at once sustain themselves and contribute to the life of the whole survived. Those that proved unable to find or create their niche of service expired. Continuously experimenting, interrelating, creating, building, the evolving web of life unfolded into a living tapestry of astonishing variety, beauty, awareness, and capacity for intelligent choice.

Then, a mere 2.6 million years ago, quite near the end of our 15-billion year story, there came the most extraordinary achievement of all, the creation of a being with a capacity, far beyond that of any creature that had come before, to reflect on its own consciousness, to experience with awe the beauty and mystery of creation, to articulate, communicate and share learning, to reshape the material world to its own ends, and to anticipate and intentionally choose its own future. It was the living spirit's most daring experiment and a stunning co-operative achievement.

Each of these creatures, humans they were called, was comprised of from 30 to 70 trillion individual living, self-regulating, self-reproducing cells. More than half the dry weight of each human consisted of the individual micro-organisms required to metabolise its food and create the vitamins essential to its survival. Altogether, it took more than a 100 trillion individual living entities joined in an exquisitely balanced co-operative union to create each of these extraordinary creatures.

These new beings—these humans— had such potential to contribute to the journey of the whole. Yet their freedom to choose their own destiny carried a risk. Failing to recognise and embrace their responsibility to the whole, they turned their extraordinary abilities to ends ultimately destructive of the whole of life, destroying in a mere 100 years much of the living natural capital it had taken billions of years of evolution to create.

Some attribute this tragedy to a genetic flaw that doomed humans to the blind pursuit of greed and violence. Yet the vast majority of humans were generous and caring. More compelling is the argument that the ideology of what humans called their Scientific Revolution stripped humans of their sense of meaning, called forth their greed and violence, and made generosity and caring seem somehow naive. This ideology taught that matter is the only reality and that the universe is best thought of as a giant clockwork set in motion at the beginning of creation and left to run down as the tension in its spring expires. It further taught that life is only an accidental outcome of material complexity, consciousness an illusion. Though such beliefs defied logic, denied the human experience, stripped life of meaning, and were contrary to reality, they became a foundation of the dominant Western culture.

Thomas Hobbes, a noted philosopher of the Scientific Revolution, elaborated on these flawed beliefs to articulate a theory of human behaviour and a moral philosophy that ultimately became the theoretical and philosophical foundation of humanity's dominant economic system. He argued that since life has no meaning and human behaviour is determined solely by appetites and aversions, good is merely that which gives oneself pleasure; evil that which brings pain. The rational person seeks a life of material indulgence unburdened by concern for others. These beliefs became the foundation of a cultural system known as modernism and an economic system known as capitalism.

Though there was much ado about a conflict between scientists and theologians, they actually arrived at a mutual accommodation in many of their core views. In an act revealing of human hubris, Western theologians had long before created their God in their own image, an elder male with a white beard who ruled a kingdom called heaven. This God was so powerful that by the estimate of the Western religions, he created the cosmos, the earth and all its living beings in a mere six days—presumably for the sole benefit of the humans he created on the sixth day. On the seventh day, his work thus done, he took a rest.

The main issue on which scientists and theologians were inclined to consequential differences centred on whether or not God returned after his vacation to tend to the needs of those humans he chose to favour. The theologians generally believed that he returned to keep a book on who, by his rules, was naughty or nice, reward the worthy with material abundance, and punish the unworthy with sickness and poverty. Some noted that by this characterisation God bore a striking resemblance to a mythical figure humans called Santa Claus.

Those with wealth and power were, by definition, worthy in God's eyes and the poor and powerless were unworthy. Thus it was that Western theology affirmed the righteousness of both materialism and political oppression and absolved humans of responsibility either for one another or for the Earth. Furthermore, since humans were the end product of creation, not an instrument of its continued unfolding, it followed that what ever the deficiencies of the world as any individual might find it, it was to be accepted as God's will.

Some believed that God would return, in his own good time, to establish peace and justice for all. Others looked to the afterlife for perfection and considered their time on Earth as something akin to a short layover in a cheap hotel on their way to paradise. Either way it was in the hands of a god who resided apart in a far place.

Nowhere was the rejection of human responsibility for the lot of society greater than in the economic system humans called capitalism. One of capitalism's defining features was a consumer culture cultivated by saturating the media with an endlessly-repeated message that consumption of whatever product was advertised would bring meaning and love to the empty and lonely lives of the otherwise unworthy. When consumption inevitably failed to substitute for meaning, more consumption was pre-scribed as the solution.

Increasingly the creative energies of the species turned to building institu-tions dedicated to endlessly increasing consumption through a process called economic growth. Growth became such an obsession that no one seemed to care what was consumed. Nor did they seem to notice that the basic livelihood needs of the many went unmet while a fortu-nate few gorged themselves on luxuries. Indeed, a privileged minority became so obsessed with the futile attempt to fill their empty lives with stuff they failed to notice that the growth they so prized was destroying the life support system of the planet and the social fabric of the society, and the lives of billions of people.

Even more perverse was the role of what humans called money—a mysteri-ous kind of sacred number that was cre-ated out of nothing by banks by loaning it into existence. Though most humans had little idea where money came from, they were socially conditioned to accept it in exchange for things of real value like their labour, food, land, and shelter. Since money was the ticket that allowed people to accumulate stuff, those who already had so much stuff they didn't know what to do with it turned their attention to accumulating sacred numbers called money that banks happily stored for them in computers. As this accumulation served no evident purpose, its practition-ers turned it into a competitive game in which the winner was the one with the most financial assets. The top players were called billionaires. A well-known magazine called *Forbes* regularly pub-lished their current scores and rankings.

This game became life's purpose for those few who had the means to play. The most dedicated redesigned human insti-tutions to allow them to achieve ever more inflated scores. Any human with

extra cash was encouraged to join in by placing it in the hands of professional gamblers called money managers who traded currencies, bonds, and corporate shares in a great cyberspace casino called a financial market. In the course of their play, the money managers moved tril-lions of dollars around the world at the speed of light, trashing the currencies and economies of hapless countries whose policies displeased them and the share

> One of capitalism's defining features was a consumer culture cultivated by saturating the media with an endlessly-repeated message that consumption of whatever product was advertised would bring meaning and love to the empty and lonely lives of the otherwise unworthy.

prices of corporations that produced less profits than they expected. In the wake of their moves whole governments fell and hundreds of thousands lost their jobs.

These corporations were a frightfully perverse sort of legal entity designed to allow the accumulation of massive finan-cial power with little or no accountabili-ty for the consequences of its use. Some corporations were served by the labour of hundreds of thousands of people and received millions of dollars in subsidies from government. Yet the law stipulated that only shareholders were entitled to share in its profits. Employees were expected to leave their personal values at the door when they reported for work. Workers could be fired without notice or recourse. Whole communities were abandoned when a corporation found it more profitable to move its factories elsewhere.

To satisfy the money managers, corporations gave politicians huge sums of money in return for which the politicians voted corporations subsidies and special privileges. Tiring of the inconvenience involved in doing deals with politicians one country at a time, the major players created something called the World Trade Organisation—or WTO. Here unelected trade representatives loyal to the corporate interest established international rules that obliged all countries to extend special rights and privileges to global corporations. Incredibly, the WTO could require any country to change its laws to conform to WTO rules, even though such action might be contrary to the interests and preferences of its own citizens. Invariably the rules of the WTO gave corporations ever greater freedom to roam the world converting the living wealth of society and planet into money.

They turned the natural living capital of the earth into money by strip-mining forests, fisheries and mineral deposits, producing toxic chemicals and dumping hazardous wastes. But it isn't just natural capital they placed at risk. They also turned human capital into money by employing workers under substandard working conditions that left them physically handicapped. They turned the social capital of society into money when they paid substandard wages that destroyed workers emotionally, leading to family and community breakdown and violence. They turned the living trust of public institutions into money by bribing politicians with campaign contributions to convert the taxes of working people into inflated corporate profits through public subsidies, bailouts and tax exemptions.

Then, as the year 2000 dawned, a remarkable thing happened. Millions of humans started waking up, as if from a deep trance, to the beauty, joy, and meaning of life. They began to reject consumerism and took to the streets by the hundreds of thousands demanding a restoration of democracy, an end to corporate rule, and respect for the needs of all people and other living things. The process of building a new politics and a new consciousness was set in motion. It was, however, as yet a tiny spark of hope in comparison to the forces of corporate capitalism that were consuming the Earth.

There are indications that humans may be on the threshold of a new intellectual and social maturity as new scientific findings continue to demonstrate the fallacies of the old story and its underlying belief systems. Yet so far they still resist coming to terms with the social implications of their scientific understanding that matter exists only as a continuing dance of flowing energies, that creation is an ongoing self-organising process, that life is fundamentally a co-operative process, and that Earth's successful species are those that learn to meet their own needs in ways that serve the larger web of life.

Perhaps with time they will come to grasp the deeper philosophical implications of these findings. For example that the material world is largely illusion, conscious intelligence is the ground from which all else is manifest, and humans are an instrument of creation's continued unfolding—not its end accomplishment. Though embodied in ancient human wisdom, human's largely dismiss these and other truths as superstition. Perhaps their rediscovery will bring them a renewed sense of life's profound meaning, inspire a search for their own place in service to life's incredible journey, and lead them to transform their values and institutions in ways that unleash potentials within their being beyond their current imagining.

This story, of course, is our story, the choices are our choices. The challenge before us is to transform a global society dedicated to the love of money into a global society dedicated to the love of life and the continuing exploration of its possibilities.

To help us better understand the nature of this challenge, I want to establish a framework that may enable us to understand the ideal of a civil society and

sionary power inherent in the ability to control access to the means of living, as well as to material luxuries.

- Culture is the sphere in which the society defines the values, symbols, and beliefs that are its sources of meaning and identity. It holds the normative power to determine what is valued and to legitimate institutions and the uses

THREE SPHERES OF COLLECTIVE LIFE

SPHERE	FUNCTION	POWER
POLITY	set and enforce rules governing relationships between members of society	threat: monopoly of coercive police and military power
ECONOMY	produce and exchange valued goods and services	exclusionary: control over access to means of living
CULTURE	define values, symbols, and beliefs that provide meaning and identity	normative: determine what is valued and legitimate

the larger possibilities of the global democracy movement. This framework divides society into three primary spheres of collective life: polity, economy, and culture.

- Polity is the sphere in which rules are formalised and enforced regarding the rights and obligations that govern relationships among members of the society. It holds the threat power inherent in its monopoly over police and military power.
- Economy is the sphere that organises the production and exchange of valued goods and services. It holds the exclu-

of the power resources of polity and economy. Though cultural power may seem weak compared to the powers of coercion and exclusion, it is ultimately the decisive power in any society, as it is the foundation on which all else rests, including the powers vested in the formal institutions of the polity and the economy.

To complete our framework setting, let's turn to the question: What is the meaning of the term 'civil society'? Is it simply another term for the institutions of the nongovernmental, non-profit sector as implied by its customary use? Or is it something more? Jean Cohen and Andrew Arato, in their classic study Civil Society and Political Theory trace the idea of a civil society back to ancient Greece and Aristotle's concept of a politike koinonia or political community, later translated into Latin as societas civilis, or a civil society. For Aristotle the civil society is an ethical-political community of free and equal citizens who by mutual consent agree to live under a system of law that expresses the norms and values they share. The law thus becomes a codification of the values and practices of the shared culture and is largely self-enforcing. The requirement for coercive intervention by the state to maintain order is minimised because the necessary coherence of society is achieved primarily through self-organising processes that maximise the freedom of the individual in return for voluntary self-restraint that flows from a sense of shared values and civic responsibility.

The common contemporary practice of treating civil society as synonymous with all the varied organisations that are both non-governmental and non-profit—essentially the residual institutional space not occupied by the institutions of government and business—captures nothing of the more profound idealism embodied in the classical Aristotelian concept of a civil society. I think it also significant that our use of the term civil society is most often evoked by groups and individuals engaged in a struggle to reclaim social spaces for democratic engagement by free and equal citizens.

This suggests we might properly use the term civil society in two ways. The first is to refer to a society that has achieved the ideal of democratic civility. The second is to refer to those elements of a society that are actively engaged in expanding the social spaces in which the practice of democratic civility is both practised and valued as a step toward the creation of a civil society in the larger sense.

Now let's put the pieces of this puzzle together to see more clearly how the ideal of a civil society contrasts with the existing global capitalist economy. This schematic representation of a civil soci-

SOCIETY: CIVIL OR CAPITALIST ?

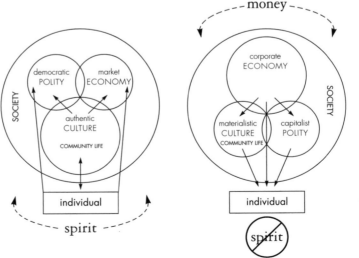

inspired by Nicanor Perlas, Shaping Globalization.

ety, which is adapted from a book on *Shaping Globalisation* by my Philippine colleague Nicanor Perlas, incorporates the underlying premise of the cosmic story I shared with you earlier that all being is a manifestation of a spiritual energy or intelligence. I realise that there will surely be some among you who find this premise in conflict with your own belief system. I honour that and ask only that you consider with me the ways in which our views of society and human possibilities may ultimately depend on our spiritual beliefs. One of the tragedies of our time is that we rarely discuss such issues with one another, even in private, and thus rarely subject our deepest beliefs to critical examination.

As a Hobbesian denial of the existence of spirit leads logically to a rejection of individual responsibility for anything other than one's personal material gratification, a recognition of the spiritual foundation of all existence leads naturally to a profound and freely embraced sense of responsibility for the whole and the mindful personal engagement of the individual in community, political, and economic life that is the necessary foundation of a truly civil society.

An authentic culture is the product of the active community life of individuals who are in contact with the spiritual energy that expresses itself through them. The shared values, symbols, and beliefs of an authentic culture are in turn the foundation on which the civil society's more formalised institutions of polity and economy are built. The life-affirming values of an authentic culture lead naturally to the creation of an authentically democratic polity based on a deep commitment to openness, active participation in political discourse, and to one person, one voice, one vote equality and the kind of consensus based decision making that our youth were practis-

ing in the streets of Seattle and in other equally sophisticated protest actions around the world. They also lead naturally to the creation of an authentic market economy comprised of local enterprises that provide productive and satisfying livelihoods for all, and vest in each individual a share in the ownership of the productive assets on which their livelihood depends. Such a society would be radically self-organising and predominantly co-operative in the manner of all healthy living systems, and would maximise the opportunity for each individual to develop and express their full creative potential in service to the life of the whole.

The contrast between a civil society so defined and our contemporary capitalist society is stark indeed. In the capitalist society, denial of the spirit results in a self-aggrandising materialism that looks to money as the defining value. Global financial markets that value life only for its liquidation price become the ruling institution. The control of productive resources becomes consolidated in global mega-corporations answerable only to the managers of huge investment funds who in turn are answerable only for the financial returns produced on their portfolios. The wages of working people are suppressed to increase the returns to those who already command vast financial holdings. Economic affairs are centrally planned by the heads of corporations that command internal economies larger than those of most states. Through ownership of mass media, influence over school curricula, commercialisation of the arts, and mass advertising, corporations dominate the processes of cultural regeneration—reinforcing the values of materialism and consumerism that strengthen corporate legitimacy, lead us to accept corporate logos as the sources of our identity and meaning, and alienate us all from our sense of connection to both our inner spirit and to the web of planetary and community life.

Similarly, the concentration of financial power in the corporate-ruled economy, combines with media control to allow corporate domination of the institutions of polity. The result is a one-dollar, one-vote democracy that concentrates control over the rule-making system in the hands of a wealthy élite and a persistent bias toward the passage of laws that favour yet further concentration of financial wealth at the expense of life. The excluded majority become increasingly alienated from political participation—lose interest even in voting, and by default yield even more power to big money.

As dependence on money for access to the necessities of life and the sources of identity increases, individual attention comes to centre on making money at the expense of spiritual and community life. Spiritually impoverished and dependent on corporations for money and what it will buy, individuals face enormous pressure to embrace the values of the corporate culture. Ideals of equity are out the window and individual freedom becomes largely illusory as the majority of people find themselves deeper in debt and giving ever more of their life energies over to the imperatives of the money machine. Those for whom the corporate system finds no use are simply discarded like so much trash.

Because it is destructive of life and spirit, the capitalist economy must be considered a social pathology. Even its apparent capacity to create vast wealth is largely illusory, because though it is producing ever more sophisticated gadgets and diversions, it is destroying the life-support systems of the planet and the social fabric of society. It is therefore destroying our most important wealth. Its institutions function as cancers that forget they are part of a larger whole and seek their own unlimited growth without regard to the consequences.

It is a powerful testimony to the reality and power of humanity's spiritual nature that millions of people all around the world are waking up from the cultural trance into which they have been lulled by capitalism's relentless siren song of material indulgence. Their resistance is not confined to street protests. They are also engaged proactively in creating civil alternatives, protecting nature, democratising the polity, rebuilding local market economies, and applying the values of civility in their own organisations. The resulting enclaves of civility are both expanding and melding. We call it globalising civil society, but we could as well call it the civilising of global society. Either way it is an extraordinary and increasingly powerful self-organising, bottom-up process of cultural and institutional transformation only partially understood even by its leaders.

One key to understanding the nature and significance of what is happening is to realise that though it has its political dimension, what is becoming manifest is predominantly a cultural movement that draws its increasingly powerful energy from a deep, yet still largely unrecognised global-scale culture shift toward the values of an authentic or integral culture. This values shift is creating the cultural foundations of a truly civil society.

Paul Ray, a values researcher tracing cultural change in the United States provides a compelling framework for documenting and understanding this shift, which of course is happening not only in the United States, but as well all around the world. Ray identifies three major cultural groupings.

• The Modernists—who are still the largest cultural group in America—actively prize materialism and the drive

CULTURE SHIFT IN AMERICA

GROUP	VALUES	ADULT AMERICANS
CULTURAL CREATIVES	family, community, environment and feminism, diversity, personal growth and spiritual development	50 million (26%) and growing rapidly
MODERNS	materialism, consumerism, and the drive to acquire money and property	93 million (48%) and steady
TRADITIONALS	traditional ways of life and gender roles, religious fundamentalism	48 million (25%) and declining rapidly

to acquire money and property. They tend to spend beyond their means, take a cynical view of idealism and caring relations, and value winners. Their numbers are relatively stable.

• The Traditionals want to return to traditional ways of life and traditional gender roles. They tend toward religious conservatism and fundamentalism. They also believe in helping others, volunteering, creating and maintaining caring relationships, and working to create a better society. Their numbers are in rapid decline.

• The third group—Ray calls them the Cultural Creatives—is a product of the reaction against modernism's lack of authenticity. Its members are distinguished by the embrace of the values of an integral culture that honours life in all its dimensions, both in their inner spiritual experience and in their outward commitment to family, community, the environment, internationalism and feminism. They have a well-developed social consciousness and are generally optimistic about the possibilities of humankind. They are interested in alternative health-care practices, personal growth and spiritual development, and they are careful, thoughtful consumers.

Most significant in terms of our present discussion, as Ray documents in his forthcoming book, *The Cultural Creatives*, most Cultural Creatives are activists. The typical Cultural Creative is likely to be involved in several groups working for social change. Furthermore, most social change initiatives in the United States, including those involved in the Seattle protests, are headed by Cultural Creatives. Cultural Creatives are the vanguard of the global democracy movement—and their numbers are growing fast. Now 50 million in number in America alone, they are 26 per cent of the adult American population. As recently as the early 60s they were less than 5 per cent.

Politically and socially active, the Cultural Creatives are crafting a new ecological and spiritual world view, a new literature of social concerns and a new problem agenda for humanity. At the same time they are pioneering psychological development techniques, restoring the centrality of spiritual practice to daily living, and elevating the importance of the feminine—all building blocks of a civil society.

Yet Cultural Creatives remain invisible to the corporate media, which is dominated by modernist values. And their values are unrepresented by a political system that is still defined by the struggles between moderns and traditionals. Unaware of their own numbers and potential power, most Cultural Creatives feel culturally isolated, out of step with the mainstream, and politically disempowered. To actualise their true potential as a force for change, they must first become visible to one another and to the larger society. For this reason, perhaps the most important consequence of the Seattle WTO protests was the message it sent to Cultural Creatives everywhere in the world that they are not alone in their discomfort with the cultural, economic and political forces of modernism and corporate globalisation and their belief in the possibility of creating a better world for all—even in America, the world centre of materialism and corporate arrogance. Most cultural creatives I know found it to be a powerfully energising moment.

A variety of international surveys reveal that the patterns identified in America by Ray are part of a generalised global trend toward an embrace of the values of an authentic or integral culture. The pattern includes a loss of confidence in hierarchical institutions—including those of government, business, and religion—and a growing trust in their inner sense of the appropriate. Interest in economic gain is decreasing, while desire for meaningful work and interest in discov-

ering personal meaning and purpose in life is increasing.

Beyond the struggle to resist the destruction being wrought by the global corporate juggernaut, the civilising citizen movements are awakening to two critical priorities. One is to articulate and demonstrate alternatives to corporate globalisation in order to counter the fatalistic modernist mantra that 'There is no alternative.' The second is to recognise that the movement's greatest strength is cultural power and to devote serious attention to helping Cultural Creatives recognise that they are part of a large and increasingly powerful cultural group, find one another, and strengthen the alliances that are linking them into a global mega-movement. The greater the visibility of this new cultural formation the greater its power and the more rapidly disaffected moderns and traditionals will be drawn to its ranks.

A great deal of my own energy is going into an organisation called The Positive Futures Network, publisher of *YES! A Journal of Positive Futures*, which is working on both of these agendas by telling the stories of those who are working for the deep changes required to create a world that works for all and by providing people with the information resources they need to connect with one another and to link the movement's many elements. It just happens that I've brought some sample copies of *YES!*, along with subscription forms for those who are interested. Or check it out at <yesmagazine.org> on the web.

Overall, the goal of claiming the cultural mainstream may be more nearly within the reach of the civil society movements than even the most optimistic of us may imagine. Once this happens, transformation of the institutions of polity and economy to complete the civilising of society will follow.

I believe we live at one of the most critical and exciting moments in all of human history. The ability to choose is one of the defining characteristics of life. As a species we find ourselves confronted with a profound choice—to take the step to a new level of understanding and function in service to the whole of life or to risk our own extinction. We face both the necessity and the opportunity to reinvent human society. I find the creative possibilities incredibly exciting. Though the optimistic thrust of my comments may suggest I consider the outcome to be foreordained, that is far from the actual case. I am in fact only presenting what I consider to be possibilities to sharpen our understanding of the options. The great struggle between humanity and its institutions—between a culture of life and a culture of money—is far from resolved. But let us hope that Aristotle's dream of a truly civil society—a dream shared by countless millions throughout human history—is an idea whose time has finally come. It's in our hands.

rights of money versus
rights of living persons

DAVID C. KORTEN

Property rights should be limited by law to prevent those who have more than enough using them to deny others their right to the means of making a livelihood. Moreover, companies should be banned from political activities of any kind because political rights reside only in real people.

Proponents of market liberalism claim the free market is the essential foundation of political democracy—a guarantor of the rights of people against the abuse of state power. They neglect, however, the important ways in which the unfettered market tends to function as a profoundly undemocratic institution.

Political democracy vests rights in the living person, one person, one vote. By contrast, the market recognises only money, not people—one dollar, one vote. It gives no voice to the penniless, and when not balanced by constraining political forces can become an instrument of oppression by which the wealthy monopolise society's resources, leaving the less fortunate without land, jobs, technology or other means of livelihood. Only when wealth is equally distributed can the market be considered democratic in any meaningful sense.

Global markets are now dominated by global mega-corporations—among the most undemocratic and unaccountable of human institutions. By its nature the corporation creates a legal concentration of power while shielding those who wield that power from accountability for the con-

sequences of its use. Many mega-corporations command more economic power than do the majority of states and dominate the political processes of nearly all states. Their growing unaccountable power poses a serious threat to the basic economic and political rights of people everywhere.

The time has come to re-examine some of our most basic assumptions about the nature of democracy, human rights, and the institution of the corporation. The survival of our political freedoms depends on recognising that economic rights are an essential foundation of political democracy. Consider for example two of the most fundamental of all human rights—the right to a means of living—literally the right to live—and the right to participate in making the decisions that affect our lives.

THE RIGHT OF ACCESS TO A MEANS OF LIVING
The earth's life-sustaining resources are a common heritage of all life. All people are born with an inalienable right to a sufficient share of these resources to create a secure and fulfilling life for themselves and their families. They have a corresponding responsibility to share and steward these

resources to the benefit of all persons and other living things.

Since the most basic requirements of living depend on the products of the earth, there is a fundamental—though often neglected—connection between livelihood rights and property rights. English philosopher John Locke set forth a moral justification for property rights in *The Second Treatise of Government* published in 1689. Locke argued that where unused land is abundant, a man has a right to appropriate for his private and exclusive use the land which he tills to produce for his basic subsistence needs. It is through the application of his labour to make the land produce that he acquires this private right. Locke stressed that given the condition of abundance, such appropriation in no way deprived others of similar opportunity. Locke was also clear that the rightful claim to a property right followed only from the application of one's personal labour. Furthermore, he said, this claim legitimately extended only to such property as required to meet one's own material needs—suggesting that a property right is virtually synonymous with a livelihood right,

Locke, however, went beyond this relatively unassailable moral argument to seek justification for actions of those who accumulate property rights far beyond their personal needs. Presuming that property rights are most likely to be accumulated by clever and industrious persons who seek to realise their full productive potential, Locke argued that the result of this accumulation would be to maximise the wealth of society and thereby the well-being of all. It is essentially the same argument that economists make to this day in defence of inequality based on the assumption that the surpluses created through investments of the wealthy in a growing economy will be widely distributed through society in the form of high-paying jobs and well-funded public services.

It is noteworthy that the moral defence of inequality imbedded in Locke's thesis and the work of most modern economists rests on two inadequately examined assumptions: 1) natural wealth is abundant relative to need; and 2) the benefits of an overall increase in economic activity are widely shared even when wealth is distributed unequally. Unfortunately, for several billion people who find their livelihoods increasingly at risk, neither premise is valid in our present world. To the contrary, the poor are being excluded from access to land, technology is eliminating jobs faster than it is creating new ones, and public services are being systematically dismantled—all to increase the riches of those whose wealth already exceeds any conceivable need. In short, property rights are being used routinely to justify the exclusion of those without property from access to a decent means of living.

As suggested by Locke's argument, the rightful purpose of a property right is to protect a person's right of access to a means of livelihood or to secure for the individual a just reward for entrepreneurial initiatives that create a better life for all. A property right loses its legitimacy when its exercise by those who have more than they need denies others of their rightful means of livelihood or otherwise diminishes their opportunities for a full and meaningful life. The livelihood rights of the many come before the property rights of the few. Recognition in our laws and public culture of this limitation of property rights is fundamental to the market's socially efficient function.

THE RIGHT TO PARTICIPATE IN DECISIONS THAT AFFECT ONE'S LIFE AND COMMUNITY
Born with reason, conscience, and the capacity for intelligent choice, all people have the inalienable right—indeed the obligation—to use these gifts to participate actively in the decisions that affect

their lives and communities. The rights of speech and assembly derive from this basic right to participate. The right to participate resides in the person and does not rightfully extend to any corporation.

In the economic realm the exercise of the right of participation extends far beyond choosing among those products the market finds it profitable to offer us. It includes the right to participate in setting standards and priorities for the economic affairs of our communities, the uses to which our local resources will be put, and the conditions under which we will engage in external trade and invite the participation of others in our domestic economies.

This right is under attack by the world's mega-corporations that seek to establish

There is nothing democratic about an unregulated market that responds exclusively to the needs of the wealthy and subordinates human rights and interests to corporate rights and interests.

their own right to move across the face of the planet without restriction to extract resources, exploit unorganised and unprotected labour, evade taxes and environmental regulations, and monopolise indigenous knowledge and genetic materials without regard to the human and environmental consequences. Their weapons of choice are international agreements on trade and investment that take precedence over the rules and regulations established by people and their governments to govern local commerce. Negotiated in secret and implemented without full public discussion and democratic assent, these agreements are systematically eroding the democratic rights of people to regulate their own local and national economies, and to set rules for commerce consistent with their own values and judgements regarding their personal

and community needs. The interests of money and the fictitious legal persona of the corporation are thus placed ahead of the interests of living persons and their communities—all in the name of market freedom.

It is useful to recall that Adam Smith, the patron saint of free marketeers, favoured a market comprised exclusively of small buyers and sellers. Smith considered the corporation to be an instrument for monopolising markets and saw no place for such institutions in a properly functioning competitive market economy. By his reckoning the corporation is an anti-market institution.

A corporation comes into being only through the public act of the government that issues the corporate charter. The creation of a corporation is thus a public, not a private, act and its only justification is to serve a public purpose. Whatever privileges or authority the corporation may enjoy are derived from the authority of government, which is itself derived from the will of the people. It therefore follows that the corporation is rightfully subject to the will of the people and to whatever laws people freely chose to establish governing its function.

Nor does a corporation rightfully enjoy any privilege beyond the jurisdiction of the government that issued its charter unless and until the people of another jurisdiction explicitly chose to grant it such privilege. It is the proper function of the corporation to implement the laws that people establish through their governments, not to participate in their creation. Indeed, it is essential to the integrity of democratic governance that corporations be barred from political participation of any kind on the theory that political rights reside only in real people.

The idea that corporations should enjoy the rights of flesh and blood persons—including the right of free speech—grew out of a US Supreme Court decision in 1886 that designated corporations as legal persons entitled to all the rights and protections afforded by the Bill of Rights of the US Constitution. Significantly, the US Constitution makes no reference to corporations. It was a decision without legal or moral foundation made by a corrupted court system.

As citizens it is our right to revise existing legal codes to make clear that human rights belong only to flesh and blood persons. Similarly, it is our right to replace trade and investment agreements that abrogate the most basic political and economic rights of people with international agreements that protect the rights to economic and political choice of all people against infringement by democratically unaccountable institutions—either state or corporation.

Markets are important institutions and they have an essential place in any democratic society—functioning within a framework of democratically determined rules and public safeguards. There is nothing democratic, however, about an unregulated market that responds exclusively to the needs of the wealthy and subordinates human rights and interests to corporate rights and interests. In the end only an active and politically engaged citizenry can assure the protection of our human rights from the arbitrary use of power by either states or corporations. Institutional power and legitimacy flow from the will of people, and when any institution usurps our natural rights, it is right of the people to restructure, replace, or eliminate, that institution.

This article was first circulated by the People-Centered Development Forum in May 1997.

life after capitalism

DAVID C. KORTEN

Capitalism destroys the main planks on which most of us wish to build our societies—democracy, a market economy, and an ethical culture. Consequently, we need to adopt policies which are almost exactly the opposite of those being followed at present.

We live in a world being pillaged by the institutions of global capitalism to enrich the few at the expense of the many. It has become more than just a political issue. We have reached the point in human history at which the very survival of civilisation and perhaps our species depends on replacing these rogue institutions with institutions supportive of democracy, market economies, and ethical cultures that function in service to life and community. Yes, your heard me right. We must replace the global capitalist economy with democracies and market economies. Now how's that for a radical idea?

For those of us who grew up believing that capitalism is the foundation of democracy, market freedom, and the good life it has been a rude awakening to realise that under capitalism, democracy is for sale to the highest bidder, the market is centrally planned by global mega-corporations larger than most countries, the elimination of jobs and livelihoods is rewarded as an economic virtue, and the destruction of nature and life to make money for the already rich is viewed as progress. Let us speak truth tonight. Global capitalism is not democratic and it systematically violates every principle of a market economy.

Under global capitalism the world is ruled by a global financial casino staffed by faceless bankers, money managers, and hedge-fund speculators who operate with a herd mentality that sends exchange rates and stock prices into wild gyrations unrelated to any underlying economic reality. With reckless abandon they make and break national economies, buy and sell corporations, and hire and fire corporate CEOs—holding the most powerful politicians and corporate managers hostage to their interests. When their bets pay off they claim the winnings as their own. When they lose, they run to governments and public institutions to make up their losses with cries that the financial skies will fall if they are forced to suffer the market's discipline.

Contrary to its claims, capitalism's relationship to democracy and the market economy is much the same as the relationship of a cancer to the body whose life energies it expropriates. Cancer is a pathology that occurs when an otherwise healthy cell forgets that it is a part of the body and begins to pursue its own unlimited growth without regard to the consequences for the whole.

The growth of the cancerous cells deprives the healthy cells of nourishment and ultimately kills both the body and itself. Capitalism does much the same to the societies it infests.

Another way of characterising our situation is that we find ourselves unwitting participants in an epic contest between money and life for the soul of humanity. And it comes down to a fairly literal choice as to which we value more—our money or our lives.

The cultural and institutional choices we must now make in the favour of life will require changes of a scope and speed unprecedented in human history. Fortunately, we find ourselves facing this challenge at the very moment in our history at which we have acquired the knowledge, the technology, and the organisational capacity to negotiate the required changes successfully. The main question to be resolved is whether we will find the collective wisdom and the will to act in time.

It is a question that must be resolved individual-by-individual, community by community, and nation by nation. In some places, citizen movements are already engaging it on a national scale—as in the Philippines, Chile, and Thailand. Just last month I had the privilege of participating in new initiatives emerging in Hungary, Finland, and Norway.

But to my knowledge there is no country in the world in which the process has gained so much momentum as here in Canada in a wide range of initiatives such as alternative budgeting exercises, the Citizen's Agenda and MAI inquiry processes being led by the Council of Canadians, and initiatives of many groups such as the Parkland Institute and the Western Affairs Committee.

This momentum gives you a special opportunity for global leadership. It also means you face the special challenge always presented to those who choose to sail in uncharted waters. You have no map and I have no map to offer, but I do hope to leave you with a few useful navigational devices.

At its core, the root cause of our collective crisis is two fold: a failure of our values and a failure of our institutions. We have created a global culture that values money and materialism over life itself. In our pursuit of money we have given the institutions of money—banks, investment houses, financial markets, and publicly traded corporations—the power to rule over life. Recognising only financial values, accountable only for money's replication, and wholly unmindful of the needs of life, these institutions are wantonly destroying life to make money. It's a bad bargain.

Our flawed choice results in part from our nearly universal failure to distinguish between money and real wealth. An experience I had a few years ago in Malaysia illustrates the distinction I have in mind. I had a brief encounter with the minister responsible for Malaysia's forests. Seeing that I was Western and assuming I was probably an environmentalist, he wasted no time in poking my buttons by explaining to me that Malaysia would be better off once its forests are cleared away and the money from the sale is stashed in banks to earn interest, because the financial returns will be greater. The image flashed into my mind of a barren and lifeless Malaysian landscape populated only by branches of international banks, with their computers faithfully and endlessly compounding the interest on the profits from Malaysia's timber sales. It is a metaphor that sums up all too well the future to which our confusion of money and real wealth is leading us.

The very vocabulary of finance and economics is a world of double speak that obscures such essential distinctions. For example, we use the terms money, capital, assets, and wealth interchangeably, leaving us with no simple means to express the difference between money—a number that by social convention we agree to accept in return for things of real value—and real wealth—which includes such things as trees, food, our labour, fertile land, buildings, machinery, technology—even love and friendship—things that sustain our lives and increase our productive output. It leaves us prone to the potentially fatal error of assuming that when we are making money we are necessarily creating wealth.

> *As we become ever more dependent on money to acquire the basic means of daily life, we give over to the institutions and people who control money's creation and allocation the power to decide who among us shall live in prosperity and who shall live in destitution.*

Similarly, we politely use the term investor when we speak of the speculators whose gambling destabilises global financial markets. Indeed we favour them with tax breaks and special protections. Language makes a difference. If we called them by their real names—speculators, gamblers, and thieves, they would be subjects of public outrage—as they should be.

As a medium of exchange money is one of the most important and useful of human inventions. However, as we become ever more dependent on money to acquire the basic means of daily life, we give over to the institutions and people who control money's creation and allocation the power to decide who among us shall live in prosperity and who shall live in destitution— even suffer premature death. With the virtual elimination of subsistence production the increasing breakdown of community and public safety nets, our modern money system has become possibly the most effective instrument of social control and extraction ever devised by human kind.

The term 'capitalism' now means much

the same thing it did in the mid-1800s when it was coined to refer to an economic and social regime in which the ownership and benefits of productive assets are appropriated by the few to the exclusion of the many who through their labour make the assets productive. Modern capitalism has taken this concentration of wealth to a truly unconscionable extreme. In 1991 there were 274 billionaires in the world. By 1996 their numbers had increased to 447. Their total assets were roughly equivalent to the total combined incomes of the poorest half of humanity. Between 1996 and 1997, a single billionaire, Bill Gates of the Microsoft Corporation increased his net worth by $18 billion, a gain roughly equal to the total income shared by the 11 million people of Zimbabwe over that same one year period. Dwell on that for a moment. An income ratio of 11 million to one.

As outrageous as such inequality is, the most sinister aspect of modern capitalism is not its concentration of wealth in the hands of a tiny, greedy élite. It is about an institutional system of autonomous rule by money and for money that functions on autopilot beyond the control of any human actor and is unresponsiveness to any human sensibility. This is perhaps the most critical distinction between a market economy and our contemporary global capitalist economy.

In a healthy market economy enterprises are human-scale and predominantly locally owned. Economic exchanges are shaped and controlled by people through the expression of their cultural values, their purchasing decisions, their democratic participation in setting the rules by which the market will function, and their ownership of local enterprises as local stakeholders with an interest in the community and its well-being. It is a dynamic and interactive system in which people participate in many roles and bring their human sensibilities to bear on every aspect of economic life—a distinction I attempt to capture in the figure below.

Political democracy and the market economy work well together as means of organising the political and economic life of a society to allocate resources fairly and efficiently while securing the freedom and sovereignty of the individual. They provide an institutional foundation for self-organising societies able to function with a minimal need for central coercive control. The special magic of the market is its ability to reward those who do productive work responsive to the self-defined needs of others as they add to the total wealth and well-being of society.

Capitalism, by contrast, is about using money to make money for people who already have more of it than they need. It rewards the monopolist and the speculator at the expense of those who do productive work. Its institutions, by their very nature, breed inequality, exclusion, environmental destruction, social irresponsibility, and economic instability while homogenising cultures, weakening the institutions of

democracy, and eroding the moral and social fabric of society.

I am amused when I hear the apologists for capitalism saying that the mistake in Russia was to introduce capitalism too fast before the values and institutions of capitalism were put into place. In fact Russia demonstrates capitalism's values and institutions at their most advanced state of development. It is a country with virtually no rules and no government in which the strongest and best organised are free to steal whatever they can get their hands on. I'll return to the Russian experience later.

We are often told that deregulation and economic globalisation are necessary to free the market. In fact, efficient market function depends on both regulation and borders. What deregulation and economic globalisation actually free are the forces of capitalism's attack on democracy and the market. Without regulation and borders, financial markets merge into a single unregulated electronic system able to create money with reckless abandon through bank lending to support speculative excesses. Similarly, global corporations consoli-

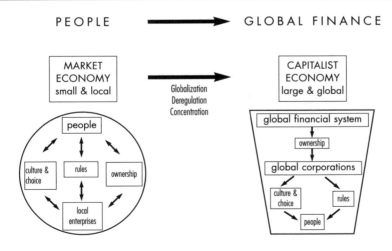

POWER SHIFT

PEOPLE ⟶ GLOBAL FINANCE

MARKET ECONOMY
small & local

Globalization
Deregulation
Concentration

CAPITALIST ECONOMY
large & global

people

culture & choice   rules   ownership

local enterprises

global financial system

ownership

global corporations

culture & choice   rules

people

date and concentrate their power through mergers, acquisitions, and strategic alliances beyond the reach of any state. Economic power becomes formally delinked from concern for any person or place as absentee ownership and its dysfunctions become institutionalised on a global scale through the aggregation of savings into professionally managed retirement, trust, and mutual funds that have a legal fiduciary responsibility to maximise financial returns to their clients without regard to social and environmental consequences.

Acting as proxy owners of the corporations whose shares they hold, the fund managers expect the managers of these corporations to take a similarly narrow view of their responsibilities and send them a powerful message. A fair profit is not enough. Annual profits must be constantly increased at a rate sufficient to produce the 20 to 40 per cent annual increase in share price the markets have come to expect. The corporate head that succeeds is well rewarded. The average annual compensation of the head of a US corporation, much of it in stock options, is now $7.5 million a year. Those who fail lose credibility with the financial community and may invite a take-over bid or ejection by large shareholders. How the corporation increases it profits isn't the market's concern. As they say at the Nike Corporation: 'Just do it.'

The global corporation responds by using its great power to reshape cultures, limit consumer choices, pass costs onto the public, and press governments to provide subsidies and rewrite the rules of commerce in their favour. Commonly the corporation responds in ways that destroy the most precious of all wealth, the living capital of the planet and the society on which all life and the fabric of civilisation depend.

It destroys living capital when it stripmines forests, fisheries and mineral deposits, aggressively markets toxic chemicals and dumps hazardous wastes. It destroys human capital by maintaining substandard working conditions in places like the Mexican maquiladoras where corporations employ once vital and productive young women for three to four years until failed eyesight, allergies, kidney problems, and repetitive stress injuries leave them permanently handicapped and they are replaced with a new batch. It destroys social capital when it breaks up unions, bids down wages, and treats workers as expendable commodities, leaving society to absorb the family and community breakdown and violence that are inevitable consequences. It destroys institutional capital when it undermines the function of governments and democracy by buying politicians, weakening environmental health and labour standards, and extracting public subsidies, bailouts and tax exemptions which inflate corporate profits while passing the burdens of risk to governments and working people.

Living capital, which has the special capacity to continuously regenerate itself, is ultimately the source of all real wealth. To destroy it for money, a simple number with no intrinsic value, is an act of collective insanity—which makes capitalism a mental, as well as a physical pathology.

Once we look seriously at the issue of externalised costs we begin to see just how grossly inefficient global capitalism actually is. Ralph Estes, a certified public accountant who teaches at American University in Washington, DC, developed an inventory of studies that have produced serious estimates of the costs that corporations impose on US society each year through such things as defective products, unsafe working conditions, and environmental discharges. He didn't even include direct subsidies and tax breaks. He came up with a figure of $2.6 trillion a year in 1994 dollars. That is five times corporate profits for that year and 37 per cent of US

GDP. We would never tolerate such inefficiency from government.

Beginning with Adam Smith, market theory has been quite explicit that market efficiency results from small, locally owned enterprises competing in local markets on the basis of price and quality for consumer favour. By contrast, what we know as the global capitalist economy is dominated by a handful of gigantic corporations and financial speculators with billions of dollars at their disposal to reshape markets and manipulate prices. If we consider the gross sales of a corporation to be roughly the equivalent of the GDP of a country, we find that of the world's 100 largest economies, 51 are economies internal to corporations. Only 49 are national economies.

This has an interesting implication. The proponents of capitalism continuously tell us that market economies are more efficient and responsive to consumer needs than centrally planned economies. But the economy internal to a corporation is not a market economy. It is a centrally planned economy—centrally planned by corporate managers to maximise financial returns to themselves and their shareholders. No matter what authority the head of a corporation may delegate, he can withdraw it with a snap of his fingers. In the US system, which is rapidly infecting Europe and the rest of the world, the head of a corporation can virtually hire and fire any worker, open and close any plant, change transfer prices, create and drop product lines almost at will—with no meaningful recourse by the persons or communities affected. Indeed, the power of a corporate head to dictate policy and action within the corporation's internal economy would have made any Soviet planner green with envy.

Ironically, the global victory of capitalism is not a victory for the market so much as it is a victory for central planning. Capitalism has simply shifted the planning function from governments—which in theory are accountable to all their citizens—to corporations—which even in theory are accountable only to their shareholders.

The global capitalist economy is dominated by a handful of gigantic corporations and financial speculators with billions of dollars at their disposal to reshape markets and manipulate prices.

We are moving very fast toward ever-greater consolidation of this unaccountable corporate power. In the United States the total value of corporate mergers and acquisitions has increased at a rate of nearly 50 per cent a year in every year save one since 1992. We see a similar pattern being played out around the world as Wall Street investment banks bring their gun slinging ways to the rest of the world.

Just to give you an idea of the degree of concentration, in 1995 the combined sales of the world's top 200 corporations equalled 28 per cent of total world GDP. Yet these corporations employed only 18.8 million people, less than one third of one per cent of the world's population.

The direct destruction of life to make money is only one of the destructive features of global capitalism. Another centres on the processes by which speculators seek to make money from money without any intervening involvement in productive activity. It is known as the stage of finance capitalism. It is here we encounter the source of the financial instability that has devastated economy after economy—from Brazil and Mexico, to Japan, Thailand, Malaysia, Indonesia, South Korea, and Russia.

The scale of the speculation involved is suggested by the fact that nearly $2 trillion now change hands in the world's currency markets each day. This is far more money than controlled even by the most powerful of central bankers. Only about 1 per cent of this $2 trillion is related to trade in any sort of real goods or services. The rest of it is purely speculative money looking for quick returns when the boom is on and safe havens when the bubbles are bursting. Though unrelated to anything real, these money movements do have real world consequences.

Last month when I was visiting Norway they told me how a speculative raid on the Norwegian Kroner forced Norway's interest rates up by 2 per cent, raising the cost of living for every Norwegian. A few weeks ago the integrity of the entire US banking system was threatened when bets on the Russian rouble made by a single hedge fund called Long-term Capital Management went bad. It turned out that the fund had $25 in bank loans for every dollar in equity and a financial risk exposure of more than $1 trillion in derivatives. The total borrowing was sufficient to threaten the financial integrity of a number of large banks if the fund were to go bankrupt. Some hedge funds are leveraged as high as 100 to one and there are an estimated 4000 such funds in the world trafficking in trillions of dollars in financial derivatives— most of which are little more than sophisticated gambling instruments.

During a two-day period last month, the US dollar fell by 15 per cent against the yen—primarily the result of large hedge funds unwinding from bad bets they had made based on expectations that the yen would fall against the dollar. This fundamentally changed the terms of trade between the two countries, resulting in significant changes in the sales prospects for thousands of legitimate businesses in both countries, with all the related implications for their workers, suppliers and the communities in which they are located.

These swings had nothing to do with any change in underlying economic reality. When a currency collapses due to the actions of speculators there is no change in either the country's productive capacity or in the needs of its people. There is often, however, a drop in actual output for the simple reason that banks left with uncollectable loans stop lending and the money supply dries up—leaving the economy with insufficient money to finance real production and exchange. The cases of Thailand and Russia are especially instructive.

In 1997, financial market's turned Asia's much-touted financial miracle into the Asian financial meltdown. While the details differed by country, Thailand's experience is illustrative of the basic dynamic.

During the latter days of its economic miracle period, Thailand was attracting large inflows of foreign money with high interest rates. These inflows fuelled rapidly growing financial bubbles in stock and real estate prices. The inflated bubbles attracted still more money. Much of the money was created by international banks eager to profit from loans to the speculators. Generally the inflated assets secured these loans. Little if any of the inflow of foreign money was used to finance any increase in the country's productive potential. Most commonly it financed a rapid growth in the importation of luxury consumer goods— which created the illusion of prosperity and a booming economy.

Since speculation in stocks and real estate was producing much higher returns than were productive investments in industry and agriculture, the real entrepreneurs who had invested in productive industrial and agricultural enterprises stopped investing in maintaining the productive potential of the own enterprises, instead siphoning off the cash flow to participate in the speculative frenzy. Real production stagnated or even declined in both agriculture and industry. Exports also began to decline. Thus the faster so called 'foreign investment' flowed in, the faster real productivity capacity and the possibility of paying off the skyrocketing foreign debts declined. Once the speculators realised their money was at increasing risk, they started pulling out their money and the meltdown phase began. Stock and real estate prices plummeted, banks and other lending institutions were left with large portfolios of uncollectable loans. Financially impaired, the banks stopped making loans even for legitimate businesses, a liquidity crisis ensued and financial collapse threatened.

The Wall Street bankers and investment houses that had helped to create the crisis through their speculative excesses and reckless lending—inveterate champions of the free market when the profits were rolling in—responded in typical capitalist fashion. They ran to governments and the IMF for public bailouts.

In the case of Russia I don't recall that there ever was a time when people were talking about Russia's miracle economy. Yet most of us do recall that not so long ago the Soviet Union was considered a major industrial power and a significant military threat by the West.

Now, having embraced capitalism under the tutelage of the IMF and legions of Western advisors, Russia has become an economic and social basket case. Over a seven-year period GDP has fallen at least by half and possibly by as much as 83 per cent. Capital investment has fallen by 90 per cent, meat and dairy livestock herds by 75 per cent. Except for energy, the country is no longer able to produce much of anything. Most consumer goods, especially in the large cities, are now imported. Tens of millions of people are not receiving earned salaries. Male life expectancy has fallen to 57 years. An estimated 15 million people are actually starving and malnutrition has become the norm among school children. Money is so scarce that an estimated half of all transactions are by barter.

Yet in spite of the economic depression, in 1997 Russia had one of the world's highest performing stock markets—fuelled by generous loans from Western bankers. Then in the late spring of 1998, the market turned downward and investors started pulling money out of the country. Russia suspended payment on its foreign debt, depositors were unable to withdraw their money from Russian banks, and store shelves emptied of goods as foreign suppliers cut off deliveries.

Real economies are becoming mortgaged to the global financial system as domestic capacity to sustain real beneficial production declines.

We see important parallels in the Thai and Russian experiences. Both involve implementing IMF recommended policy actions to remove barriers to the free flow of goods and money in and out of the country, while maintaining high domestic interest rates. This encouraged large inflows of foreign money as loans and stock investments. Those who were invested in productive enterprises found the returns did not compete with the returns from stock and real estate speculation. So real enterprise were decapitalised and domestic production fell. Export earnings fell as dependence on imports to meet daily needs increased. This in turn meant that ever-greater foreign portfolio investments were needed to finance consumer imports. Since there was no prospect of being able to repay the now inflated foreign financial claims, financial collapse became inevitable—all thanks to what the IMF and World Bank tout to the world as sound economic policies.

There is reason to believe that something similar is happening to nearly every country in the world. Real economies are becoming mortgaged to the global financial system as domestic capacity to sustain real beneficial production declines.

I now draw your attention to the figure below. A study by McKinsey and Company found that since 1980, the financial assets of the OECD countries have been growing at two to three times the rate of growth in gross domestic product (GDP)—a result of inflating assets values through pumping up financial bubbles. This means that potential claims on economic output are growing from two to three times faster than the growth in output of the things that money might be used to buy.

The distortions go far deeper, however, because an important portion of the output that GDP currently measures represents a decrease, rather than an increase, in our well-being. When children buy guns and cigarettes, the purchases count as an addition to GDP—though no sane person would argue that this increases our well-being. An oil spill is good, because it generates expensive clean up activities. When a married couple gets divorced, that too is good for GDP. It generates lawyer's fees and requires at least one of the parties to buy or rent and furnish a new home. Other portions of GDP represent defensive expenditures that attempt to offset the consequences of the social and environmental breakdown caused by harmful growth. Examples include expenditures for security devices and environmental clean up. GDP further distorts our reality by the fact that it is a measure of gross, rather than net domestic product. The depreciation or depletion of natural, social, human, institutional, and even human-made capital is not deducted. So when we cut down our forests or allow our physical infrastructure to deteriorate, there is no accounting for the loss of productive function. We count only the gain.

Economists in the United States, the UK, Germany, the Netherlands, and Australia have adjusted reported GDP for their countries to arrive at figures for net beneficial economic output. In each instance they have concluded that in spite of substantial economic growth, the economy's net contribution to well-being has actually been declining or stagnant over the past 15 to 20 years.

Yet even the indices of net beneficial output are misleading as they do not reveal the extent to which we are depleting the underlying base of living capital on which all future productive activity depends. I know of no systematic effort to create a

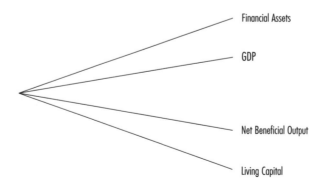

MAKING MONEY, GROWING POOR

Financial Assets

GDP

Net Beneficial Output

Living Capital

unified index giving us an overall measure of the state of our living capital. However, what measures we do have relating to the depletion of our forests, soils, fresh water, fisheries, the disruption of our climatic systems, the unravelling of our social fabric, the decline in educational standards, the loss of legitimacy of our major institutions, and the breakdown of family structures give us reason to believe that the rate of depletion of our living capital* is even greater than the rate of decline in net beneficial output. This is represented by the sharply downward sloping line.

The indicators of stock market performance and GDP our leaders rely on to assess the state of the economy create the illusion that their policies are making us rich—when in fact they are impoverishing us. Governments do not compile the indicators that reveal the truth of what is happening to our wealth and well-being. And the power holders, whose financial assets are growing, experience no problem. In a global economy their money gives them ready access the best of whatever real wealth remains. Those whom capitalism excludes have neither power nor voice.

We are just beginning to wake up to the fact that the industrial era has in a mere century consumed a consequential portion of the natural capital it took evolution millions of years to create. It is now drawing down our social, institutional and human capital as well.

As we watch the social and economic devastation that capitalism spreads in its wake across the globe the time has come for some serious truth telling, starting with the stark truth that unbridled capitalism is a disastrous failure.

Those familiar with market theory know that a market can function efficiently only within a framework of rules that maintain certain necessary conditions. There must be rules and incentives to limit the growth and power of individual firms, encourage local ownership, and require firms to internalise their costs. Therefore, our goal should not be to eliminate necessary regulation, but rather to make it sensible and effective.

It is here that we experience the new global capitalism at its most perverse. NAFTA, GATT, the World Trade Organisation, and the proposed Multilateral Agreement on Investment all turn the necessary practice of market regulation on its head. To restore market efficiency and the equity essential to the legitimacy of its institutions, we must police global corporations to insure their adherence to essential market principles. Yet the international agreements and institutions in place and under negotiation not only fail to serve this need, they do exactly the opposite. They install corporate dominated mechanisms to police democratically elected national and local governments to keep them from protecting the public from the excesses of global financial markets and the world's largest and most powerful corporations.

The Multilateral Agreement on Investment—the infamous MAI—is only the most recent of such agreements. It seeks to create a global ruling class comprised of stateless corporations and absentee owners who enjoy the automatic rights of citizenship everywhere, but with none of the obligations that citizenship normally implies. It would also establish that the right of a corporation to profit at the expense of society takes priority over the right of a country's people to protect their prosperity, health, and safety from harmful products and practices.

---

* This was correct when this talk was given but in 1998, the World Wide Fund for Nature (WWF), the World Conservation Monitoring Centre and the New Economics Founcation published the *Living Planet Index*. This showed that 'the Earth has lost nearly one third of its natural wealth' since 1970. (Eds)

The MAI is designed to guarantee the presumed right of global corporations to deplete living capital for profit and of financial speculators to create or flee financial bubbles without restriction or regard for the economic disruption thereby created. And it obligates governments to protect the property of absentee owners from the actions of irate citizens whose jobs, health, and economic security are being destroyed for short-term profit. It is possibly the most actively anti-democratic international agreement ever proposed by supposedly democratic governments.

It will take more than protest to save us from capitalism's destructive powers. We must work together to create a positive vision of the world that can be. I believe we stand at a defining moment in our own history and in the evolution of life on this planet. The time has come when we, as a species, must accept conscious collective responsibility for the consequences of our presence on the planet.

To create a world in which life can flourish and prosper we must replace the values and institutions of capitalism with values and institutions that honour life, serve life's needs, and restore money to its proper role as servant. I believe we are in fact being called to take a step to a new level of species consciousness and function. That is the primary thrust of my book *The Post-Corporate World: Life After Capitalism*. It is also the focus of the group I helped to found, and whose board I chair, called the Positive Futures Network, publishers of *YES! A Journal of Positive Futures*.

We must face up to the obvious fact that capitalism's failures are an inevitable consequence of embracing values and institutions that favour money over life. To create a world in which life can flourish and prosper we must recreate our economies based on values and institutions that honour life, serve life's needs, and restore money to its proper role as servant.

Once we recognise that capitalism is the mortal enemy of the democracy, market economy, and ethical culture on which most of us want to build our societies, it is not surprising that to get where we want to go requires policies nearly the opposite of those advanced by capitalism.

Whereas capitalism prefers giant global corporate monopolies with the power to extract massive public subsidies and avoid public accountability, the efficient function of markets depends on rules that keep firms human-scale and require producers to internalise their costs. Whereas capitalism institutionalises a system of absentee ownership that keeps owners far removed from the consequences of their choices, a proper market economy favours ownership by real stakeholders—workers, managers, suppliers, customers, and communities—to bring human sensibilities to economic decision-making. Whereas capitalism encourages and rewards the speculator, a proper market economy encourages and rewards those who contribute to wealth creation through their labour and productive investment. Whereas capitalism places the rights of money above the rights of persons and seeks to free it from restriction by national borders, a proper market economy seeks to guarantee the rights of persons over the rights of money and honours borders as essential to the maintenance of economic health. Whereas capitalism believes all assets and functions should be privatised, market theory recognises the need for public services and an equitable sharing of common property resources. Whereas capitalism prefers the economic man or woman to the ethical man or woman, a proper market economy assumes an ethical culture that nurtures in its participants a mindfulness of the social and environmental consequences of their behaviour.

I want to focus here for a minute on the central importance of an ethical culture. One of capitalism's many myths is the idea that by some wondrous mechanism the market automatically turns personal greed into a public good—because Adam Smith said so. In truth, the market has no such mechanism and Adam Smith never said it did. Efficient market function absolutely depends on a culture of trust and mutual responsibility. To emphasise this fact, I refer in my forthcoming book, *The Post-Corporate World*, to the mindful market to underscore the importance to efficient market function of an ethical culture that encourages individuals to act with mindfulness of both their personal needs and the needs of the whole.

Most of the responsibility and initiative in negotiating a transition from capitalism to democracy and mindful market economies must come from citizen movements at local and national levels. Supporting nations and localities in this task should become the core agenda of the United Nations under its security agenda, since the protection of people and communities from predatory global corporations and finance is arguably the central security issue of our time.

Among the more specific actions we must take, some are simple and straightforward, like favouring products made by smaller local enterprises and maintaining our savings and checking accounts with local community banks. Others are more challenging, such as dismantling the World Trade Organisation, the World Bank, and the International Monetary Fund. In a world of mindful market economies we have no need for global institutions whose primary function is to open national and local economies to penetration and colonisation by global capital and to police governments to prevent them from protecting their citizens from economic predators.

What we need at the level of global economic management is an open and democratic institution with the mandate and

power to set and enforce rules holding those corporations that operate across national borders democratically accountable to the people and priorities of the

> *The modern corporation is a direct descendant of the British Crown corporations such as the British East India company and the Hudson Bay company that were created to exploit the resources and markets of colonised people. Such an institution has no evident place in a mindful market economy.*

nations where they operate and to regulate and tax international financial flows and institutions. Call it the World Organisation for Corporate and Financial Accountability. The creation of such an institution should perhaps be a centre piece of initiatives toward the drafting of a citizens' MAI as an alternative to the agreement being promoted by our governments.

The citizens' MAI is itself an important initiative in which civil society groups in Canada have established a leading role. In my view such an agreement should recognise and secure the right of each individual country to set its own economic priorities and standards and to determine the terms under which it will trade with others and invite others to invest in its economy. It should recognise that tariffs and financial controls are necessary instruments of market regulation and that trade goals are appropriately subordinated to social, environmental, and even other economic goals.

Another institution that we must seek to eliminate is the publicly traded, for-profit corporation. It is an organisational form specifically designed to concentrate economic power without public accountability and it institutionalises an extreme form of absentee ownership. Bear in mind that the modern corporation is a direct descendant of the British Crown corporations such as the British East India company and the Hudson Bay company that were created to exploit the resources and markets of colonised people. Such an institution has no evident place in a mindful market economy.

There are several things that must be done to eliminate the corporation as we know it. One is to eliminate the legal fiction that corporations are legal persons entitled to the rights and privileges of natural persons. We must simultaneously engage in radical campaign finance reform to get big money and corporations out of politics. A second is to eliminate corporate welfare and require that corporations bear the full cost of their operations. This would involve eliminating corporate subsidies and tax breaks. It would also involve assessing public fees covering the full costs of the burdens the corporation's activities impose on the environment and on society. A third is to eliminate absentee ownership in favour of stakeholder ownership. This means putting in place policies that favour stakeholder owned enterprises such as family enterprises, community enterprises, co-operatives and worker owned enterprises. We can salvage a good deal from existing corporate structures through policies that encourage mega-corporations to break themselves up into human-scale, stakeholder owned firms. If we get corporations

out of politics, restore the integrity of economic borders and eliminate corporate welfare most mega-corporations will probably become unprofitable. This should make their managers and shareholders receptive to selling off the component businesses to stakeholders at appropriately depreciated prices.

While some of our leaders are now talking about the need to tax and regulation international money flows, they are far from facing up to the fact that roughly 99 per cent of the money sloshing around the world is engaged in unproductive speculation. Our goal should be to eliminate virtually all international flows of money not related to the purchase of goods and services on the ground that they serve no useful purpose. A larger goal should be to eliminate speculation in purely financial assets. One important step in this direction would be to prohibit banks from lending for financial speculation. This, for example, would eliminate bank loans to hedge funds and the purchase of stocks on margin.

We can restore democracy and create mindful market economies. We can create cultures and the institutions of the just, sustainable, and compassionate world of which we all dream. And it is our right to do so. We can have life after capitalism. And Canadians are well positioned to lead the way.

(From a talk given to groups from Edmonton, Calgary and Saskatoon in November 1998.)

JAMES ROBERTSON

from the Feasta conference
'money, energy and growth'
march 2000

sharing the value of common resources through taxation and public expenditure

JAMES ROBERTSON

Radical changes in the taxation system and the introduction of a Citizen's Income would help the move towards sustainability. Changes in government spending would assist, too.

PART 1: A RESTRUCTURED TAX SYSTEM & A CITIZEN'S INCOME.

The earth shall become a common treasury to all, as it was first made and given to the sons of men.
                    Gerrard Winstanley (1649)

Pressures are growing for a general restructuring of taxation and welfare benefits. At present they encourage inefficient use of resources—over-use of natural resources (including the environment's capacity to absorb pollution and waste), and under-use and under-development of human resources. By failing to discourage environmentally damaging activities, they fail to encourage innovation for sustainability and a larger share of the growing world market for environmental technologies and services. They discourage both employment and useful unpaid work like parenting. Means-tested benefits discourage saving, as well as the earning of income. They create poverty and unemployment traps which reinforce social exclusion and raise costs for educa-

tion, health, and law and order. The cost of the welfare state is already at crisis level in many countries.

For the future, an ageing society will find it even more difficult to tax fewer people of working age on the fruits of their employment and enterprise in order to support a growing number of 'economically inactive' people. In the medium term at least, a competitive global economy will exert pressure for lower taxes on personal incomes and business profits in order to attract inward investment.

That is the context for the proposal to combine:

- ecotax reform (i.e. a shift of taxation away from employment, incomes and savings, on to resource-depleting and environmentally damaging activities),
- the further replacement of existing taxes by another resource tax—a tax on land site-values, and
- the introduction of a Citizen's Income.

This combination would be phased in over a period of years. It would embody a new social compact for a new era of equitable and sustainable development, in which full employment of the conventional kind, a welfare state of the conventional kind, and economic growth of the conventional kind, had become obsolete goals.

1A *Ecotax Reform*

Environmental taxes have been seen as pollution taxes, reflecting the 'polluter pays' principle. In economists' jargon, they would 'internalise' costs previously 'externalised' by polluters.

They are now coming to be seen more broadly as taxes on the use of natural resources—the capacity of the environment to absorb pollution and wastes being one such resource. Energy taxes, water charges, and traffic congestion charges are other resource taxes. The principle is that people should pay for the benefits they get from using 'commons' of all kinds, meaning resources and values created by nature or society and not by themselves. For example, in its 1995 Report the British Government Panel on Sustainable Development supported taxing people 'on the value they subtract' rather than 'the value they add'.

Ecotax reform is concerned not just with ecotaxes themselves, but with how the revenue from them should be used. The European Commission's White Paper on *Growth, Competitiveness, Employment* of December 1993 proposed to use ecotax revenues to reduce taxes on employment. This approach has now been developed in many official and unofficial studies and reports, and has in some instances (as in the UK's landfill tax) been put into practice.

But there is a serious problem. If existing taxes on incomes, profits and savings are simply replaced with environmental

JAMES ROBERTSON's early career was as a British civil servant; he accompanied Harold Macmillan on his prime-ministerial 'Wind of Change' tour of Africa in 1960. After setting up and directing the Inter-Bank Research Organisation, and contributing to enquiries on government, civil service, parliament, and London's future as a financial centre, he became an independent writer and speaker in 1974.

Between 1975 and 2000 he and his wife, Alison Pritchard, circulated the twice-yearly **Turning Point** (latterly **Turning Point 2000**) newsletter. In 1984–5 they helped to set up The Other Economic Summit (TOES) and the New Economics Foundation. He is a patron of SANE (South Africa New Economics Foundation), set up following his visit there in 1996.

His recent books include **Creating New Money: A Monetary Reform for the Information Age** (New Economics Foundation, 2000) co-written with Professor Joseph Huber, **Beyond The Dependency Culture** (Adamantine/Praeger, 1998), **The Transformation of Economic Life** (Schumacher Briefing No 1, Green Books, 1998) and **A New Economics of Sustainable Development**, a 'Briefing for Policymakers' written for the European Commission in 1997 (Kogan Page, 1999). He lives in Oxfordshire.

and resource taxes on consumers, they will hit poorer people relatively harder than richer. Regardless of the taxes they replace, ecotaxes are bound to have this regressive effect if they are applied 'downstream' at the point of consumption. For example, value-added tax (VAT) on household energy hits poorer households harder than richer ones, because they do not have the money to pay the higher cost of the tax or to invest in greater energy efficiency; and similarly, fees and charges to reduce urban congestion will hurt small tradespeople who need to use their vehicles for their work, but will be painlessly absorbed by users of chauffeur-driven limousines. If ecotaxes are to replace existing taxes significantly, this problem will have to be solved. How?

First, ecotaxes should, as far as possible, be applied 'upstream'. A tax on fossil fuels and nuclear energy, *collected at source* and cascading down through the economy, will raise the cost of the energy content of all goods and services. This will have three advantages. It will reduce pollution, because pollution mostly arises from energy-intensive activities. It will be seen to be fair because, by raising costs for producers as well as prices for consumers of energy-intensive goods and services, it will clearly hit the salaries, dividends, capital appreciation, etc. of big producer interests and not just the pockets of small consumers. And it will be simpler administratively and easier to understand than a proliferation of separate ecotaxes on individual consumers and polluters.

Second, a tax on land will help to offset the regressive effect of ecotaxes. A site-value tax is a resource tax that is progressive. It is the rich, not the poor, who become rich from the value of land.

Third the revenue from ecotaxes should be used progressively. A German study (DIW, 1994) concluded that, if part of the revenue from an energy tax were distributed to households as an ecobonus, the change would have positive economic and employment effects, and would reduce the net tax burden on low-income households. A Swiss study (von Weiszacker, 1994, p.76) concluded that if the revenue from levying two Swiss francs per litre of petrol were distributed to all adults as an ecobonus, people driving less than 7000 kilometres a year would benefit, while people driving more would lose.

So, could ecobonuses add up to a Citizen's Income? And could a Citizen's Income be financed from from resource tax revenues? We'll explore that later on.

1B *Site-Value Land Taxation*

The proposal is to tax the annual rental site value of land. That does not include the value of developments carried out by the owner and his predecessors (which should not be taxed). It is the value of the land as provided by nature and as affected for better or worse by the activities and regulations of society. Estimates for Britain in 1990 suggest the relative size of these values (£bn) for various land uses: housing 66.4; commerce 19.0; public services 10.2; industry 9.3; farm, woodland and forest 2.4 (Taken from David Richards, *The Land Value of Britain, 1985-1990*, Economic and Social Science Research Association, London.).

This tax has attracted favourable comment from economists since Adam Smith. Ricardo (1817) pointed out that a 'tax on rent would affect rent only; it would fall wholly on landlords and could not be shifted to any class of consumers'. In 1879, in *Progress And Poverty*, the American economist, Henry George, showed that to shift the burden of taxation from production and exchange to the value of land would stimulate employment and the production of wealth; the selling price of land would fall; land speculation would receive its death-blow; and land monopolisation would no longer pay. Leading economists since then have agreed that the tax on economic rent is the most neutral and most efficient of all taxes, inducing no distortions and generating no loss of welfare (Fred Harrison in Ronald Banks [ed.], 1989). Various political parties in Europe during the 20th century have included site-value taxation in their policies, and it provides a component of local taxation in a number of countries today. But mainstream policy analysts and economists in recent years have shown a strange lack of interest in it. Merely a case of professional groupthink? Or, as some suggest (Mason Gaffney and Fred Harrison, 1994) the result of an intellectual conspiracy originally inspired by landowning interests early this century?

Some past advocates of the site value tax have put people off by insisting that, as the 'single tax' needed to finance all public spending, it should replace all others. Today, its more forward-looking advocates present its claims as one resource tax among others. Their arguments for a system of public finance based on socialising (i.e. taxing) the rent of land *and other natural resources*, and privatising (i.e. not taxing) people's wages and savings, appear wholly convincing.

1C *Citizen's Income (or Basic Income)*

The proposal is to distribute a Citizen's Income (CI)—often known as a Basic Income—as a tax-free income paid by the state to every man, woman and child as a right of citizenship. It will be age-related, with more for adults than children and more for elderly people than working-age adults. CI for children will replace today's child benefit, and CI for the elderly will replace today's state pensions. There will be supplements for disability, housing benefits, and other exceptional circumstances. Otherwise CI will replace all existing benefits and tax allowances. The amount of a person's CI will be unaffected by their income or wealth, their work status, gender or marital status.

The idea of a basic income goes back to Thomas Paine in the 1790s and to the Fourierists and John Stuart Mill in the first half of the nineteenth century. In Britain in the 1920s Major C.H. Douglas proposed Social Credit as a response to unemployment. More recently, support has come from distinguished economists, including Samuel Brittan and James Meade. Most contemporary CI supporters have assumed that CI would be financed out of income tax, but opinion within the CI movement is now shifting towards financing it from 'sources reflecting a 'common endowment'".

Support for CI continues to grow, especially in Britain and Western Europe. A recent study (Clark, C. and J. Healy, 1997) showed that a full Citizen's Income could be introduced in Ireland over a period of three budgets. It would result in nobody receiving less than the poverty line of income; all unemployment and poverty traps being eliminated; and it always being worthwhile for an unemployed person to take up a job. The principle underlying the proposal was that 'Nature and its resources are for the benefit of all'.

1D *Targeting or Universality?*

At first sight, it seems more sensible and less costly to target benefits strictly to those who really need them, rather than to distribute them to everyone. But targeting involves means testing. There is no other way to establish need and eligibility. And means testing has serious disadvantages: it is experienced as demeaning and socially divisive; to avoid it, many people fail to take up benefits to which they are entitled; it tightens the unemployment and poverty traps, by reducing incentives to earn and save; and people who have earned and saved enough to disqualify themselves from means-tested benefits, feel resentment against those who have not—creating more social divisiveness.

The universality of a Citizen's Income avoids these disadvantages. But the total direct cost of CI to government will be much higher than the cost of selective benefits based on means-tested need; and it is argued that poor people should not be given an unearned income as a hand-out from the state. (It is noticeable that the unearned incomes which rich and middle-income people derive from 'enclosure of the commons' are seldom similarly questioned!) However, these objections can be met by combining a CI with a restructured tax system, whereby the CI's value (or more) will be clawed back from better-off people via taxes on their use or monopolisation of common resources, and CI will be seen as every-one's share of the value of those resources.

The result will be doubly progressive. The CI will be progressive because the same amount of money is worth relative-ly more to poor people. The taxes will be progressive because richer people will pay more for the disproportionately large financial benefits they now enjoy (in terms of salaries, dividends and capital appreciation) from the ownership of land and the use of common resources.

1E *Towards A New Social Compact*

Part of the transition, then, to a people-centred, environmentally sustainable future will be a package of reforms based on:

· the introduction of taxes and charges on the use of common resources and values, particularly including energy and the site value of land;

· the reduction, and perhaps the even-tual abolition, of taxes and charges on employment, incomes, profits, value added, and capital; and

· the introduction of a Citizen's Income, to which ecobonuses will contribute, paid to all citizens as of right in place of all tax reliefs and many existing welfare benefits.

The ecotax reform movement has been gathering strength in mainstream policy-making and academic research but still faces serious problems. The movements

for site-value taxation and Citizen's Income are growing stronger but yet have to mobilise mainstream momen-tum. Over the next few years the poten-tial synergies between the three will become clear. Beyond the practical argu-ments for treating them as a package, an integrating vision will emerge.

It will be a vision of a people-centred society—less employer-centred and state-centred than today's—which does not tax people for what they earn by their useful work and enterprise, by the value they add, and by what they contribute to the common good; in which the amounts that people and organisations are required to pay to the public revenue are based on the value they subtract by their use or monopolisation of common resources; and in which all citizens are equally entitled to share in the annual revenue so raised, partly by way of ser-vices provided at public expense and partly by way of a Citizen's Income.

The citizens of such a society will be more equal with one another in esteem, capability and material conditions of life than now. They will find it easier to get paid work, but they will no longer be as dependent as they are now on employers to provide them with incomes and organ-ise work for them. The modern-age class division between employers and employ-ees will fade—as the old master/slave and lord/serf relationships of ancient and medieval societies have faded. It will be normal for people to work for themselves and one another. It will become an aim in many fields of policy to enable people to manage their own working lives.

The social compact of the employment age is now breaking down. The time is passing when the great majority of citi-zens, excluded from access to land and other means of production and from their share of common resources and values, could nevertheless depend on employers to provide them with adequate incomes in exchange for work, and on the state for special benefit payments to see them through exceptional periods of unemployment. A new social compact will encourage all citizens to take greater responsibility for themselves and their contribution to society. In exchange, it will recognise their right to share in the value of the 'commons', enabling them to become less dependent than they are today on big business and big finance, on employers, and on officials of the state.

PART 2. PUBLIC EXPENDITURE PROGRAMMES

In prehistoric times there might have been some parliamentary control over public expenditure, but there certainly has not been in my parliamentary experience.

Arthur Balfour, 1905

The need to transform the major part of welfare spending into a Citizen's Income has been discussed. What about the rest of public spending?

2A *Perverse Subsidies and the Market Economy*

The need to remove perverse subsidies in many areas of the economy was noted above. The UK Goverment's Panel on Sustainable Development has estimated (January 1997) the total value of environmentally damaging subsidies in Britain at more than £20 billion a year. Estimates of the worldwide value of perverse subsidies range between $500bn (Wuppertal, 1997) and $1500bn (Myers, 1998). Perverse subsidies are worse than merely a waste of citizens' money. They skew the price structure of the economy in favour of socially and environmentally undesirable activities, just as perverse taxes do.

But how are subsidies defined? What do they include? In addition to subsidies in the narrow sense, there are other forms of *de facto* subsidisation which artificially improve the competitive position of some products and activities against others by influencing market prices in their favour. Examples include: discriminatory taxes, such as the *de facto* subsidy to energy consumption due to its lower rate of Value Added Tax than on energy-saving equipments; higher public spending on R & D in one field than in competing fields, as on nuclear power against energy efficiency and energy conservation; higher public spending on one type of transport infrastructure than on others, such as road against rail; and the *de facto* subsidy given by today's tax system to energy-intensive production and distribution, against employment and useful unpaid work.

The point is that the whole array of public spending programmes and taxes existing at any one time, together with the non-existence of public spending and taxation on other things, moves market prices in favour of certain kinds of activities against others. As we have said, some such framework has to exist. It should be designed to encourage social equity, environmental sustainability, and economic efficiency and enterprise, and to minimise the need for *ad hoc* government interventions in the workings of the market.

Democratic control over the nature of this framework and its effects is virtually non-existent. At the least, parliaments should insist on governments publishing a comprehensive annual statement on the social and environmental impacts of subsidies provided under each spending programme. If representatives of NGOs and pressure groups were included in the teams drawing up these statements, their effectiveness would be enhanced.

2B Should There Be Any Subsidies At All?

Should subsidies be given to activities and products that positively contribute to people-centred sustainable development?

In the short term there is probably a case for this. For example, the favourable tax treatment recently introduced in the Netherlands for environmental investment funds may encourage some savers to consider green investments sooner than they would otherwise have done, and may help to stimulate banks and other financial concerns to provide environmental investment services. As a temporary measure, it and other comparable subsidies, for example to support conversions to organic farming, may serve a useful purpose.

But, if introduced at all, such subsidies should be seen as strictly temporary. In each case the same questions need to be asked: What are the distortions in the economy that make it necessary to subsidise this desirable activity? How can those distortions be removed? In almost every case the answer will be that price distortions arising from perverse subsidies or perverse taxes bias the economy against the activities desired. It is better to remove existing perverse taxes and subsidies than to introduce additional subsidies to counteract their effects. Environmental investment and organic farming, for example, will both get a bigger boost from ecotax reform than from subsidies.

In today's business-centred, employer-centred, government-centred economy, the use of public funds to encourage the provision of goods and services and jobs by businesses, employers and government rather than by citizens for themselves and one another, may be understandable. But, in a more people-centred economy that offers citizens greater freedom of choice and enables them to take more responsibility for themselves and one another, it will be increasingly questioned. It will become obvious that much existing expenditure on government programmes would more appropriately finance a Citizen's Income.

2C Lower Total Public Spending?

That is one reason to look for a reduction in conventional public spending programmes over the coming years. There is another.

A high proportion of public expenditure now is remedial. It deals with the after-effects of crime, unemployment, social exclusion, ill-health, environmental damage, humanitarian disasters, breakdowns of law and order, and so on. Reorientation of public policy and public spending towards the creation of conditions leading to less crime, social exclusion, ill-health, environmental damage, and so on is a high priority.

To take one of many possible examples, there is growing evidence that diets, deficient in certain vitamins and trace elements and containing certain additives and other chemical substances, are a significant cause of attention deficit and hyperactivity in children, which can develop into anti-social and criminal behaviour as they grow older. But few professionals in the police, prisons and other law-and-order services, in the education and employment services, in the medical and health (i.e. sickness) services, or in the drug companies, are interested. How a dietary approach might help such children, their families and society in terms of improved quality of life, improved education, improved economic capacities and improved life prospects, and what existing costs it might save, is still largely unexplored.

In general, a new approach to public spending is needed, to identify possibilities for re-orientating it toward prevention instead of cure. But, to be realistic, the professions which have grown up in remedial fields of public service, and the bureaucracies and commercial interests which support them, are likely to be unenthusiastic. How many health practitioners and health officials, for example, can we expect to contribute to health-creating innovations in transport, energy, employment, planning, taxation, welfare benefits, or food and farming? The initiative to reorientate public policy from cure to prevention will have to come mainly from outside today's remedial professions.

As the changes in taxes, benefits and public spending proposed here are phased in over the years, they will help people and localities to meet for themselves many needs now met by government programmes. This will bring phased reductions in total public spending. That will allow corresponding reductions in the overall burden of taxation. So we should not worry too much that resource and pollution taxes may be so effective in reducing resource use and pollution that the revenue they are able to raise will eventually decline.

REFERENCES

Banks, Ronald, (ed.), (1989), *Costing the Earth*, Shepheard-Walwyn, London.

Clark, C. and J. Healy (1997), *Pathways to a Basic Income*, CORI, Dublin.

DIW, German Institute for Economic Research (1994), 'Ecological Tax Reform Even if Germany Has to Go It Alone', *Economic Bulletin*, Vol.37, Gower, Aldershot.

Gaffney, M. and F. Harrison (1994), *The Corruption of Economics*, Shepheard-Walwyn, London.

Myers, N. (1998), *Perverse Subsidies: Their Nature, Scale and Impacts*, International Institute for Sustainable Development, Canada.

von Weizsacher, E.U., (1994) *Earth Politics*, Zed Books, London.

Wuppertal Bulletin, Summer 1997, 'Guide to Global Subsidies Jungle.'

WORLD ENERGY OUTLOOK

FROM THE FEASTA CONFERENCE
'MONEY, ENERGY AND GROWTH'
MARCH 2000

the imminent peak of global oil production

COLIN CAMPBELL

Humanity has already burned nearly half of its endowment of oil and, within the next five years, its most convenient form of energy will become increasingly scarce.

The world's economic prosperity over the best part of the last century was driven by an abundant supply of cheap oil-based energy. This energy source has also played a critical and increasing role in agriculture, which has successfully fed a rapidly growing population. Given this dependency on oil, it is surprising that more attention has not been given to studies of its endowment in Nature, including its distribution, and above all, its depletion. All finite natural resources are subject to depletion which follows a general bell-shaped curve, starting and ending at zero with a peak in between.

The oil industry has made great technological advances since exploration began 150 years ago. These achievements have not, however, been matched in properly defining oil and gas or reporting discovery and production. The unreliable database has given many vested interests the opportunity to mislead and confuse. Explorers have a vested interest in exploration; economists have a blind faith in market forces; engineers have a belief in technology; managers have no alternative but to sing to the investment community, whose interest is confined to short-term financial gain; and governments

rely on voters with a thirst for good news. So far, this obfuscation and denial has not particularly mattered as oil production from past discovery continued to grow, although it has indirectly led to damaging fluctuations in oil price. But now the moment of truth approaches as the peak of discovery in the 1960s delivers the corresponding peak of production. The world is ill-prepared to face this historic turning point.

It is now too late to make many useful preparations, and the effort has to concentrate on education. Governments and the people at large need better information if they are to react sensibly.

THE GENERATION OF OIL AND GAS

Advances in geochemistry over the past twenty years have made it possible to relate the oil in a well with the source-rock from which it came, and to map the productive trends, once the critical information has been gathered from key boreholes. In fact, the bulk of the world's oil comes from only a few epochs of extreme global warming, which caused the proliferation of algae, effectively poisoning seas and lakes. The resulting organic material was preserved in favourable plate-tectonic settings. Thus, most of the oil from the United States to northern South America, including the vast degraded deposits of Venezuela, comes from a few hundred meters of clay, deposited 90 million years ago. Another such event, 140 million years ago, is responsible for most of the oil in the North Sea, the Middle East, and parts of Russia.

Gas was more widely generated in Nature than was oil, but this is offset by its tendency to leak from geological traps. Salt and permafrost form the most effective seals. The presence of salt is an important factor contributing to the preservation of large amounts of oil and gas in the Middle East.

The world has now been so extensively explored that virtually all the productive trends, at least in the accessible parts of the world, have been identified, leaving much less scope for surprise than was previously the case.

The world is not about to run out of oil, but it is about to face the peak of production. To determine the date and size of peak involves identifying the many different categories of oil and gas to see how each can contribute. Each category has its own endowment in Nature, its own costs and characteristics, and above all, its own depletion profile. There is obviously a world of difference between a Middle East well flowing at 30,000 barrels per day and processing a few barrels a day from a tar-sand or oil 'shale'.

It is convenient to distinguish *Conventional* oils, which have produced most oil to-date and will continue to dominate all supply far into the future, from *Non-conventional* oils, but there is no standard definition by which to do so. Here, the following categories are treated as *Nonconventional*:

- Oil from coal and 'shale' (actually immature source-rock)

COLIN CAMPBELL obtained his doctorate in geology from Oxford University in 1958 and has worked since then as a petroleum geologist with companies including BP, Texaco, Fina and Amoco. He was exploration manager for Aran Energy, Dublin, in 1978–9. More recently he has been a consultant to the Norwegian and Bulgarian governments, and to Shell and Esso.

In 1998, he and a colleague, Jean H. Laherrère, were largely responsible for convincing the International Energy Agency that the world's coventional oil output would peak in the next ten years. He is the author of two books and numerous papers on oil depletion and has lectured and broadcast widely on the topic. He lives in Ballydehob, Co. Cork.

- Bitumen (defined by viscosity)
- Extra-Heavy Oil (less than 10° API. API is an index which measures viscosity—the lower, the thicker)
- Heavy Oil (10-17.5° API)
- Deepwater oil and gas (more than 500 m water depth)
- Polar oil and gas
- Coalbed methane, gas in tight reservoirs, gas in geopressured aquifers, hydrates etc.

Gas liquids, comprising condensate, liquids from processing and new Gas-to-Liquids technology, belong to the gas domain and should be treated apart from crude oil, although the industry's database does not distinguish these adequately.

Economists tend to picture a seamless transition driven by market forces, such that as the production of one category becomes expensive another will take its place, making it difficult to measure anything. It is therefore better to base measurements on physical attributes, although economic and technological factors do influence extraction.

Since peak production is controlled mainly by *Conventional oil,* we will concentrate on it here.

THE SIZE OF DISCOVERY

An oilfield contains what it contains, having been filled in the geological past. Its size will be known exactly only on the day of its final abandonment, but reasonable estimates may be made earlier. The terminology and practices of reserve estimation and reporting are subjects in themselves. But to simplify greatly, we need to use the estimate most likely to result in revisions being statistically neutral: the best estimate for this purpose is that commonly termed *Proved & Probable.* Published reserves are generally reported as *Proved,* although in reality they are

closer to *Proved & Probable,* save in the onshore USA. Revisions have to be backdated to the discovery of the field containing them to obtain a valid discovery trend. The amount discovered at any given reference date is the sum of *Cumulative Production* and the *Reserves.*

THE ILLUSION OF 'RESERVE GROWTH'

Many claims are made that technology will extract more oil from known fields, giving what is termed *Reserve Growth.* However, plotting annual production against cumulative production for most major fields shows unequivocally that technology barely affects the reserves. The observed upward revision of reserves is primarily an artefact of reporting practices.

THE SIZE OF THE YET-TO-FIND

It is possible to obtain a good estimate of what is yet-to-find in mature basins by extrapolating the discovery curve with a

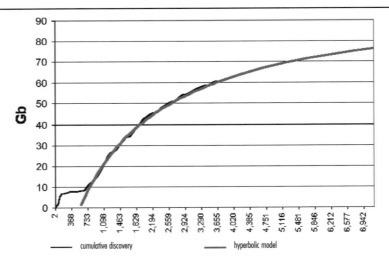

SHELL'S CREAMING CURVE

The cumulative number of exploratory wells—wildcats—drilled by the Shell oil company is plotted on the horizontal axis and the cumulative amount of oil they discovered is shown in billions of barrels (Gb, or giga-barrels) on the vertical one. The graph makes it clear that recent drilling has discovered much less oil per wildcat than in the early days.

so-called creaming curve that plots cumulative discovery against cumulative wildcats or over time. The plot of a particular geological province is hyperbolic because the larger fields are found first, being too large to miss. Other statistical techniques involving size distributions and geological habitats also contribute to the estimate. Given that the world has now been thoroughly explored, most future discovery will be in ever smaller fields in currently producing basins.

ULTIMATE RECOVERY

The sum of *Cumulative Production*, the *Reserves* and the *Yet-to-Find*, comprises the *Ultimate Recovery*. The key parameters of the world's oil based on a realistic assessment of each country's conventional crude oil for end 1999 are follows (Gb stands for billion barrels):

Cumulative Production to date		822 Gb
Remaining Reserves	+	827 Gb
Discovered	=	1649 Gb
Yet-to-Find	+	157 Gb
Ultimate	=	1800 Gb
Used to date	–	822 Gb
Yet-to-Produce	=	978 Gb

These numbers are quoted as computed but need to be generously rounded, given the inaccuracy of the input. In principle, they apply to conventional crude oil only, but it is recognised that they include some condensate and *non-conventional* heavy oil, which cannot be properly identified in the industry's database.

MODELLING DEPLETION

There are several ways to model depletion once the resource base has been established to within at least reasonable limits. A simple practical model distin-

guishes five Middle East OPEC countries as swing producers, making up the difference between world demand, under various scenarios, and what the non-swing countries can produce. Peak production comes close to the midpoint of depletion, when half the *Ultimate* has been consumed. The non-swing countries may in turn be divided into post- and pre-midpoint groups. In the post-midpoint group, production is assumed to decline at the current *Depletion Rate*, which is annual production as a percentage of the *Yet-to-Produce*. In the pre-midpoint countries, production is assumed to rise to midpoint on the current trend or as otherwise determined. Since midpoint in most such cases is now close, alternative assumptions about the rate of increase have little overall impact. The treatment of the individual swing countries is more complex, but generally, it is assumed that each country produces in relation to its share of the regional aggregate *Yet-to-Produce* to midpoint, when production declines at the then depletion rate, with the balance being made up by Saudi Arabia.

The base case scenario assumes that demand grows at 1.5 per cent a year until swing share passes 35 per cent. That is taken to trigger a price shock sufficient to curb further demand increases, leading to a plateau of production until share reaches 50 per cent, when the swing countries can no longer meet the demands made upon them as they themselves are approaching their own depletion midpoints. World production thereupon falls at the then depletion rate.

Swing share is an important element. It was 38 per cent at the time of the First Oil Shock in 1973, but sank to 18 per cent in 1985 because new provinces, such as the North Sea, were flooding the world with flush production from giant fields, which are found early in the exploration

SWING SHARE AND THE PRICE OF OIL

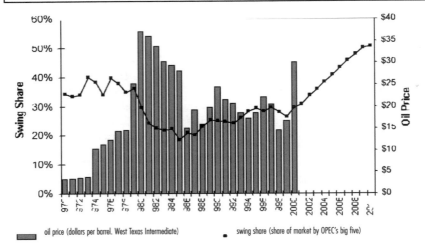

oil price (dollars per barrel. West Texas Intermediate)   swing share (share of market by OPEC's big five)

Whenever the share of the world oil market held by the five big OPEC producers in the Middle East has exceeded 30 per cent, they have had the power to push oil prices up sharply—and have done so.

process. It is stressed that these new provinces had been found before the shock, and were not a consequence of it, as is so often claimed. Swing Share has been rising since 1985 to reach about 30 per cent by end 1999. This time, it is set to continue to rise because there are no major new provinces ready to deliver, or indeed in sight, save perhaps the Caspian, whose potential has been much exaggerated.

SCENARIO

Applying the model to the database summarised above, gives a price shock in 2002 and the onset of terminal decline in 2009. The intervening plateau is likely to be anything but flat as it will be a time of tension and volatility. A general peak for conventional oil at about 61 Mb/d (million barrels per day) can be said to arise in the middle of the plateau, namely around 2005. Adding *non-conventional* oil and gas-liquids will delay the overall peak by about five years, when production may total about 85 Mb/d. Gas itself,

which is not considered in detail here, is likely to peak around 2020.

There are of course other scenarios that could advance or delay peak, but the onus rests on their proponents to demonstrate exactly where they expect the necessary production to come from and at what rate and cost. The deepwater areas, whose oil is here treated as *non-conventional*, are not as well known as the rest of the world. It appears, however, that deepwater oil prospects depend very much on unusual plate-tectonic conditions as found principally in the Gulf of Mexico and South Atlantic, where oil reservoirs are underlain by the rock from which the oil came. In other areas where ancient river deltas are now found in deep water, drilling is more likely to yield gas than oil. Overall, the deepwater domain is likely to yield about 85 Gb, peaking with heroic effort at about 9 Mb/d by 2010.

DENIAL AND OBFUSCATION

The foregoing scenario is based on a realistic assessment of the reserves as known

WORLD OIL PRODUCTION, PAST & FUTURE

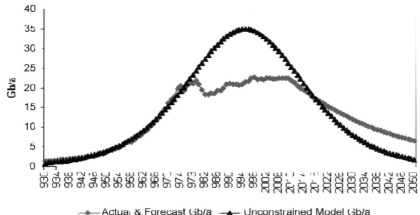

Actual & Forecast Gb/a   Unconstrained Model Gb/a

The darker line in the graph above is the so-called Hubbert curve and shows how oil production would have expanded and then contracted if it had been governed solely by physical constraints. The lighter line shows the amount of oil actually produced until today and what is likely to be produced in the future. As can be seen, the actual curve followed the theoretical curve very closely until the early 1970s when the five powerful Middle Eastern OPEC producers gained control of more than 30 per cent of the world market. They took advantage of their situation and pushed up prices, thus limiting oil demand. High oil prices can be expected to cause world oil demand to stay on a plateau until around 2010. After that, output will fall whatever the price because fields will be becoming exhausted.

to the oil industry with the *yet-to-find* estimate coming from an extrapolation of past results. The industry has indeed made remarkable technological progress in virtually all spheres of operation, and it has systematically searched the world for the biggest and best remaining prospects. It is, therefore, very reasonable to give weight to the past record in predicting the future, and to treat with skepticism claims that some remarkable and unforeseen technological breakthrough might open unknown doors. In any event, it is better to base plans on realism and not dreams.

It is worth examining how and why governments, international institutions and oil companies are reluctant to look reality in the face. It is difficult to penetrate the many layers of denial and obfuscation that envelope their pronouncements. We need the skills of a detective to determine whether we are dealing

with ignorance, culpable ignorance, or fraud and deception.

OIL COMPANIES
Shell overcomes its reluctance to admit to depletion by claiming that its record of forecasting has been poor, so that it prefers to develop a range of well-reasoned scenarios to cover the spectrum of possibility. In effect, it evades the issue on the grounds that it has no single viewpoint, although it does confess that at least one of its scenarios contemplates an Ultimate of about 2600 Gb for all liquids with a peak around 2010. This is close to the above assessment.

Another major oil company, BP Amoco, has made a public presentation showing that discovery peaked in the 1960s, even if failing to draw the obvious conclusion that peak production must follow. It has changed its logo to a sunflower and says that its initials stand for

'Beyond Petroleum', which is a very oblique reference to the depletion of its principal asset. Its chairman and chief executive sit on the board of an investment bank, Goldman Sachs, which in 1999 commented:

The rig count over the last 12 years has reached bottom. This is not because of low oil price. The oil companies are not going to keep rigs employed to drill dry holes. They know it but are unable and unwilling to admit it. The great merger mania is nothing more than a scaling down of a dying industry in recognition of the fact that 90 per cent of global conventional oil has already been found.

It would be surprising if this did not convey the opinion of the BP board. At the time it was making large acquisitions, the company stated that oil prices would remain low for the foreseeable future, but now admits that the world depends on the Middle East.

Lee Raymond, chief executive of Exxon-Mobil comments: *'So technology is one of the key reasons why I am excited about the prospects of our industry. Our raw resources may be the same, but our processes and technology are truly state-of-the-art'*. In other words, he admits that technology does not change how much oil a field contains, with all that that implies.

In shining contrast are the chief executives of Arco and Agip who, when they felt free to speak on leaving office, both stated that they expected global production to peak by 2005.

GOVERNMENT INSTITUTIONS

The US Geological Survey has made periodic assessments of the world's oil and gas endowment, the latest of which was issued in 2000. In a press release on the eve of a critical OPEC meeting, it claimed that *'there is still an abundance of oil and gas in the world'* and announced an estimated *Undiscovered* of 649 Gb for the world outside the USA and 612 Gb of

'Reserve Growth'. The report itself later revealed a very wide range from 239 to 1376 Gb for the Undiscovered with for example a *Mean* expectation from East Greenland of 49 Gb on the basis of a comparison with mid-Norway, which has yielded about 10 Gb after many years of search. To attribute five times more to an undrilled, unknown province demonstrates an absence of common sense. The reserve growth claim also ranges from 192 to 1031 Gb based mainly on onshore US experience, failing to appreciate that most 'growth' is a reporting phenomenon, primarily related to large onshore fields. Only the low end of the ranges can be taken at all seriously. At the same time, the Geological Survey separately released an unpublicised poster that did depict an imminent peak of production accompanied by a text stressing the consequential crisis. It has diplomatically covered the full spectrum of possibility with a wide range of estimates and contradictory material.

The International Energy Agency was established by the OECD governments in the aftermath of the oil shocks of the 1970s to monitor supply and demand. In 1998, it presented a report evaluating a so-called 'business as usual scenario' whereby demand grew to 112 Mb/d (Million barrels per day) by 2020 with prices rising to $25/b. It showed how this demand would be met, admitting that the non-Middle East peaked and declined, while the Middle East share grew to 62 per cent by 2020. Even this was not enough, causing the IEA to introduce a 'balancing item' of unidentified unconventional oil, whose production miraculously rises from zero in 2010 to 19 Mb/d ten years later, while the identified unconventional makes a ceiling of only 2.4 Mb/d by 2010. A moment's reflection tells us that oil will not be $25/b when the Middle East supplies 62 per cent, and that the 'balancing item' is a euphemism for rank shortage.

These few examples illustrate the scale of denial and obfuscation that surrounds this subject.

CONCLUSIONS

There is no particular technical difficulty in assessing the size of a field's reserves or in assessing the world's undiscovered potential. It is easy to see that the true impact of technology is to hold production as high as possible for as long as possible, without materially affecting the reserves themselves, which are set by Nature. The relationship between peak discovery, which is a matter of historical fact, and a corresponding peak of production is also evident from a moment's thought.

So far, the world has been reluctant to admit that the production of one of its principal fuels is close to peak without sight of any substitute that can come close to matching its convenience and low cost. It is now too late to make any useful preparations, but much remains to be done to inform. Governments need to understand, so as to react better, and the people at large have to know, so that they will be willing to give governments the mandate for tough decisions.

The world is not about to run out of oil, but production is about to peak. The sky does not fall in at peak, but the perception of the future changes. It is likely to lead to severe political and economic tensions, including economic recession, a stock-market crash, and financial instability from the huge flows to the Middle East. There are obvious dangers of misguided military intervention as the United States, Europe and the East vie for access to Middle East oil. The inequality between rich and poor nations will be

more severe. Agriculture is at risk because it is now heavily dependent on synthetic nutrients and irrigation, both directly and indirectly dependent on petroleum. The global market may wither from high transport costs.

This is not necessarily a doomsday picture, for the end of cheap oil-based energy may carry long-term benefits. Countries will have to become more self-sufficient and self-reliant, finding ways to live in closer harmony with their environments. The excesses of capitalism that seem to have created a virtual economy, based on the notion of perpetual growth, may be curbed, and the kleptocrats who run it may be reined in. The risks to the climate from human activity may recede.

It is time to wake up, for the alarm has sounded.

REFERENCES

Bentley R.W, *et al*, 2000, *Perspectives on the future of oil*; Reading University.

Campbell C.J., 1997, *The Coming Oil Crisis*, Multi-Science Publishing Company, Brentwood, UK.

Campbell C.J., and J.H. Laherrère, 1998, The end of cheap oil, *Scientific American*, March, pp. 80–6.

Campbell C.J., 2000, Myth of spare capacity; *Oil & Gas Journal*. March, p. 20.

Fleming D.,1999, The next oil shock?, *Prospect*, April 1999.

International Energy Agency, 1998, *World Energy Outlook*, Paris.

Laherrère J.H., 1999, Reserve growth: technological progress, or bad reporting and bad arithmetic, *Geopolitics of Energy*.

Perrodon A., J.H. Laherrère, and C.J.Campbell, 1998, *The world's non-conventional oil and gas*; Petroleum. *Economist*, London.

Schindler J and W. Zittel, 2000, *Fossile Energiereserven*, LB-Systemtechnik. Ottobrunn, Germany.

US Geological Survey, 2000, *World Petroleum Assessment*, DDS-60.

Youngquist W., 1997, *Geodestinies: the inevitable control of earth resources over nations and individuals*; Nat. Book Co., Portland.

www.oilcrisis.com (various items)

WORLD ENERGY CONSUMPTION
1970–2015

World Energy Consumption

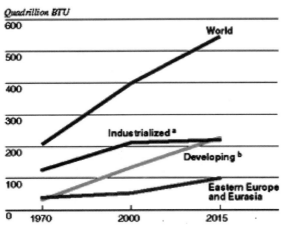

Quadrillion BTU

a Includes: United States, Canada, Mexico, Japan, United Kingdom, France, Germany, Italy, Netherlands, other Europe, and Australia.

b Includes: Developing Asia (China, India, South Korea, other Asia), Turkey, Africa, Brazil.

World Energy Consumption by Fuel Type

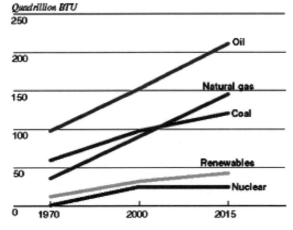

Quadrillion BTU

Source: International Energy Outlook, 1998; US Department of Energy.

OIL SCARCITY...

A report published by the US Central Intelligence Agency in December 2000 does not anticipate any problems in meeting the world's rising demand for fossil fuels over the next 15 years. The relevant section of the report touches on several issues discussed in this Review besides oil depletion. It reads:

"Sustained global economic growth, along with population increases, will drive a nearly 50 percent increase in the demand for energy over the next 15 years. Total oil demand will increase from roughly 75 million barrels per day in 2000 to more than 100 million barrels in 2015, an increase almost as large as OPEC's current production. Over the next 15 years, natural gas usage will increase more rapidly than that of any other energy source—by more than 100 percent—mainly stemming from the tripling of gas consumption in Asia.

Asia will drive the expansion in energy demand, replacing North America as the leading energy consumption region and accounting for more than half of the world's total increase in demand.

- China, and to a lesser extent India, will see especially dramatic increases in energy consumption.
- By 2015, only one-tenth of Persian Gulf oil will be directed to Western markets; three-quarters will go to Asia.

Fossil fuels will remain the dominant form of energy despite increasing concerns about global warming. Efficiency of solar cells will improve, genetic engineering will increase the long-term prospects for the large-scale use of ethanol, and hydrates will be used increasingly as fuels. Nuclear energy use will remain at current levels.

Meeting the increase in demand for energy will pose neither a major supply challenge nor lead to substantial price increases in real terms. Estimates of the world's total endowment of oil have steadily increased as technological

NO PROBLEM SAYS CIA

progress in extracting oil from remote sources has enabled new discoveries and more efficient production. Recent estimates indicate that 80 per cent of the world's available oil still remains in the ground, as does 95 per cent of the world's natural gas.

- The Persian Gulf region—absent a major war—will see large increases in oil production capacity and will rise in its overall importance to the world energy market. Other areas of the world—including Russia, coastal West Africa, and Greenland—will also increase their role in global energy markets. Russia and the Middle East account for three-quarters of known gas reserves.
- Latin America—principally Venezuela, Mexico, and Brazil—has more than 117 billion barrels of proven oil reserves and potentially 114 billion barrels of undiscovered oil, according to the US Geological Survey. With foreign participation, Latin American production could increase from 9 million barrels per day to more than 14 million.
- Caspian energy development is likely to be in high gear by 2015. New transport routes for Caspian oil and gas exports that do not transit Russia will be operating.

Oil-producing countries will continue to exert leverage on the market to increase prices but are unlikely to achieve stable high prices. Energy prices are likely to become more unstable in the next 15 years, as periodic price hikes are followed by price collapses.

By 2015, global energy markets will have coalesced into two quasi-hemispheric patterns. Asia's energy needs will be met either through coal from the region or from oil and gas supplies from the Persian Gulf, Central Asia, and Russia. Western Europe and the Western Hemisphere will draw on the Atlantic Basin for their energy sources at world prices. **//**

Not surprisingly, the increased level of economic activity will have serious environmental consequences but, realistically perhaps, the CIA does not expect effective international action to be taken to counteract these.

// Contemporary environmental problems will persist and in many instances grow over the next 15 years. With increasingly intensive land use, significant degradation of arable land will continue as will the loss of tropical forests. Given the promising global economic outlook, greenhouse gas emissions will increase substantially. The depletion of tropical forests and other species-rich habitats, such as wetlands and coral reefs, will exacerbate the historically large losses of biological species now occurring. (…)

Global warming will challenge the international community as indications of a warming climate—such as meltbacks of polar ice, sea level rise, and increasing frequency of major storms—occur. The Kyoto Protocol on Climate Change, which mandates emission-reduction targets for developed countries, is unlikely to come into force soon or without substantial modification. Even in the absence of a formal treaty, however, some incremental progress will be made in reducing the growth of greenhouse gas emissions. **//**

Colin Campbell's comment (4 January 2001) on the CIA's report was: 'This organisation is in the business of subterfuge and deception, so we should not expect otherwise when it addresses oil supply. Its motive for exaggerating the world's oil supply is to undermine the Middle East's confidence in its ability to control world oil supply and thereby price. The US is already facing the onset of recession, partly triggered by high oil price. It is a situation that can only get worse.' (Eds)

The full CIA report can be downloaded from:
http://www.odci.gov/cia/publications/global-trends2015/index.html#link8c

after oil

DAVID FLEMING

The extraordinary prosperity of the twentieth century was built on cheap oil and gas. When they are no longer either cheap nor reliably available, the economic consequences will be far greater than can easily be imagined.

Beneath the seabed off the coast of Saudi Arabia, there is an oil field called Manifa. It is a giant, and its riches are almost untapped.[1] There is, however, a snag. Its oil is heavy with vanadium and hydrogen sulphide, making it virtually unusable. One day, the technology may be in place to extract and dispose of these contaminants, but it will not be for some time and when, or if, it does happen, it will do no more than slightly reduce the rate at which world oil supplies slip away towards depletion. However, even this field has advantages relative to the massive reserves of oil which Middle East suppliers are said to hold ready to keep oil prices low and secure the future of civilisation. Unlike those fantasy fields, Manifa actually exists.

For the last twenty five years, there has been a tacit consensus that oil depletion has almost no place on the environmental agenda. This is partly a reaction to the criticism of the Club of Rome's (1972) study, *The Limits to Growth*, which drew attention to the existence of limits to the oil resource.[2] The study was revisited and ably defended,[3] but the weight of criticism was crushing, and environment policy turned instead to sustainable develop-

ment. The question of resources—oil included—came to be regarded as an embarrassing phase in the environmental movement's early days.[4]

But now, it is back with a vengeance. In region after region, the story is of ageing oilfields, of the wrong sort of oil, of nitrogen being pumped into wells to keep up the flow, of exploration turning to unpromising areas such as West-of-Greenland. The UK's North Sea oil is past its peak, as are the giant fields in Alaska, the former Soviet Union, Mexico, Venezuela and Norway. The United States' own oil production has been declining since 1970 and now accounts for less than half its needs. The only producers who still possess an oil resource which may be capable of keeping oil flowing into the world market at a roughly constant level in the first decade of the century are the Middle East OPEC Five—Saudi Arabia, Iran, Iraq, Kuwait and the United Arab Emirates. And even with these countries, it seems, the closer you look at the detail, the less they have to offer.

Much of Saudi Arabia's reserves of oil are held in one huge field, the Ghawar. It has been pumped continually since 1948 and not surprisingly, it is showing signs of exhaustion, with its southern end now flooding with water. Saudi Arabia can keep its production roughly constant for between seven and ten years before it, too, has used up half its total oil resource and rolls over towards depletion. Then it will turn to smaller fields, producing smaller amounts, followed by poor-quality fields with real problems like Manifa. Saudi Arabia's legendary oil wealth is now coming up hard against the geology.

Reality intervenes in the case of the other Gulf states, too. Iran, which in the past was one of the young giants of the world oil business, could not now sustain a higher output for long, and there are suspicions that some of the production credited to Iran in recent years has actually consisted of oil piped over the border from Iraq. Kuwait and one of the Emirates, Abu Dhabi, could increase production and may well do so, but development would take several years, and their reserves are small relative to the world's demand for oil. There is, however, one country with potential for a serious increase in output, on a scale that could make a difference. The snag in this case is that the country is Iraq.

Unlike every other region with major oil potential, Iraq's oil geology is not fully explored, but there are some well-informed guesses. One estimate is that there are 110 billion barrels there, equal to more than three UK North Seas, or more than one third of the total resource once possessed by Saudi Arabia—enough to keep world oil production rising for a few more years. It lies, however, in a country which is armed to the teeth, consumed by loathing of the West, and just waiting for the threat of armed intervention from America to make its day. Iraq was prevented from selling off its oil during the 1990s, when prices were lower than they will ever be again; it will soon

DAVID FLEMING is an independent policy analyst specialising in the impact that environmental change will have on the global market economy in the early decades of the twenty-first century. His forthcoming book **The Lean Economy** describes the consequences of the coming oil price shock and climate change. It discusses four types of solution: lean production, lean distribution, lean design and lean culture. He holds an MBA and has worked in the textile, detergent, advertising and financial services industries. He was economics spokesman of the English Green Party between 1977 and 1980 and chairman of the Soil Association between 1988 and 1991. In 1979 he began studies in economics at Birkbeck College, University of London, completing an MSc in 1982 and a PhD on the economics of the market for positional goods in 1988. He lives in London.

be well placed to apply its own sanctions to the rest of the world by fine-tuning its oil production and naming its price.

The most shocking quality of this story is that it is not new. The essential problem has been known for a very long time. It is a well established fact, written up exhaustively in the literature, that the period around the turn of the millennium would mark the end of growth in the world production of oil, and the start of its long decline towards depletion. Consistent forecasts of the 'peak'—the moment when oil production turns down—have been routine for half a century.[5] In 1956, the geologist King Hubbert correctly forecast that America's oil production would peak around 1970.[6] In 1970, Esso forecast that that total world petroleum deposits would turn out to be about 2,100 billion barrels, very close to Colin Campbell's current estimate.[7] In 1976, the UK's Department of Energy warned that the North Sea production would peak around the end of the century—about the same time as the peak in world oil production; it would therefore be a good idea, its report concluded, to be ready with alternative supplies of energy.[8] The *Global Report to the President*, commissioned by President Carter and published in 1982, noted that if there were no constraint in demand, the peak would occur in the 1990s, but this would be slightly postponed if (as happened) there were to be any attempt to enforce higher prices: 'Convenient, easily transported, relatively clean-burning petroleum and natural gas resources are being depleted.' It recommended action: 'As these resources become increasingly scarce, a transition to other forms of energy must be made.'[9]

An oil-price shock is likely in the opening years of the twenty-first century.

The procession of unheeded warnings has continued. Individual energy analysts, notably Colin Campbell, Buzz Ivanhoe, Jean Laherrère and, more recently, Roger Bentley, have produced a series detailed empirical studies showing that the turning point for oil would occur around the turn of the century.[10] In November 1998, the International Energy Agency (IEA) showed (although it required a little deduction to decode the message) that growth in world oil output could not be expected to continue beyond about 2001. And, in mid 2000, a member of the conservative United States Geological Survey (USGS), published in an Internet master-class on 'the Big Rollover—when the demand for oil outstrips the capacity to produce it'. It concludes, 'Hang on tight. If we don't recognise the problem soon and deal with it, it's going to be quite a ride!'[12]

The reputable forecasts, then, have consistently indicated that an oil-price shock is likely in the opening years of the twenty-first century, and that its impact will get worse over time. Why, then, have they been ignored? If the problem were really serious, surely—in this society rich with economists and experts—we would have been told? Not necessarily. The principles of economic thought which are so confidently used as an aid to understanding what is going on in the market economy break down when they are applied to natural resources such as oil.

There are four ways in which the unquestioned principles of market economics do not apply in this case. The first arises from the fact that the price of oil has virtually no influence on the rate at which it is discovered. In market economics, the rules of supply and demand hold good: if, owing to increased demand, the price of something goes up, then this gives a signal to supply more of it; new suppliers will pile into the market until the price settles down again. In the oil market, price does not have this effect. In the early days, the best and biggest fields of conventional (i.e. liquid and accessible) oil were quick to be found, and very cheap to pump. In fact, a new well did not have to be pumped at all; it just gushed. This cheap-to-produce and very useful fuel was immensely profitable, so the world's resources were prospected rapidly and, with the help of digital seismic technology, the discovery of oil grew to a peak in the mid 1960s. Since 1965, however, the rate of discovery has declined by approximately 70% and is falling fast.[13]

This means that we are using oil now that was discovered over forty years ago, in the period when it was being found in huge quantities. That period of discovery is over. There is no conceivable increase in prices, nor any prospective technological advance,[14] which will bring it back. As we use up more of the oil fields which were found in the past, it is becoming harder and harder to sustain the growth of production. Soon production will decline. The famous 'price signal' which is supposed to kick in at that point will have absolutely no effect. It is an *impasse* to which the well-behaved theories of prices, supply and demand are irrelevant.

The second breakdown in the well-behaved thinking of market economics occurs with a failure to grasp the significance of the 'peak' in the supply of oil. There is still a large quantity of oil in the ground; we are probably not yet even half way through the total quantity of recoverable conventional oil, and there will always be some left to trickle up, if it is pumped hard enough, as proved by the oil donkeys in Pennsylvania which are still nodding away after more than a hundred years. What matters is not the quantity of oil that remains, but the turning point at which the flow of oil hits its peak—when producers are forced to turn to the smaller wells from which it is impossible to sustain the massive flows of former years. It is here that we come to the parting of the ways between what the market needs and what the oil industry can produce.

The third way in which oil insults the received rules of economics is that it cannot usefully be discussed in abstract terms such as 'reduced dependency' and 'falling percentages.' The British press and government have persistently argued that the world's dependency on oil has declined during the last three decades, and this, it is claimed, means that the market is much less vulnerable to prices and disruptions affecting oil than it was in 1973. Certainly, this was the UK government's position at the time of the first ominous price rises of 1999–2000: 'In effect, people have substituted away from oil and oil product consumption', wrote John Battle, the Energy Minister, and his successor, Helen Liddell, agreed: 'The declining reliance of the world economy on oil' is one of several factors which 'counterbalance fears regarding the peak in oil production'.[15] *The Financial Times* admiringly quoted calculations of the effect of high oil prices on corporate profits. $40 a barrel?—that would merely

reduce corporate profit growth from 13% to 12%. No problem. It summarised:

These projections reflect the fact that the corporate sector—and western economies as a whole—have become far less dependent on oil. As a proportion of output, OECD oil and gas imports were three and a half times higher in 1978 than they are now.[16]

Less dependent? Even if oil accounted for no more than one percent of the total quantity of energy used, and that one percent provided the fuel for transport, then disruptions to the supply of oil could close the economy down within days. Arcane calculations about the impact of oil prices on growth rates are irrelevant. While it is true that oil declined from 45 percent to 33 percent of all energy used in the UK between 1973 and 2000, the volume of transport, which depends entirely on oil, doubled. We are twice as dependent on transport as we were in 1973. The economists' arguments about 'reduced dependency' would be entirely correct were it not for one little snag: we do not fill up our cars with percentages.

Our reliance on a secure flow of oil to underpin our economic and social order is total.

The 'reduced dependency' argument, then, is absurd. The world uses 30% more oil now than it did in 1970, and the fact that its consumption of gas has doubled does not mean that it is less dependent on oil; it simply means that it has become more dependent on gas, too. In the case of the UK, the contribution of gas and oil combined grew from 50% to 70% of energy consumption between 1973 and 2000. Secure supplies of gas itself cannot be expected to last significantly beyond 2020;[17] this date would be brought forward substantially if there were any large-scale switch from oil to gas for transport, and the switch itself would require a transition period of 5-10 years in order to become a serious solution. There is therefore not a shred of justification for arguing that we are less dependent on oil. Our reliance on a secure flow of oil to underpin our economic and social order is, at present, total.

Expertise, it seems, wipes the mind clean of common-sense.

The fourth way in which well-behaved economic analysis throws us off the scent of the oil shock is that it prefers to ignore time-lags. Specifically, it makes simple assumptions that other sources of energy, from renewable sources—such as solar and wind power—will come on stream as soon as the 'price signal' of high oil prices kicks in; when it does so, renewables will flood into our homes and cars and solve our problems. The belief is persistent that ingenuity will come to the rescue— to take the case of transport alone—with shared, gas-powered and much smaller cars (goods vehicles too, maybe), opening up a smooth and speedy path to post-oil economy. What is really worrying the OPEC countries, according to Anatole Kaletsky in *The Times*, is the danger of alternative energy sources bringing the demand for oil to a premature end: 'The Saudis, in particular, realise that oil demand could collapse well before their kingdom has the chance to sell off its oil reserves.'[18]

The problem is, however, that the development of those alternative energy sources will take a long time. Look at the scale of the task, to take just the transport case again: build solar / wind / biomass facilities to generate electricity; use the electricity to produce hydrogen; distrib-

ute this hydrogen at an ultra-low temperature (-150°C) to 'petrol-stations' fitted with the robots that are needed to deliver it into cars and trucks fitted with fuel-cells, cut dependency on road transport by some 75% ... Natural gas clearly has a useful contribution to make here but, given the time it would take to switch to natural gas and the coming peak in the flow of gas itself, this contribution will be quite limited. For energy as a whole, the UK government's own target in 2000 was that renewable sources should, by 2010, account for just 2% of current final demand. A detailed study, published by the LTI-Research Group in Mannheim in 1998, found that, if the development of renewable energy systems were supported as an urgent priority by decisive, well-co-ordinated action by governments, then it would be possible to provide energy from them equal to as much as 35% of the energy used at present—but it would take fifty years to do so.[19]

If more efficient ways of using energy (e.g. conservation methods and super-efficient technologies) were both developed at the same time as a reduction in the need for energy services (e.g. more compact ways of using land), this 35% might conceivably give us all the energy we needed in fifty years, and if it were given the highest possible urgency, then, perhaps, it could be done in twenty-five years. It follows that, if we wait in the approved manner for the market to give the 'price signal' that renewable forms of energy should now be developed, we shall ensure that the job starts twenty five years too late. It also follows that, even if the shock were not imminent after all and, instead, were postponed for ten years, while an intensive programme to develop renewables started straight away, it would still have started fifteen years too late to avoid a destabilising 'energy gap' before the alternatives are functioning properly.

In fact, our twenty-five year estimate of the time needed for a shift from dependency on oil is doubly optimistic, because the LTI-research group's own estimate of fifty years is based on the assumption of the comfortable background of a fully functioning economy with no disruptions to transport or industry or to any of the other conditions of normality. In reality, the building of the renewables-based economy will have to take place against a background of the oil shock, with all its consequences, which will make it difficult to put into effect a decisive co-ordinated programme on anything at all.

It is evident therefore, that one of the reasons for this surreal situation, with imminent and devastating change unrecognised by the experts and discounted by government, is that the problem falls outside the mind-set of market economics. Expertise, it seems, wipes the mind clean of common-sense. Maybe, for a moment, we should stop thinking, and just feel the reality of energy famine. It starts in the poorer countries, when the cost of paraffin which they use for cooking places it beyond their reach; after the peak, consumers all over the world are in trouble, not because oil is expensive, but because it is not there.

The economics of oil is now dominated by its close proximity to the peak, and the graph below shows the peak that could be expected in 2005. In fact, the global peak will not take the usual form of a simple turning-point; instead, as production begins to slow down, price increases will begin to speed up, suppressing demand and slowing the rate of growth in production even more. The market will go into 'contango'. Buyers will want to *buy more oil today*—i.e. for delivery straight away,

Gh/a

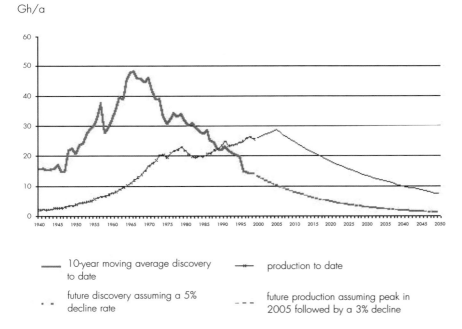

```
60

50

40

30

20

10

0
  1940 1945 1950 1955 1960 1965 1970 1975 1980 1985 1990 1995 2000 2005 2010 2015 2020 2025 2030 2035 2040 2045 2050
```

——— 10-year moving average discovery to date

——•—— production to date

• • future discovery assuming a 5% decline rate

– – – future production assuming peak in 2005 followed by a 3% decline

The steep decline in the discovery of oil since 1965 means that, at some point, production must begin to decline itself. This is expected to happen around 2005.

since it will be cheaper than oil in the future, while sellers will have an incentive to *hold back the supply of oil today*, since the oil that is still in the ground is appreciating in value. This increase in demand for today's oil, combined with limited supply, will tend to raise its price while the expectation that oil in the future will be still more expensive will tend to increase the price of future oil too, though not quite so fast. Eventually, the price of today's oil will catch up with that of future oil, returning the market to order and equilibrium, but at a much higher price. Oil production will flatten off towards a plateau for a period, followed by a relatively abrupt downturn onto the path towards exhaustion.

The three main purposes for which oil is used world-wide are food, transport and heating. Agriculture is almost entirely dependent on reliable supplies of oil for cultivation and for pumping water, and on gas for its fertilisers; in addition, for every calorie of energy used by agriculture itself, five more (mainly from oil and gas) are used for processing, storage, and distribution.[20] Since farming and the food industry is not famous for spending money unnecessarily, there must be a presumption that there is very little short term 'slack' which would allow its demand for energy to be reduced at short notice without disruptions in food supplies. In the case of transport and heating fuel, there is more scope for saving energy at short notice; cutting leisure journeys, for instance, wearing extra pullovers and, in the slightly longer term, driving smaller cars have a role to play while, in the longer term, there is totally different low-energy paradigm waiting to be developed. But it is the short term that has to be survived first, and in that short term, the competition for oil for food, transport and heating will be real and raw.

One hitherto cuddly competitor which will abruptly reveal another side to its character will be the United States. America will fight hard and dirty. Its economy is organised irrevocably around the assumption of cheap transport, and any failure to keep its automobile economy moving would be even more damaging there than it would in other developed economies. It has, at the moment, a lot of money, and it can afford to bid high. And, America has the additional problem that it is facing not just a shortfall in the supply of oil but, at the same time, a progressive reduction in the supply of gas; it already relies on gas imports from Canada, whose own reserves are now depleting rapidly.[21] The timing is vicious: just at the moment when the world's supply of oil starts to decline, the United States will have a new and pressing incentive to *increase* its consumption of oil. American households will have the choice of freezing in unheated homes or—for only as long as the purchasing power of the dollar lasts—paying very high prices for oil.

The world market as a whole will strain to cope with the prices, but the scarcities themselves will intensify. There will be serious economic contraction and destabilisation. Unless the installation of alternatives to replace both oil and gas moves ahead at an extraordinary speed, the deconstruction will get rapidly worse as the supplies of oil, and then gas, go into decline. The market economy in its present form will not survive this sudden loss of cheap and abundant energy.

REFERENCES
1. This discussion of oil supplies is a revised and expanded version of the article published in David Fleming (2000), 'After Oil', *Prospect*, November, pp. 12-13.
2. Donella Meadows, Dennis Meadows, Jorgen Randers and William Behrens (1972), *The Limits to Growth*, London: Earth Island. It was

criticised in (for instance) H.S.D. Cole, Christopher Freeman, Marie Jahoda and K.L.R.Pavitt (1973), *Thinking about the Future: A Critique of 'The Limits to Growth'*, London: Chatto and Windus for Sussex University Press; William D. Nordhaus (1973), 'World Dynamics: Measurement without Data', *Economic Journal,* December; Wilfred Beckerman (1990), *An Introduction to National Income Analysis*, London: Weidenfeld and Nicholson, (third edition; first published 1968); Robert M. Solow (1974), 'The Economics of Resources or the Resources of Economics', *American Economic Review*, Papers and Proceedings (May); Mancur Olson and Hans H. Landsberg, eds. (1975), *The No-Growth Society*, London: Woburn Press.

3. Richard Douthwaite, (1992), *The Growth Illusion*, Hartland: Green Books; Donella Meadows, Dennis Meadows and Jørgen Randers (1992), *Beyond the Limits*, London: Earthscan. See also Meadows et al's successful refutation of the criticism in Cole et al (1973).

4. David Fleming (2000), 'The Limits to Sustainable Development', *Where Next? Reflections on the Human Future*, London: Royal Botanical Gardens, Kew.

5. The decisive paper on this was by M. King Hubbert (1949), 'Energy from Fossil Fuels', *Science*, 109, pp. 103-9. See Hardin, Garrett (1993), *Living Within Limits: Ecology, Economics and Population Taboos*. London: Oxford University Press, p.138.

6. M. King Hubbert (1956), 'Nuclear Energy and the Fossil Fuels', American petroleum Institute of Drilling and Production Practice, *Proceedings*, Spring Meeting, San Antonio, Texas, pp.7-25.

7. The Editors of *The Ecologist* (1972), *Blueprint for Survival*, London: Penguin Books, p.18.

8. UK Department of Energy (1976), *Energy Research and Development in the United Kingdom*, Energy Paper Number 11, Her Majesty's Stationery Office.

9. Gerald O. Barney (1982), *The Global 2000 Report to the President: Entering the Twenty-First Century*, Penguin, p.351. The report showed that, if demand were held constant at the level it reached in 1975, the turning point to a precipitous decline into depletion could be postponed until about 2025 while, in the absence of any attempt to control prices (by, for instance, the OPEC cartel), the peak

would occur at the start of the 1990s. On this basis, the slight constraint that has actually occurred in demand, due to relatively high prices over much of the period 1975-2000, would have been expected to lead to a peak in the period of 2000-05.

10. Colin Campbell (1997), *The Coming Oil Crisis*, Brentwood, UK: Multi Science. L.F. Ivanhoe (1996), 'Updated Hubbert Curves Analyse World Oil Supply', *World Oil*, November pp.91-4. Jean Laherrère discovered the 'parabolic fractal', (as explained by Campbell (1997), p.176), 'the law of distribution stating that objects in a natural domain plot as a parabola when their size is compared with their rank on a log-log format. For example, the populations of the larger towns can be plotted to yield the population of a country down to the smallest settlement. It means that when the larger oilfields have been found, their size distribution can be used to predict what the *Ultimate* recovery will be.' (Jean Laherrère (1996), Distributions de type <fractal parabolique> dans la nature', *C.R. Acad. Sci.*, Paris 322 Iia 535-41; cited in Campbell (1997)). Roger Bentley's (1998 and later revisions), *UK Energy: The Next 5-10 Years*, a report submitted without effect to the Department of Trade & Industry, UK, by the Department of Cybernetics, University of Reading, is a summary-synthesis of all the main relevant data on oil discoveries, reserves and future supplies. See also: Hooshang Amirahmadi (1996), 'Oil at the Turn of the Twenty First Century', *Futures*, 28, 5, pp.433-52.

11. IEA (International Energy Agency) (1998), *World Energy Outlook*, Paris: OECD. This is analysed in David Fleming (1999), 'The Next Oil Shock?' *Prospect*, April, pp.12-13; and in David Fleming (1999b), 'Decoding a Message about the Market for Oil', *European Environment*, 9, 4, July-August, pp.124-34. The IEA's forecast took the form of an analysis of showing what would have to happen in order to achieve a sustained production growth of 1.8% a year, allowing the reader to decide for himself whether that scenario was plausible or not. The Agency later confirmed, as concluded in the above papers - that this was in effect issued a coded warning of a turning point in oil supplies around 2000.

12. www.oilcrisis.com/magoon/ (2000).

13. This analysis is set out in various forms in the references cited above, but see also Matthew Simmons (2000), *An Energy White Paper*, http://www.simmonsco-intl.com/research/: 'The reality of the world's oil production base as we begin the twenty-first century is that all the super giant fields are now very old with high water cuts and steep decline curves. Most of these giant fields are now mere pygmies through rising decline rates'.

14. Confidence in 'technological improvements relating to discovery and recovery rates' was expressed by, for instance, by Helen Liddell, the UK's Energy Minister at the time, in her reply to a letter from Tim Yeo, Shadow Agriculture Minister, 10 May 2000.

15. Letters to Tim Yeo, MP, 8 April, 1999 and 10 May 2000.

16. 'Pouring Oil on Troubled Markets', Leading article, *Financial Times*, 30 September, 2000.

17. The International Energy Agency's projections of gas supplies on the basis of business as usual (BAU) suggest that gas production from all OECD sources will peak in 2015, and that the OECD's share of the market will fall from around 45% at present to 30% and falling in 2020. The major sources of supply will be the Transition Economies (the former Soviet Union), the Middle East and South & East Asia, which will, collectively, have a 55% share of the market, while China, significantly, will have only a 2% share. This concentration of supply, the declining production from the OECD and the political tensions arising from gas-rich economies bordering on a gas-poor China suggest the probability of both price- and geopolitical-instability in the gas market. Moreover, the rise in oil pries means that there will be both a higher demand and higher prices for gas than the BAU projections indicate. This suggests that the estimated peak in OECD gas output should be brought forward to around 2010. After that, gas prices will be much higher, and a global peak in production, with severe price volatilities, can be expected to develop during the second decade of the century. See also J.H. Laherrère, A. Perrodon and C.J. Campbell (1966), *The World's Gas Potential*, Geneva: Petroconsultants S.A., and IEA (1998); USGS (1) and (2) CHECK

18. Anatole Kaletsky (2000), 'This Oil Shock Will Not Put the Skids under Growth', *The Times*, 3 October, p.27.

19. LTI-Research Group, Ed, (1998), *Long-Term Integration of Renewable Energy Sources into the European Energy System*, Heidelberg, Physica-Verlag. The study finds that, in order to meet energy demand within the European Union from renewables, demand would have to be reduced from 4500 watts per capita in 1990 to 1700 W/cap in 2050.' p.4.

20. Maurice Green (1978), *Eating Oil*, Boulder: Westview.

21. Francis Harper (1999), 'Ultimate Hydrocarbon Resources in the 21st Century', American Association of Petroleum Geologists Conference, *Oil & Gas in the 21st Century*, 12-15 September, Birmingham, UK, cited in Roger Bentley (2000), 'Global Oil & Gas Depletion', E.U. Conference, *What Energy Options for Europe in 2020?*, 4-5 December, Brussels. Bentley writes, 'Going by the North American experience (which is more-or-less at peak on gas), [the] proportion for the gas peak is around three-quarters. However, unlike oil which declines gently when the peak is reached, gas production past peak falls off a cliff.' (p.3)

WEBSITE CONNECTIONS
The oil peak: www.hubbertpeak.com and www.oilcrisis.com/magoon/
Fuel rationing www.dtqs.org

bye-bye, Irish energy pie

KEVIN HEALION

Ireland needs an annual intake of energy from various sources to keep active. Major changes in the country's energy diet are required in the next few years. Unfortunately, government policy documents are only just beginning to take this into account.

You could say that Ireland is at the adolescent stage. In the last few years, the nation has put on a massive spurt of growth. From a small kid we've grown to be a gangly teenager so fast that we've surprised ourselves and all the neighbours. And like any teenager, our appetite has become voracious—we consume 70 per cent more energy pie in the year 2000 than we did in 1980. And it is projected that our energy consumption will be 26 per cent greater in 2010 than it is today—if 'business as usual' continues. Our energy pie in divided into three slices of roughly equal size: heat, electricity and transport. Our demand for energy in all three sectors has grown significantly since 1980 and our need for extra helpings of electricity and transport seems insatiable.

Irish demand for heat has increased by nearly 40 per cent since 1980. It is required by all sectors of the economy: industry, agriculture, the public and private service sectors and in the home. Its main sources are oil, natural gas, peat, coal, wood and electricity.

Irish electricity demand has doubled since 1980, and continues to increase. During the past year, there have been a number of red alerts at ESB headquarters

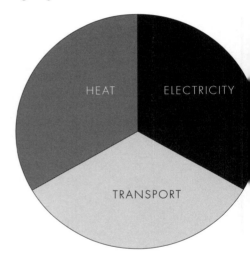

when the demand for electricity came uncomfortably close to the supply capacity available. An ESB report[1] on generation capacity requirements from 2000 to 2006 says that there is an immmediate need for extra capacity. Using the Economic and Social Research Institute's projections of GDP growth, it concludes that around 1000 megawatts should be installed over the time period. This would be enough to supply one million homes. Present installed capacity is about 4700 megawatts (MW).

Ireland's need for transport, both passenger and freight, is also increasing at a rapid rate. This has resulted not just in increased congestion on the roads, but also an increased demand for petrol and diesel. Total final consumption of energy in the transport sector is now more than double what it was in 1980.

The ingredients for the pie are getting scarcer

One of the stated objectives of Irish energy policy is to ensure the security of energy supply (that is, make sure our economy/society has sufficient quantities of energy resources available at acceptable prices). Together oil and natural gas provide 77 per cent of our energy requirement at present, and this figure could grow to 83 per cent by the year 2010. To help ensure the security of supply of oil and gas, Ireland has its own oil refinery, its interconnector to the European (and beyond) natural gas network is to be duplicated, and the provision of natural gas storage capacity has been considered. However, it appears to me that there has been a major omission from the security of supply discussion: the future global availability of oil and natural gas.

What is being said about the future availability of oil? Figures produced by Shell forecast[2] that global oil production will peak around 2012. Another forecast was presented by Dr Colin Campbell at the Feasta 'Energy, Money and Growth' conference in March 2000. As his paper in this Review makes clear, Dr Campbell's message was that the end of cheap oil is coming soon. He estimates that peak conventional oil production globally will be reached about the year 2005. Plausible estimates of global peak oil production are therefore in the range 2005 to say 2015. After peak production is reached, oil supplies will decrease, thus causing significant and permanent oil

KEVIN HEALION is from the village of Rosenallis in the Slieve Bloom mountains, Co. Laois. He studied biotechnology in Dublin City University and environmental engineering in Trinity College Dublin. He worked initially as an environmental consultant, specialising in sewage sludge management and renewable energy production from wood. Now living in Thurles, Co. Tipperary, he teaches environmental science and systems on the National Diploma in Sustainable Rural Development at the Tipperary Institute. He is presently completing studies in adult and community education at NUI Maynooth. His project and research work is focused on the community-based development of bioenergy, and he is the current Treasurer of the Irish Bioenergy Association (IrBEA). He may be contacted on 0504 28105 or khealion@tippinst.ie.

price increases. In other words, a 'permanent oil shock' is coming. Dr Campbell's advice is that all governments should plan seriously for this foreseeable oil supply crisis.

Take a few seconds to think through the possible implications of a permanent oil shock. Think how dependent the transport sector is on oil (in fact, oil sup-

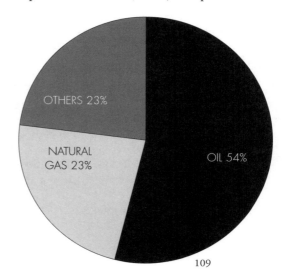

plies 95 per cent of the energy required for the world's land, sea and air transport fleet). Remember also that mechanised food production in the developed world is now highly dependent on oil and oil-derived products. Now think of how dependent on transport we have become in the globalised market economy—all those imports, exports (including food) and tourists moving between countries. Increased oil prices will also make it more expensive to develop other energy resources. Factor in that 10 to 15 per cent of oil supplies go into the production of petrochemicals, including plastics and other substances and materials which we have come to take for granted. So a long term steep increase in oil prices could force us into ways of running things that are very different from those at present.

The argument has been made that natural gas will replace oil. Indeed, Ireland has moved significantly to natural gas in both the electricity and heating sectors. At present, the Republic of Ireland imports gas via a pipeline to Scotland, built in 1993. The interconnector was designed to meet all of Ireland's needs until 2015. However, Ireland's rapid economic growth, its pattern of energy use and the fact that a number of large new natural gas power stations have been proposed, now means that additional gas supplies must be made available by the winter of 2003/2004. The 'Gas 2025' project was commissioned by the Department of Public Enterprise to examine options for the supply of gas up to the year 2025. The report[3] concludes that additional interconnector capacity is required soon. However, it appears that the terms of reference of the 'Gas 2025' study did not include consideration of the security of supply of gas at a global level.

So what is being said about gas resources globally? Firstly, it should be said that gas resources are much more difficult to assess than oil resources. There are differences in the views of energy experts on the extent of the resource but the plausible estimates for global peak gas production are in the range 2020 to 2050. In addition to conventional natural gas, there are opportunities to develop the use of natural gas liquids, and the large deposits of what is termed 'non-conventional gas'. However, there is another aspect to the security of supply of natural gas—what part of the world is it coming from? The European Union is expected to be 46 per cent dependent on imported natural gas this year, 2001. Supplies are, and will continue to be, from quite far away. Ireland's dependence on natural gas in electricity generation could reach 80 per cent if Moneypoint is switched to natural gas by 2008, as is proposed in the National Climate Change Strategy[4] published in October 2000. This has serious implications for security of supply if significant new indigenous gas supplies do not materialise.

While the estimates of future supplies of oil and gas vary to some extent, I believe that Ireland would be wise to plan its energy policy based on the 'precautionary principle'. This is an environmental management principle which advocates proceeding cautiously in situations where there is a high degree of uncertainty over the effects and impacts of your actions—the 'better safe than sorry' approach. There is certainly uncertainty that oil supplies and prices will remain stable in the long term. The possible negative impacts on our society and economy of significant and sustained oil price increases are huge. Natural gas should be seen as merely a stepping stone to a more sustainable energy future based on using less energy and getting this to a large extent from renewable sources.

The US is in a major power and natural gas supply crisis at present (January 2001). This is due to increasing electricity demand, declines in US and Canadian gas production, and limitations in the electricity generation and transmission infrastructure due to deregulation. New deeper gas wells and long pipelines will take time and money to develop. The capacity to manufacture and install gas turbines is stretched to the limit. Two major utilities in California face bankruptcy, which has led to a fall in the share-prices of the banks that lent the utilities money. It is not too difficult to see how an energy crisis could spiral into an economic crisis. And remember how dependent Ireland is on the well-being of the US economy. The US crisis can only be solved by reducing electricity, gas and oil use. EU and Irish energy policy makers should take note.

Despite the uncertainties over future oil and gas supplies, the Green Paper on Sustainable Energy[5] published by the Department of Energy in November 1999 does not address the issue. Nor does the most recent report[6] of the Energy Advisory Board, which brings together representatives of the major energy players in Ireland to provide the Minister for Public Enterprise with policy advice on energy efficiency, renewable energy and related areas of research. Nor does the National Climate Change Strategy. Even the Energy Panel report[7] of the Technology Foresight Ireland exercise, carried out by the Irish Council for Science, Technology and Innovation, under Forfás, does not consider the issue of global oil and natural gas reserves in detail. There seems to be an implicit belief in Irish energy policy that oil and gas will remain readily available for the foreseeable future.

The key aims of Irish energy policy seem to be to ensure the competitiveness of the Irish economy while meeting our international commitments on greenhouse gas emissions at least cost. It's a case of 'Where you stand determines what you see'. There does not seem to be any impetus to move away from dependence on oil as quickly as possible, nor to reduce our natural gas use. If such a 'status quo' policy was based on a convincing analysis of the future of oil and gas supplies, it might be acceptable. But I have not seen such an analysis in any of the various documents on Irish energy policy. Surely a major omission? A study of the future global availability of oil and gas and its implications for Irish energy and economic policy could be carried out for a reasonable cost. It should be undertaken as a matter of priority.

Can we get by on less pie?

As I stated earlier, Irish energy consumption will be 26 per cent greater in 2010 than it is today if 'business as usual' continues. Both the Green Paper on Sustainable Energy and the National Climate Change Strategy stress the importance of reducing the forecast levels of energy use, and describe a comprehensive range of possible methods to achieve such reductions.

A key component of the implementation programme set out in the Green Paper is the development of appropriate economic instruments to reduce the use of fuels contributing most to greenhouse gas emissions. The fuel with the highest greenhouse gas emissions per unit of energy produced is peat, followed by coal, then oil, then natural gas. Renewable energy sources have about zero greenhouse gas emissions (see diagram). Economic instruments such as greenhouse gas taxation (including a 'carbon tax'), energy taxes and tradable permits are a key component of the National Cli-

CARBON DIOXIDE EMISSIONS FROM ELECTRICITY GENERATION

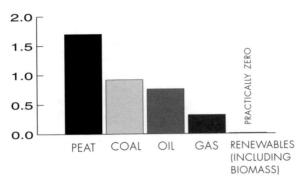

KG CO2 PER
KWH ELECTRICITY

2.0
1.5
1.0
0.5
0.0

PEAT COAL OIL GAS RENEWABLES (INCLUDING BIOMASS)

PRACTICALLY ZERO

mate Change Strategy. (A system of tradable green credits was launched recently by the renewable energy company Eirtricity, with Waterford Glass signing up as its first customer). These instruments will reduce the cost of renewable energy in comparison with fossil fuels and provide exciting new opportunities for sustainable products and services. It has already been announced that carbon energy taxation will be introduced in Budget 2002. This will be a fundamental shift towards a policy framework that promotes the sustainable use of resources and makes the polluter pay.

Energy efficiency standards and energy labelling for buildings and appliances are also proposed in the Green Paper. The Irish Energy Centre is to be significantly strengthened, increasing its role in energy efficiency promotion and market stimulation. Improvements to the energy efficiency of pre-1980 housing stock and Government and local authority buildings are to be made. The Green Paper mentions the possibility of improvements in the conversion efficiency of heating equipment, referring to the fact

that oil-fired condensing boilers can be up to 95 per cent efficient, compared to 75 per cent for conventional boilers, thus giving a saving of 33 per cent on annual fuel use and consequent emissions. However, there is no comprehensive treatment of the heat sector per se in the Green Paper.

The National Climate Change Strategy reinforces the proposals in the Green Paper—energy efficiency is to be promoted in both existing and new houses through upgrading of local authority housing, energy rating, an adjustment to the New House Grant, improvement in building regulations and the construction of demonstration and experimental housing. The current boom in house building will give Ireland one of the most modern housing stocks in Europe by 2010, with a high energy efficiency standard. The Strategy again stresses the role of the Irish Energy Centre in demand side management (that is, controlling the amount of power people use), education, awareness creation and information provision. The local energy agencies are also seen as a very important resource, and will work closely with the Irish Energy Centre. Local authorities will have a new role in promoting energy efficiency and renewable energy.

In addition to the measures proposed in the Green Paper, the Government's Technology Foresight Ireland Energy Panel made exciting suggestions for energy efficiency research, development and training, and for personal tax relief for energy conservation measures in private housing. The National Development Plan[8] 2000–06 allocates £146 million to the energy sector (mainly for the implementation of recommendations in the Green Paper), but the vast bulk of the capital investment in the energy sector over the period to 2006 will take place outside the National Development Plan.

112

It is expected that the market will cater for the investment needs of the power generation and gas sectors. The current ESB programme to upgrade the electricity network is also outside the National Development Plan.

As regards energy use in the transport sector, the Green Paper proposes integrated planning for land use and transport planning, charging for road use, the promotion of cheap public transport, and energy standards and labelling for road vehicles. Further details on plans for the transport sector are contained in the National Development Plan. More than £8.5 billion from the Plan is to be spent on the provision of transport infrastructure. £4.7 billion is to be invested in national roads, £1.6 billion in non-national roads, up to £1.6 billion in public transport in the Greater Dublin Area, over £650 million in regional public transport and £60 million for seaports and regional airports (the pie chart shows the breakdown between roads, rail, bus and other measures).

The £1.6 billion allocated to public transport in the Greater Dublin area concentrates on:

- developing the bus network;
- constructing the LUAS light rail network;
- developing the suburban rail network;
- promoting transport integration though park and ride facilities,
- integrated public transport ticketing and public transport interchange facilities; provision of further cycle infrastructure and facilities;
- implementation of traffic management measures; and
- transport demand management.

The £1.6bn figure also includes a contingency sum for possible rail developments outside Dublin. The Strategic Planning Guidelines for the Greater Dublin Area state that the future spatial development of the region must be based around public transport. Housing investment under the National Development Plan (in and outside Dublin) is to be co-ordinated with public transport development. The National Development Plan money allocated for regional public transport includes £500 million for mainline rail, supporting the Iarnród Éireann 'On Track 2000' programme. Bus Éireann is also to receive substantial funding to improve its urban and rural bus fleets. £3.5 million is allocated to encourage local or community-based initiatives to provide bus services in rural areas—all welcome developments.

Here again, the National Climate Change Strategy builds on the proposals in the Green Paper. It describes how increased fuel efficiency, transport demand management and shifts in mode of transport used will help control greenhouse gas emissions from the transport

BREAKDOWN OF THE £8.5 BILLION SPEND ON TRANSPORT IN THE NATIONAL DEVELOPMENT PLAN

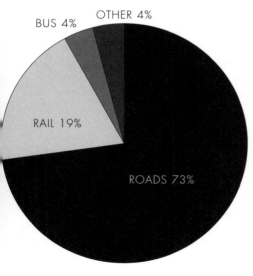

BUS 4% OTHER 4%

RAIL 19%

ROADS 73%

sector. Increased fuel efficiency will result from voluntary agreements at EU level with car manufacturers, from energy labelling and modifications to Vehicle Registration Tax and road tax rates to promote efficient fuel use and low carbon fuels. Integrated spatial, transport and energy planning is also seen as an essential element in greenhouse gas abatement.

Roads account for 96 per cent of passenger traffic and 90 per cent of freight transport inside Ireland. The total investment in roads under the National Development Plan is £6.3 billion, almost three quarters of the total Plan spend on transport infrastructure. The Plan explains that roads must continue to be the first priority for investment in transport, given the immediate infrastructural bottlenecks in the transport sector, the heavy reliance on roads for the transport of people and goods and the lack of alternative networks of real scale for inter-urban transport in Ireland.

These are all very sensible reasons from one point of view. The National Climate Change Strategy argues that this investment will contribute to greenhouse gas emission reduction by making road transport more efficient and by implementing charges for road use (e.g tolls) on a wider basis. However, I come back to my previous point regarding the future availability of oil supplies: road transport depends almost entirely on petrol and diesel. What if transport fuel prices take a large and permanent hike upwards due to an increasing scarcity of oil resources? We are making investments that will shape our future for years to come, yet we seem to be doing so without serious consideration of one major risk factor—oil availability. The recent mini fuel crisis over petrol and diesel prices should help to focus attention on this issue. I was pleasantly amazed while reading a recent review of a new petrol/electric hybrid car in the motoring column of one of the national Sunday newspapers.[9] The correspondent wrote that worldwide oil production will have peaked within five years. And I am sure that you will have seen the recent TV advertising by Shell, with the message that renewables may one day be their biggest business. So maybe the message on future oil supplies is getting out!

The measures proposed in the Green Paper, the Technology Foresight Ireland Energy Panel report, the National Development Plan and the National Greenhouse Gas Abatement Strategy should be successful in slowing the rate of increase in energy demand across the heat, electricity and transport sectors. Unfortunately specific targets for the size of the Irish energy pie in the years to come are not set in any of documents I have read. It is therefore not clear how effective we can expect the various measures to be in reducing energy demand. Setting such targets would provide a focus for energy management efforts, and allow progress to be measured against a yardstick. We could take a lead from Denmark in this regard—the 1990 Danish Energy Plan had a specific objective to reduce energy consumption in 2005 by 15 per cent compared to the 1988 level.

Another major opportunity for reducing energy use is moving away from large scale centralised electricity generation towards small scale decentralised heat and power generation. Electricity in Ireland is produced mainly by burning fossil fuels in large electricity generating stations, and using the energy to drive turbines and generators. The dominant fuels in electricity generation, in decreasing order of importance, are natural gas, coal, oil and peat. The overall energy efficiency of electricity production from these fuels was just 36 per cent in 1998.

So 64 per cent of the energy in these fuels is wasted in the electricity generation process. The 'waste' is the heat that goes into the cooling towers or a nearby water body.

Just as fuels for heating and transport have to be distributed around the country to final consumers, so too does electricity. Energy is lost from the power lines used to move electricity around—for some consumers the loss is up to 10 per cent of the electricity generated. By having smaller units located closer to the point of consumption, power line losses can be reduced. But in the present electricity system roughly two thirds of the energy in the original fuels used for generation is lost by the time the electricity is delivered to the customer's door (and the customer might then go on to use this delivered electricity inefficiently).

Are there better options? The answer is yes. Modern power stations can achieve electrical efficiencies of around 50 per cent and over (natural gas-fired combined cycle plants, or the new gasification and pyrolysis technologies fuelled by fossil or renewable fuels). But the greatest improvement in overall energy efficiency can be achieved if the heat produced in electricity generation is also used. By making use of the heat, overall efficiencies of 75 to 90 per cent can be achieved (this is known as Combined Heat and Power, or CHP for short). Ireland has the lowest level of electricity generated by CHP in the EU at just 2 per cent. All of the Irish CHP capacity at present is fuelled by natural gas, but other fuels can also be used, including the renewable fuels wood and biogas. A CHP plant can be considered as a mini-electricity generation plant that is connected into a heating system. The heating system might be that of a hospital, an office block, an apartment building, or it could even be a district heating system

for a suburb, town or village. A district heating system consists of a network of underground insulated pipes, which distribute hot water to heat customers. The Dublin Corporation offices on Wood Quay are part of a district heating network. Such networks are quite common in other EU member states, but the Green Paper does not quantify their potential in Ireland.

So our electricity demand is climbing steadily and there is a demand for new generation capacity. How is this electricity to be supplied? Will CHP technology have a significant role to play? The Green Paper sets aside a welcome £4 million from the National Development Plan to support high efficiency CHP, and an intention is expressed to lessen the barriers to increased use of CHP. The Irish Energy Centre is to examine the future potential of CHP in Ireland and consider the continuation of Government support for CHP. While the Green Paper does not set specific targets for CHP, the National Climate Change Strategy does recognise its importance and intends to promote it strongly.

CHP also received consideration in the Technology Foresight Ireland exercise. The Energy Panel of the Foresight exercise looked to the year 2015 and asked 'How should we manage and meet Ireland's energy demand up to 2015?'. The panel was made up of nineteen people, including environment and renewable energy representatives. The recommendations of the Panel envisage a clearly defined energy research, development and demonstration programme focused on key technologies. The report is most refreshing to read, as it addresses all three energy sectors (electricity, heat and transport), recommending detailed and costed measures to improve energy efficiency and renewable energy use. It is recommended reading for all those interested in the future development of the energy sector in Ireland. The report includes a proposal for tax relief for Combined Heat and Power projects and promotes decentralised energy production. The report recommends that the Minister for Public Enterprise convene an Action Panel to secure implementation of the Panel's recommendations. A £560 million Technology Foresight Fund has now been established under the National Development Plan to support research, technological development and innovation. Unfortunately it appears that the Technology Foresight Fund is focused on information technology and biotechnology, and it is not clear if monies have been allocated to implement the excellent recommendations of the Energy Panel.

So the question remains—where will extra electricity come from? It seems that most of the demand will be met by new large centralised natural gas-fired power stations. The Commission for Electricity Regulation (CER) is overseeing the opening of the Irish electricity market to competition, as part of EU-wide moves to a liberalised energy market. A number of gas-fired power stations have been proposed by independent power producers, who are now allowed to compete with the ESB in the power generation market. The CER has a role in allocating scarce capacity in the natural gas network for electricity generation and the selection criteria are set to give preference to the larger proposed power stations. These plants will be very efficient at generating electricity, but they will not be operating in CHP mode, so much of the energy value of the natural gas will go to waste. Is this the most prudent way to use a scarce energy resource? Neither the Green Paper or the National Climate Change Strategy address this issue adequately.

Our pie is made of imported ingredients

You won't find a 'Guaranteed Irish' label on the energy pie that fuels the country. It is estimated that 86 per cent of Irish energy is supplied by imported fuels. Our own natural gas reserves have declined, and our only other indigenous energy resources are peat and renewables. Expenditure on imported fuels represents a large outflow of money from the national economy. Yet Ireland has a richness of indigenous renewable energy resources, which if harnessed to their potential would reduce energy imports nationally. Perhaps more importantly, renewable energy sources offer significant opportunities for the retention and recirculation of money within local economies.

Our pie is bad for us and for the world

Almost all of our energy pie is made up of non-renewable fossil fuels. Fossil fuels release carbon dioxide into the atmosphere when used to generate energy. There is an official consensus that carbon dioxide, along with other greenhouse

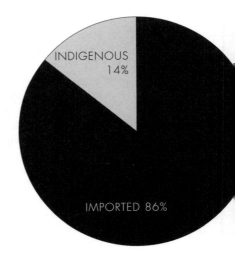

INDIGENOUS 14%

IMPORTED 86%

gases, is contributing to unnatural changes in the climate of planet Earth. Many governments from around the world came together in Kyoto, Japan in 1997 to sign a protocol to limit greenhouse gas emissions. The overall EU target is to reduce greenhouse gas emissions by 8 per cent below 1990 levels by the period 2008 to 2012 and progress towards this target must be demonstrated by 2005. To allow Ireland to develop, it was given a special derogation, and it can increase greenhouse gas emissions by 13 per cent over 1990 levels. This would allow them to rise from 56 million tonnes of carbon dioxide equivalent to 61 million tonnes. However, we have already used up all of our special allowance. Emissions in 2000 were 65 million tonnes and it is projected that without the measures in the National Climate Change Strategy they would, at 72 to 74 million tonnes, be at least 34 per cent above 1990 levels by 2010.

Ireland is likely to face significant financial penalties if it does not meet its commitments under the Kyoto Protocol. Energy use (including electricity, heating and transport) makes up over 50 per cent of the country's total greenhouse gas emissions. So if Ireland is to go anywhere near meeting its Kyoto commitments, positive actions in the energy sector are essential. The government is convinced that its National Climate Change Strategy will do the trick with its proposals for energy demand reduction and greater energy efficiency, a move from more carbon-intensive fossil fuels (peat, coal and oil) to less carbon-intensive natural gas, and a switch from fossil fuels to renewables. Implementation of the Strategy will be overseen by an inter-departmental team and progress will be reviewed every two years so that the Strategy can be revised if necessary.

Only 2 per cent of Ireland's energy is supplied by renewables. As stated in the

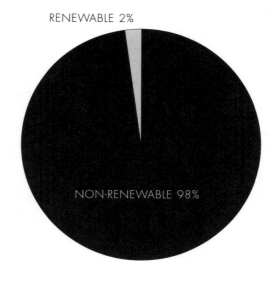

RENEWABLE 2%

NON-RENEWABLE 98%

Green Paper, the largest contribution to renewable energy at present comes from the burning of wood at wood processing plants and in open fires in the residential sector. The second largest contribution is from hydroelectricity, then electricity from wind farms and landfill gas plants. The main mechanism to encourage the expansion of renewable energy electricity production has been the Alternative Energy Requirement (AER), a competitive process in which potential project developers bid to supply power to the national grid. The AER has provided additional renewable capacity at low cost. However, the low prices paid for the renewable electricity are reflected in the low rate at which capacity has been installed in Ireland particularly when one considers the country's potential for electricity from renewables and what other countries in the EU with much less potential have done. On average, the EU gets 6 per cent of its energy from renewables, three times the Irish figure, and has set a target of 12 per cent renewable energy by 2010. Bioenergy (power from biomass) is expected to make up a large part of this increase.

The Green Paper on Sustainable Energy states that:

Government policy is to create the circumstances and conditions that will stimulate the deployment of renewable sources of energy where they have the prospect of being economically and socially attractive and to facilitate research, development and demonstration of emerging renewable energy technologies. .... It is now intended that an ambitious approach will be adopted to increase the role of renewable sources of energy in the power generation sector.

It sets a target of 500MW of additional electricity generating capacity from renewable sources for the period 2000-2005, stating that the bulk of this will come from wind energy. The target will be kept under review and additional targets will be set for 2005-2010 on the basis of this review process. It is intended to hold annual AER competitions to award contracts for new renewable electricity generation capacity. This will give confidence in the market, and allow resources to be mobilised in a planned way.

Thanks to the liberalisation of the electricity market, renewable generators are now allowed to sell green electricity directly to customers. A number of electricity companies producing wind power have been set up to take advantage of this opportunity and every Irish household now has the opportunity of buying green electricity at no extra cost. Net metering—which allows someone who generates green electricity to feed it into the grid when they have a surplus, and to draw power from the grid when they have a shortfall, and only pay for the difference—is also under consideration. It would encourage small-scale renewable energy production.

Community-based development of renewable development is to be encouraged. The existing tax relief for corporate investment in renewable energy will be continued, and other tax relief measures for renewable energy will be considered. Over £20 million from the National Development Plan will be allocated for a planned approach to grid improvements to facilitate connections from renewable energy generators. There is to be a revitalised approach to the promotion of research into the development of renewable sources of energy. The contribution of the Irish Energy Centre and its Renewable Energy Information Office to the promotion of renewable energy in Ireland to date is praised, and their role is to be developed to support the renewables strategy set out in the Paper. Finally, a very welcome development is the establishment of the Renewable Energy Strategy Group, which has been set up to examine obstacles to the further deployment of renewable energy technologies. Implementation of the measures set out in the Green Paper would mean that to almost 4 per cent of Irish energy was from renewable sources by 2005 and the National Climate Change Strategy says that the amount of power the country gets from renewables has to be maximised to help meet the Kyoto targets.

The Renewable Energy Strategy Group was established in November 1999 and examined onshore wind energy first. The Group recently published its 'Strategy for Intensifying Wind Energy Deployment' report. The principal conclusion is that three elements, electricity market, electricity network and spatial planning need to be integrated into a plan led approach to wind energy development. The report recommends that the Government send a clear signal to the renewables market by committing to hold an AER V and then an AER VI competition. The Group also recommends that the Department of Public Enterprise help the green electricity market as a temprary measure to allow renewable generators to become established in the liberalised market. The problem they face is that the AER competitions offer 15 year power purchase agreements at index-linked prices, making it easy for the successful bidders to raise project finance. Potential entrants to the green electricity market cannot offer such long term 'bankable' contracts and so do not have equal acess to capital.

So the Green Paper contains many commendable proposals. However, I believe that there are a number of serious weaknesses. The renewable energy proposals are focused entirely on renewables for electricity generation. Remember our first pie? Electricity is only about one third of our energy demand—heat and transport make up the other two thirds. There are significant opportunities for renewables to contribute to the heat sector in particular. For example, wood is the largest single renewable energy source at present. The use of wood as a fuel for heating could be significantly expanded, in the industrial, residential, agricultural, commercial and public sectors. Wood can be used in automated systems to heat large premises. Enclosed stoves for domestic use allow firewood to be used much more efficiently than in an open fireplace. Possible sustainable sources of wood fuel include sawmill and wood industry residues, some residues left in the forest after timber harvesting, wood from woodland management and tree surgery operations, and possibly waste wood that is presently being landfilled. Value-added wood fuels, such as wood pellets and briquettes, can provide convenient environmentally-friendly fuels.

Ireland also has very significant potential for the production of short rotation forestry and other energy crops, which should now be developed on a demonstration basis. On-farm anaerobic diges-

tion plants can produce methane gas for heating farm buildings and the farm homestead. The sun's energy can be harnessed via passive solar design, or solar heating systems. And heat pumps, using the low temperature heat from the ground, can also contribute to our heating requirements (a number of heat pump systems have been installed around the country). While no consideration was given to the potential for either fossil fuelled or biomass-fired district heating systems in the Green Paper, the National Climate Change Strategy does recognise the contribution district heating systems can make to greenhouse gas reduction. However, it does not mention the potential of wood as a renewable source of heat.

Wood is the largest single renewable energy source at present.

As regards renewables for electricity generation, the Green Paper is quite focused on wind. This focus has been maintained by the recent report[10] of the Renewable Energy Strategy Group. While work is being undertaken to examine the potential for offshore wind and wave, it is vital that other renewable energy sources with potential for electricity generation are not forgotten in the setting of capacity targets and the application of support mechanisms. There are considerable opportunities for micro hydro power plants. And biomass (landfill gas, anaerobic digestion and wood) could make a very significant contribution to renewable electricity generation, often while providing other environmental benefits such as reduction of methane emissions (methane is 21 times as potent a greenhouse gas as carbon dioxide). I would like to see the Renewable Energy Strategy Group focus next on the bioenergy area. Bioenergy provides alternatives to some of the proposals currently being considered to reduce greenhouse gas emissions: for example, there is considerable experience worldwide in co-firing wood with peat or coal in large power stations, thus reducing greenhouse gas emissions by displacing fossil fuel. Another interesting technical possibility is that of co-firing gas produced from the gasification of biomass with natural gas. Bioenergy also provides opportunities for renewable fuelled Combined Heat and Power, giving an alternative to fossil fuelled CHP.

Denmark has set itself the target of meeting its entire energy needs from renewables by 2030.

The Green Paper does not seem to propose any measures to promote alternative transport fuels (for example biodiesel, bioethanol, methanol, fuel cells, electric vehicles). In the chapter on transport, the Paper states that the testing and demonstration of new transport technology options can be continued in the short term with a view to increased deployment in the medium term. However, in the chapter on research and development, it is stated that bio-fuels and other alternative fuels for transport are not considered to need significant, immediate Government-supported action (disappointingly, anaerobic digestion and the production of wood biomass are also in this 'not considered' category). Ireland is described as a technology taker in the area of alternative fuels, yet significant research, development and demonstration work on biodiesel has been undertaken in Ireland by a number of organisations supported by EU energy programmes.

Biodiesel can be a means to convert waste management problems (waste cooking oil, low grade animal tallow) into an environmentally friendly vehicle fuel. However, such developments are blocked by the fact that no Irish government has reduced or removed excise duty from biodiesel, despite a long standing commitment to do so. The Green Paper mentions the possibility of a fuel taxation policy that would favour alternative fuels, but seems only to see the problems with such a measure, and not the potential benefits. It may be that alternative fuels are not considered to have a large enough potential in the transport sector to justify promotion. But why not take all of the opportunities that we can, particularly when there are benefits from a number of viewpoints? I find it hard to reconcile the negative attitude of the Green Paper to alternative transport fuels with the recommendations of the Technology Foresight Ireland Energy Panel, which states 'Given the huge anticipated growth in energy consumption in the transport sector, it is of paramount importance that alternative environmentally friendly transport systems be developed'. The Energy Panel recommends a £3 million allocation for a three-year research, development and demonstration programme, but as stated previously, it is not clear if the Energy Panel's recommendations are to be implemented. The National Climate Change Strategy does promote short rotation energy crops, anaerobic digestion, landfill gas utilisation and carbon dioxide-efficient vehicle fuels. There is now an obvious need to integrate the Strategy with the energy policy proposals from the Green Paper to produce a clear and comprehensive picture of where Irish energy policy is going in the medium to long term.

At the World Conference and Exhibition on Biomass for Energy and Industry in Spain in June 2000, biomass-based fuels for transport received a lot of attention in view of rapidly increasing vehicle numbers, particularly in the developing world. The Brazilian and United States experiences of producing ethanol for transport fuel were detailed. Visions of future transport fleets using fuels such as ethanol, methanol or hydrogen were presented. There was a nice concept of 'green' crude oil: produced by pyrolysis or other processes from plant materials, refined, and then distributed through the existing distribution channels used for fossil diesel and petrol. Experience with biogas as a vehicle fuel was also reported. It seems to me that Ireland should be taking at least an active interest, and preferably an active part, in such developments.

So while the Green Paper on Sustainable Energy contains many welcome proposals for the promotion of renewable energy, at the end of the day it is focused on electricity production from wind power, and does not adequately address the potential for other renewables to contribute to electricity production, nor the potential for renewables in the heat and transport sectors. Contrast this with Denmark which has set itself the target of meeting its entire energy needs from renewables by 2030. Wind will supply 50 per cent, bioenergy 35 per cent and solar 15 per cent. These omissions must be rectified at the next stage of Irish policy development, and a table showing the potential of all renewables across the electricity, heat and transport sectors must be part of future policy documents on renewable energy.

Time for some serious changes in diet

It has been quite difficult to assemble the information for this article. No single document considers the totality of the Irish energy picture or examines how Ireland's energy is to be produced and used in the future. We would do well to follow

the example of the United Kingdom Royal Commission on Environmental Pollution. Their report[11] 'Energy—The Changing Climate', published in June 2000, is a comprehensive consideration of the UK's energy future. The report looks to the year 2050 and first asks how much should the UK's carbon dioxide emissions be reduced, based on a equitable worldwide allocation of emission rights on a per capita basis. The size of the emission right is designed to stabilise carbon dioxide concentrations in the atmosphere at a tolerable level. This approach is known as the principle of contraction and convergence. For the UK, an international agreement along those lines could imply a reduction of 60 per cent from 1998 carbon dioxide emissions by the year 2050.

The report then goes on examine what the UK's energy picture might look like in the year 2050. The long term view taken in the report is commendable, particularly as it looks at the emission reductions that will possibly be required as far ahead as the year 2100. The report helps provide a focus for debate by presenting four possible scenarios for the year 2050. These scenarios describe how energy demand can be managed, and the ways in which energy demand could be met. The report does not see a magic source of unlimited energy with negligible environmental impact as a foreseeable prospect: for example, it is considered unlikely that a commercial-scale nuclear fusion demonstration plant would be built before 2050. So the scenarios for the year 2050 are based on energy technologies in use at present or under development. By presenting detailed quantified scenarios, the report helps the reader to visualise how the energy future might look, and provides an excellent platform for discussion on alternative courses of action. Finally, the report points out that there will be benefits from moving to a more sustainable energy economy and society, and that this could give an improved quality of life for many.

While the Irish energy policy documents produced to date are steps in the right direction, I believe that we in Ireland urgently need a comprehensive analysis of our possible energy futures, taking account of global energy resource availability and adopting a responsible role in global efforts to limit climate change. At the moment we seem to be focused on meeting international obligations at the least cost to ourselves. Why not creatively develop our potential to become a leading 'energy-fit' nation—a Celtic Cheetah rather than a Celtic Tiger?

And remember, if you live in Ireland, you consume a slice of Ireland's energy pie. While positive action at governmental level is required to help the nation move to a more sustainable pattern of energy production and use, we should all examine our own energy intake, and make efforts to cut back if possible. Responsible energy use is not pie in the sky!

NOTES

1. ESB, 2000. *Generation Capacity Requirements to 2006.* Produced by ESB at the request of the Commission for Electricity Regulation. Dublin. Available on www.cer.ie/ceresb200010.pdf
2. Campbell, C.J., 2001. Personal communication.
3. Bord Gáis Éireann and Department of Public Enterprise, 1999. *The Gas 2025 Project*

Close-out Report and Review. Dublin. Available on www.irlgov.ie/tec/energy/gasproject.htm
4. Department of the Environment and Local Government, 2000. *National Climate Change Strategy Ireland.* Dublin. Available on www.environ.ie/climatechange.html
5. Department of Public Enterprise, 1999. *Green Paper on Sustainable Energy.* Dublin. Available on www.adnet.ie/gpse/
6. Energy Advisory Board, 1998. *Annual Report 1997.* Department of Public Enterprise, Dublin. Available on www.irlgov.ie/tec/energy/energy97.htm
7. Irish Council for Science, Technology and Innovation (ICSTI), 1999. *Technology Foresight Ireland—Energy—Executive Summary.* Forfás, Dublin. Available on www.forfas.ie/icsti/statements/tforesight/energys.htm
8. Government of Ireland, 1999. *Ireland National Development Plan 2000-2006.* The Stationery Office, Dublin. Available on www.ndp.ie/
9. Spray, C., 1999. *Motoring column, Sunday Independent.* Sunday 24 September 2000. Dublin.
10. Renewable Energy Strategy Group, 2000. *Strategy for Intensifying Wind Energy Development.* Department of Public Enterprise, Dublin. Available on www.irlgov.ie/tec/energy/wind.pdf
11. Royal Commission on Environmental Pollution, 2000. *Energy—The Changing Climate.* The Stationery Office, London. Available on www.rcep.org.uk/energy.html

AUTHOR'S NOTE
This article is written in my personal capacity as a member of Feasta and is not intended to represent the views of my employer, the Tipperary Institute, or of the Irish Bioenergy Association, of which I am Treasurer. I would like to thank Richard Douthwaite, Dr Colin Campbell, Seamus Hoyne of the Tipperary Energy Agency and Paul Kellett of the Renewable Energy Information Office of the Irish Energy Centre for providing information or for commenting on drafts.

outdated thinking slows Ireland's progress towards energy sustainability

MICHAEL LAYDEN

The challenge Ireland faces in developing a sustainable energy supply is equivalent to climbing Mount Everest after a lifetime of gentle walks in Wicklow. There are really only two ways to reach the peak. One requires the climber to be fit, trained, mentally prepared, properly equipped and with no excess baggage. The other way—which is obviously the more popular—is to spend a great deal of money and hope a team of sherpas can carry you up to the top.

Irish energy policy pretends to take the former approach but increasingly resembles the latter. For example, the government has no plans to move away from infrastructural developments which will require high levels of energy use in the future even to gain a medium-term competitive advantage. Instead, it is content merely to meet EU energy and environmental legislation. Unfortunately, however, if Ireland avoids the effort required to increase the energy efficiency of its economy by more than the minimum required of it now, the country will face an almost impossible task when it seeks to raise it in the future.

THE CHALLENGE

Ireland will face increasing competition for its imported resources in the years ahead—and particularly for its energy. The sheer scale of global consumer demand is already staggering. Just one statistic gives a good indication of the amount of resources currently being consumed—there are already 770 million cars in the world even though the people of Eastern Europe, China and India are only now starting to acquire them in large numbers. So many people, so limited supplies of energy and raw materials and so many areas of instability in the world—all make our future supplies precarious.

MICHAEL C. LAYDEN, an engineer, comes from the family which ran the coal mine at Arigna, Co. Roscommon, for 120 years until low prices forced it and the ESB power station it served to close in 1990. Michael immediately went to the US to work in the wind industry while his father and sister Carol began monitoring wind-speeds in the Arigna area. Between 1994 and 1997 he and Carol developed the Arigna windfarms. He was manager of the East Connacht Energy Agency from 1997 to 2000. He now works as an independent consultant in Ireland and the US.

People still believe that brains and hard work is sufficient to enable an economy to prosper but this is no longer the case—there is no shortage of smart and hard-working people in the world. Increasingly, a country's success will be determined by its ability to meet its people's needs using the minimum input of the world's depleting stock of natural resources—in other words, its eco-efficiency. In Ireland's case, however, we are still working hard to install production systems developed years ago in other economies. This means that we are allowing other countries' past practices to dictate our place on the battlefield of future competition.

FOUR PHASES TO A SUSTAINABLE FUTURE
Building a sustainable economy or company involves passing through several stages. In Frankel's *In Earth's Company* and in Nattrass and Altomare's *The Natural Step for Business* these phases are identified as

- Compliance phase—companies see the cost of preserving the environment as a burden and do the minimum required to comply with the law.
- Beyond compliance phase—companies no longer see environmental protection as an unnecessary expense.
- Eco-efficiency phase—the environment is increasingly seen as a source of profit. Firms see that they can gain a competitive advantage by using energy wisely and striving for zero waste. Companies already at this stage include IKEA, Scandic Hotels, Xerox, Bibio, 3M.
- Sustainability phase—companies have zero waste and closed-loop manufacturing processes using sustainable energy and raw material inputs. The economy in which they operate will

bear no resemblance to that of today. Design for Environment (DfE) will be part of every manufacturing and service industry activity.

IRELAND AND THE COMPLIANCE PHASE
Ireland is clearly still in the first phase. As the Green Paper on Sustainable Energy and the Greenhouse Gas Abatement National Climate Change Strategy documents show, it is only concerned about being compliant with external legislation. Small token improvements in the public's energy awareness are hailed as a success. Jargon phrases such as 'Least Cost' and 'No Regrets' sprinkle official papers. The bigger, global picture is ignored. Extremely impressive officials produce incredibly unimpressive policy.

The reason is simple. We Irish are in love with the idea of creating a modern economy with the same level and type of infrastructure as countries which developed earlier when conditions were different. As a result, we see environmental directives from Europe and international agreements such as Kyoto as standing in our way. We therefore allow our our politicians to continue to regard environmental protection and renewable energy projects as unnecessary luxuries, to be funded sparingly—if at all.

Moving beyond the compliance phase is not automatic. Legislation is always a compromise and usually reflects the lowest common denominator acceptable to lobby groups. This is a serious problem for the achievement of sustainability as the future has no voice and almost every lobby group has a vested interest in maintaining the status quo. The Irish response to global warming shows this well. The scientific consensus is that greenhouse gas emissions need to be reduced by as much as 70 per cent to stop further warming taking place. At Kyoto in 1997, however, the EU undertook to cut its emissions by only 8 per cent from their 1990 level by 2010 and even this target may not be met as a result of the breakdown in talks on its implementation at The Hague last November. Ireland in turn has promised its EU partners to see that its emissions rise by no more than 13 per cent above 1990 levels by 2010—a clear example of the way we see our development amounting to doing what others have done before. In other words, we are leaving it to our children to make 90 per cent reductions to make up for our greed and sloth.

ECO-EFFICIENCY

Ireland has to move away from the idea that environmental protection and the substitution of renewable energy for fossil fuels are burdens and see them instead as investment opportunities. Investing in the right things now can reduce energy requirements for generations to come and help ensure that the economy is competitive (and thus able to generate our pensions) when we retire. The book *Natural Capitalism* (see review on p.175) gives many examples of buildings, businesses and cities which have invested slightly more and gained a long-term economic advantage

If we are to make massive reductions in energy use in the future, we have to look deeply into the design of our infrastructure now. At the moment, Irish energy policy only takes fuel and electricity use into consideration. It ought to consider materials as well. Once carbon taxes are introduced, or oil becomes scarce, or greenhouse gas emissions permits have to be purchased, construction materials will become significantly more expensive. Consider how even insulation might become more costly in the coming decade. Fibreglass is very energy-intensive and could triple in cost. So could rock wool if steel-making is cut back. Plastics

and foams are oil bi-products and supplies of wool and hemp are likely to be scarcer, and thus more expensive, because fertiliser applications will be cut back.

All other building materials—and particularly steel, cement, glass and aluminium—will be similarly affected, especially as the lower grade ores the world will be having to use then will require more energy for extraction. This means that in a few year years' time we will no longer be able to buy or build our ways out of problems. The more expensive solutions that we now ignore will not just be even more expensive then but completely unaffordable.

The energy embodied in most products is many times the amount required to run them. This is particularly true of cars and houses which take more energy in their manufacture than they do in the first decade or two of use. In many cases the rate of return on capital invested in energy-efficient cars, homes and equipment is already well into double figures and will grow further as energy prices rise. This is the opportunity we are missing. Now, when materials are cheap, is the time for the country to use incentives, tighter building codes and prohibitions to ensure that all investments are future-proofed.

The worst current example of a case in which our focus on mere compliance with EU directives is storing up problems for the future is in the gas and electricity system. At present, the conventional energy lobby is highlighting the fact that the gas inter-connector between Britain and Ireland will be inadequate to meet this country's demand by 2003 because it will no longer be supplemented by supplies from the Kinsale Field, which is running out. The lobby is also drawing attention to the 'appalling' level of CO_2 emissions from the coal-fired power station at Moneypoint. So what does it propose? The construction of a pipeline to the Corrib gas field as quickly as possible, the conversion of Moneypoint to natural gas and the installation of four combined-cycle gas turbines for power generation elsewhere.

This 'solution' would triple the amount of natural gas we need, maintain CO_2 emissions at their current level and burn the contents of the Corrib field—which is smaller than Kinsale and, once it is attached the European gas network, would meet Europe's total needs for only twenty days—in less than ten years. I would say 'Out of the frying pan and into the fire,' except by the time Corrib is exhausted we probably will not have anything to feed the fire. So the lobby resorts to hoping that more gas will be found in the Porcupine basin off the Mayo coast, and points out that, if not, there's always the interconnector with Europe to fall back on. But by 2010 nearly 60 per cent of Europe's natural gas is expected to be coming from Russia and Algeria, scarcely reliable sources. Until proved otherwise, the Corrib has to be treated as a strategic reserve and potentially the last great fossil fuel resource available to this country.

The easiest way to prolong the life of the Corrib field would be to install a DC powerline to North Mayo and set up a large-scale wind/gas hybrid generating station there which would fall back on gas only when the wind wasn't blowing strongly enough. This could double the life of the field. A better alternative would be for the government to require all new fossil-fuel powered generating equipment to be 80 per cent efficient. This would mean that combined cycle gas turbines, which are only 45-55 per cent efficient, would be superseded by combined heat and power stations which are 80-95 per cent efficient. This would force developers to be innovative in finding and matching heat loads to generatingfa-

THE DISTRIBUTED GENERATION REVOLUTION

The electrical system we're now using is analogous to the state of computer technology in the late 1970s or early 1980s. It's powered mostly by mainframes (large, centralised power stations). Personal computers (micropower in the form of fuel cells, microturbines, solar panels and wind) are only beginning to emerge.

The 'distributed generation' alternative to the big power plant is to build lots of smaller micro power plants. Homeowners should be offered incentives to meet much of their own needs and utilise their extra capacity during peak periods in the middle of the day when our houses are empty and we're all at work. These micro sites are then tied together into a power 'smart' network... just like we've done with our computers to accomplish 'distributed computing' or distributed processing.—
Michael Powers,
http://www.globalpowerbiz.com

cilities. This is particularly important at a time when so much construction is being carried out. Every housing estate, leisure centre, hotel, public building and industrial estate should be seen as a potential site for a generating plant. A major side benefit would be to increase innovation in our building and energy sectors which would prepare them for the new energy challenges.

MISSED OPPORTUNITIES

By concentrating entirely on the short-term price of energy rather than sustainability and our future security of supply, we are creating a centralised 1980s-style electricity system. This is unfortunate given the fact that a recent article in The Economist highlighted the growth of decentralised small-scale electricity generation of the type mentioned above as a revolution likely to be as significant as that which has taken place in telecommunications.

Ireland is very fortunate to have several renewable energy sources capable of meeting significant proportions of our power requirements. Wind, biomass and anaerobic digestion are particularly promising. So why do we not increase the funding going to these alternatives? You've guessed it—it would make electricity more expensive. Instead we do everything to keep electricity costs low, a policy which made sense in the days before we realised how limited supplies of oil and gas are and how much harm their use does to the environment. Naturally, low-cost power increases the demand for it so now the government turns round and announces its intention of introducing an energy tax within the next two years to bring our emissions down. In effect we are getting the worst of both worlds—more expensive power without the lower levels of fossil fuel use, greater sustainability and less pollution that an alternative strategy could have brought.

Immense damage has been caused by looking to the past for best practice. This is increasingly obvious in the area of wind energy where low-cost projects have alienated local populations. The concentration on cost also provides the economic justification for large scale combined cycle gas projects. They are cheaper than the older peat and coal technologies and, in addition, their lower emissions make them look environmentally superior. The fact that their emissions are higher than combined heat and power systems is overlooked.

It is time to plan for a future based on creating an economy that needs a fraction of the fossil fuel required by our competitors. If we act now, we could build the radically different infrastructure such an economy requires while material costs are low.

As things stand, the recent decisions to ban large out-of-town shopping complexes and give a £6000 tax benefit for keeping lodgers will probably save more energy in the long term than any thing else we have done as a nation. Are these moves a straw in the wind? Do they demonstrate the emergence of an awareness that Ireland does not have to do things the same way as elsewhere? One can only hope they do.

REFERENCES AND RESOURCES

Brian Nattrass and Mary Altomore, *The Natural Step for Business*, New Society Publishers, British Columbia, 1998, ISBN 0865713847

Carl Frankel, *In Earth's Company : Business, Environment, and the Challenge of Sustainability*, New Society Publishers, British Columbia, 1998, ISBN 0865713804

The US Department of Energy has an excellent site for statistics on current world energy consumption at http://www.eia.doe.gov. Its projections assume there will be no supply shortages, however. It has information on distributed generation if you use the search engine at http://www.eia.doe.gov/der

The Worldwatch Institute's July 2000 publication on micropower can be downloaded from https://secure.worldwatch.org/cgi-bin/wwinst/WWP0151

The Economist article, 'The Dawn of Micropower' appeared on 5 August 2000. It can be found at http://www.economist.com/displayStory.cfm?Story_ID=28854&CFID=37132&CFTOKEN=68859159 Alternatively, log in to www.economist.com, go to the library and use the search engine for 'micropower'.

FUTURE ENERGY USE

making western agriculture more sustainable

FOLKE GÜNTHER

The energy crisis plus a shortage of phosphates fertiliser will change settlement patterns by forcing people to source their food from local farms.

Modern Western European agriculture is heavily dependent on services that often are taken for granted. However, if we are to discuss how it can be made more sustainable we need to consider all the support systems necessary for the entire field-to-table chain. This is seldom done although several authors (Odum, H.T., 1971; Odum, E.P., 1973; Pimentel et al., 1989; Huang & Odum, 1991) have explored the topic. In particular, the support services agriculture gets from ecosystems are often left out.

Current farming cannot produce food without the following:

- Cheap and continuous supplies of fuel.
- Phosphorus ores for fertilisers.
- A distribution system for fertilisers, animal feed, fuels and agricultural products that can function even if there are disturbances outside the agricultural system.
- A support infrastructure that can maintain machinery independently of the general industrial climate.
- The uninterrupted support of ecosystems to (1) bring forth and recycle nutrients, water, carbon and other

essential production factors, (2) maintain the soil's structure and functions and (3) maintain a favourable climate and gas balance in the air.
- Specialist workers who are prepared to endure extended agricultural labour regardless of the low income and low status it brings them.

Some of these support systems are so vital that their failure would be disastrous for those who depend on the sector for their food. So how vulnerable are these systems to disruption and how can their reliability be improved?

THE DEPENDENCIES
Dependency on material and industrial energy support

Pre-industrial agriculture was a very local activity. Most equipment was made locally and agriculture was powered largely by different types of locally captured solar energy. Nutrients were collected by meadow plants and reached the arable fields (which were often situated within a few kilometers of the settlements in which their produce would be consumed) when hay was made from the plants, eaten by animals and released from the manure they had dropped when it was spread on the tillage land.

In contrast, the sun is not modern agriculture's main energy source. If the total inputs are considered, it is fossil energy of different types. This, coupled with its need for constant supplies of other inputs such as fertilisers, biocides, animal food, plastics for silage and drugs for treatment of animal diseases, gives modern agriculture a structure similar to any other throughput industry.

The higher yields produced by modern methods are not due to any enhancement of the crops' ability to capture more solar energy, but because some tasks formerly done by the crops themselves, such as extracting nutrients and warding off diseases and herbivores, are done for them by the farmer using fossil fuel inputs (Odum, 1971). This means that agriculture output levels cannot be maintained without industrial supplies. We consequently have to consider the sustainability of industry and infrastructure in any discussion of the sustainability of modern agriculture.

FOLKE GÜNTHER has an M.Sc. in Systems Ecology, from Stockholm University and lectures in Human Ecology at Lund University. His specialist area is the ecological adaptation of human settlements in response to ecological factors. He is also involved with ecological engineers and permaculturalists working on biological water purification. His homepage is at http:/etnhum.etn.lu.se/~fg/index.htm.

He originally wrote this article for a mini-conference on localisation organised by Feasta as part of the International Network of Engineers and Scientists for Global Responsibility INES 2000 conference in Stockholm in June 2000. A fuller version of it will appear in the journal **Energy & Environment**. The other INES localisation papers are on the Feasta website, www.feasta.org.

Cheap fossil energy?

Today's agriculture is heavily dependent on fossil fuels. In developed countries, the input of fossil fuel energy to agriculture equals, or surpasses, the output of

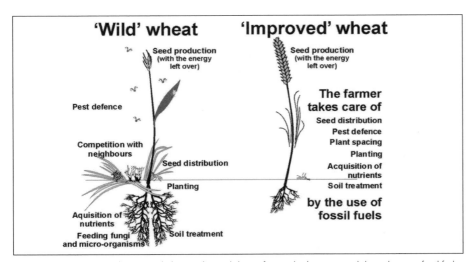

Figure 1 'Improvements' to domesticated plants and animals have often involved an increased dependency on fossil fuels.

energy in the food supplied for human consumption (Hall et al., 1986; Folke & Kautsky, 1992; Hoffman, 1995). This is why industrial agriculture has been described as a black box for converting fossil fuel energy into edible food energy . The implicit assumption underlying this conversion is that fossil fuel and the other necessary inputs will always be so cheap that they will not increase food prices beyond what the public can afford. This assumption can be questioned, however. As Colin Campbell has shown elsewhere in this *Review*, around half of the world's reserves of crude oil has already been used up and the remaining reserves can be expected to require more energy to be used for the extraction of each unit of energy they produce than those being exploited already. In other words, the energy yield per unit of energy (YPE) used in the extraction will fall.

Energy price is hard to calculate. The price for, say, petrol at the filling station

changes on a daily basis. The salary of the person who buys it changes too. The best way of saying whether the energy is 'cheap' or 'expensive' is therefore to calculate how long a person has to work in order to get a certain amount of energy. The result of such a calculation is demonstrated in (Figure 1), where the price for gasoline in Sweden is divided by the salary of a 'general' worker. It shows that the working time needed to purchase one kWh (kilo Watt hour) of gasoline in 1995 has fallen to about a tenth of the time needed in 1920. In other words, the availability of the energy to the worker has increased ten times.

The extraction of fossil fuels is energy intensive because to make the energy in fuels available energy must be used for drilling, prospecting, building an industrial infrastructure, etc. The YPE for fossil fuel extraction decreased globally during the last century. In the lower 48 states of the US, the YPE of oil production is expected to fall below 1:1 about 2005

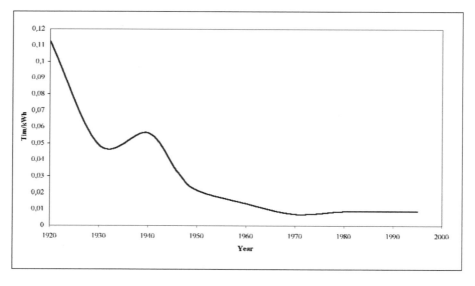

Figure 2 The working time needed to purchase one kWh of gasoline fell by about 90 per cent between 1920 and 1995. Note the increase during World War II. The 'energy crisis' during the 1970s is barely noticeable.

years from today	0	15	25	50	75
fossil energy price assuming 5 % increase per year (SEK/kWh)	0.45	0.95	1.57	5.48	19.13
direct fuel cost *per hectare* agriculture, assuming the same fuel use as 1994, in Swedish crowns (SEK)	495	1045	1727	6028	21,043

Table 1 Assuming a 5% annual increase, the price of fossil energy will rise twelvefold within 50 years. A Swedish crown is currently worth nine pence Irish.

(Hall & al., 1986; Cleveland, 1991). At this point, the oil will not be able to be considered an energy source, even if it is still extracted for other reasons.

As oil gets scarcer, its price can be expected to rise in relation to other commodities. If it increases on average by only 5% a year, its price will rise by a factor of twelve within fifty years. Swedish agriculture uses over 110 litres of fuel oil per hectare directly (SCB, 1994), plus perhaps 50% more for the production of pesticides, fertilisers, machinery etc., and for the electricity used on farms. Consequently, if the energy intensity of the food system does not change, the price of the sector's energy requirements will be very much higher (Table 1).

Moreover, a lot of fossil energy is required to process food and to transport it to the consumer. These requirements, which are substantial, will be discussed later in this paper. However, it is not too bold to assume that the total cost of the energy required to grow food, process it and deliver it to the consumer could become more than the present food production system could bear.

Phosphorus ore availability

Modern agriculture also needs a steady supply of nutrients to survive, at least as much as it loses when its products leave the farm. It is possible to use leguminous plants to fix nitrogen from the atmosphere but potassium and phosphorus have no such gaseous phases and must be made available in the soil in a soluble form.

Potassium is a quite common element and scarcity is therefore rare. Phosphorus, however, is often a limiting element for plant growth, so a constant supply of it is vital to any type of agriculture exporting produce if the nutrient content of the produce is not recycled. As modern agriculture rarely recycles its nutrients, it has to import phosphates if they are leaving the farm with the products.

Guano, the polite name for bird droppings, was used to restore phosphorus losses in nineteenth-century agriculture until the supply was exhausted after about 30 years (Brundenius, 1972; Gutenberg, 1993). Today, rock phosphate from countries like Morocco is the main phosphate source but resources of it are limited. Estimates differ but one literature survey (Pierrou, 1976) estimates the available amount of mineable phosphorus as being in the range of 3,140—9,000 Tg. (Tg stands for tera grammes, 10^{12} grammes or 1 million tonnes.) If we assume Pierrou's constant extraction rate of 12.6 Tg/year, this gives the resource a life-time of 249—714 years. However, later estimates indicate smaller resources and higher rates of extraction. Smil (1990) estimates the amount of phosphorus in the reserves to be around 2600 Tg. and says that they are being used at the rate of about 20 Tg of phosphorus a year. This means that the resource may have a lifetime of only about 130 years.

Evidently, there is great uncertainty about both the amount of mineable phosphorus ore and its average phosphorus

years ahead	0	25	50	75
price for industrial energy, SEK/kWh	0.45	1.6	5.5	19
price for extraction. of phosphorus, assuming a 3 % annual decrease in YPE, SEK/kg	3.13	34	119	415

Table 2 The energy price/YPE trap in the case of phosphorus mining, assuming 5% annual increase in petroleum prices

content. What is certain, however, is that extracting phosphorus from the ore is an energy-intensive process requiring between 18 and 32 million Joules (MJ) of energy per kilo of phosphorus, depending on the product (Smil, op. cit.). Moreover, the yield per unit of energy used in the extraction falls, just as it does in fossil fuel extraction, as lower-grade ores have to be used. (Hall & al., 1986). This could lead to a resource trap in which phosphorus reserves which could be exploited today and are therefore included in the above estimates become unavailable in the future because of the shortage of energy for extraction. Cleveland (1991) discusses this.

Phosphorus costs about 15 SEK/kg today, and the cost of the energy required for its extraction is 3 SEK. If energy prices rise at 5% per year in real terms and the amount of energy required rises at 3% a year because of the poorer ores, the energy cost for extraction will exceed 400 SEK/kg within 75 years, an increase of two powers of ten (Table 2). This is clearly an unsustainable situation worth further consideration. It is probable that such a cost would significantly limit the current method of phosphorus use.

Transport-dependent centralisation

Fossil fuel-based industrialisation and the infrastructural development which accompanied it made it possible to produce food far from the consumers and transport it cheaply to them despite the long distances. This enabled populations to congregate in urbanised—industri-

alised areas. There seems to be a close connection between the availability of cheap energy and urbanisation. Certainly, without cheap energy, large cities cannot be sustained, as the extraction, refinement and transport of their requirements would otherwise be too expensive. Any recycling of nutrients would also be impossible (Günther, 1994a).

Far more energy is currently used to supply a typical family's food in Sweden than is used to heat its house or run its car. Moreover, it would be possible to save more energy in its food production and distribution than on its heating or motor fuel. A normal house for a family of four, built according to the 1980 Swedish building standards, can be assumed to use about 17,000 kWh each year. However, energy conservation measures changing the house to an 'eco-house' could cut this figure to below 10,000 kWh. The potential for increasing energy efficiency in the building is thus about 8000 kWh/year.

Assuming the family's car travels 15,000 km/year and uses between 0.6–1 litre of gasoline per 10 km, the annual energy requirement would be about 9,000 kWh for the more efficient car and about 15,000 kWh for the other one. The potential saving from switching from a less efficient car to a more efficient one is therefore about 6,000 kWh/ year, the same sort of saving that could be made on heating the house

Food is another matter. The energy used for transportation and handling of food is to a large extent unrecognised part of the total per capita uses of energy. In Sweden the use of direct energy for transport and handling of food is conservatively estimated to be at least 10% of the total annual energy use (Olsson, 1978). Indeed, Nils Tiberg (LuTH, pers. comm.) puts the figure at about 60 TWh, or 13% of the total energy use. In Great Britain the equivalent figure was estimated to have been between 16 and 21% in 1976 . (Leach, 1976) while in the US, the energy used in the food distribution and handling system is estimated to be at least 16.5% of total energy use (Booz, 1976).

The amount of *direct energy* used to transport and handle a single person's annual food supply in Sweden is estimated to be between 5,625 and 7,500 kWh while the annual amount of energy that the food has to supply for that person's growth and maintenance is about 900 kWh. From these figures, the efficiency of energy delivery in conventionally handled food in Sweden could be computed to be about 7 : 1. However, including the energy expenditures in agriculture, which in round terms can be estimated to about 1:1, the total energy efficiency would have been about 8:1 in 1976. The figure may be higher today in view of the changes in society. Hall & al. (1986) estimates the figure for an average western society to be about 9.5 : 1. It can thus be estimated that about ten energy units are spent in growing, transportation, handling, packaging, shop maintenance, and so on for each energy unit delivered to the dinner table. A conclusion from this is that for a normal family, needing 1,000 kWh of food energy per person per year, the largest single energy use is that for food management and handling!

The vulnerability of agriculture

Industrialised agriculture is as dependent on general services from the surrounding

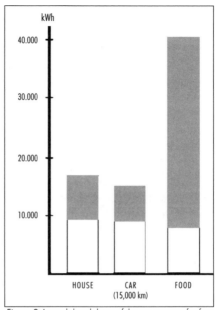

Figure 3 A rough breakdown of the energy use of a family of four in Sweden. The single largest energy user is the food system which is where the largest potential for increased energy efficiency (grey part of the bars) to be found.

society as any other industrial activity. Economic pressures have tended to increase the size of the industrial units delivering these services during past decades and to cut their number. The number of dairies and slaughterhouses has been reduced, for example. In Sweden, the total number of diaries declined from about 400 to 58 between 1960 and 1993 (SCB, 1994). 56% of the total milk production is produced in Southeast Sweden (Skåne and Halland) (SCB, op. cit.). Beside the effects of increased transportation which will be discussed later, this tendency leads to an increasingly vulnerable structure. Any malfunction of any of the larger units— perhaps as a result of disease, a strike, an electrical breakdown, problems with the delivery of supplies—will have a much more serious effect on the food supply of the population than if a smaller unit had been in trouble. The resilience (Holling, 1973) of the system has been reduced.

The same thing has happened on the farms themselves because technologies have changed and the production of their inputs—animal feed, fertilisers, seed grain, spare parts for machinery, frozen sperm for insemination and so on—has become more concentrated. About 90 % of the cows in Sweden are artificially inseminated (SCB, 1994), which means a change from farm-produced to transported services. Likewise, about 80% of the Swedish milling capacity is situated in the far south-east part of Sweden today (Jordbruksverket, 1991).

The diversity of agriculture in any given area is usually reduced when the farms there become more specialised. Half a century ago, it was still common for farms to grow a large part of the feed for their animals and to keep a wide range of them. Cows, pigs, horses, geese and chicken could be found on the same farm, together with a variety of crops and processing procedures. Today, this situation is very rare. Farmers have been forced by the increased cost of their inputs and the lower price for their output to specialise on products that can be produced in large quantities at a low unit cost. Rather than managing the land, a farmer now runs a company. State subsidies, together with the entrainment (Rosser & al., 1993) of firms into a new infrastructure, have intensified the specialisation which has lead to a decrease in diversity, reduced resilience and, consequently, to an increase in vulnerability of the food delivery system as a whole.

The specialisation of the agricultural units combined with their increase in size and decrease in number (Figure 4) and the decrease of the number of service system units has brought about not only increased delivery distances for each unit,

but meant that a malfunction in one support unit can affect several large production units that in turn produce a large part of the public's total product requirement.

With the decrease in number of production units and support units, the importance of the distribution system increases. Transportation lines are longer and the need for a safe and constant delivery of cheap energy and a well-functioning transportation infrastructure grows. Such a system is not only more likely to fail than one with shorter transportation lines and more self-sufficient production units, but the effects of the failure will be much more severe.

POTENTIAL SOLUTIONS

If we ignore changes to the agriculture itself such as organic farming or agroecology on the grounds that these have already been discussed extensively in the literature (e.g., Altieri, 1987; Pimentel, 1989), what can be done to reduce the unsustainability and potential instability of the food supply system?

1. Minimising energy use in transportation

We have seen that farming's heavy dependence on transportation is due to three factors:

- Fertilisers and other inputs are produced off the farm, and often at great distances from it.
- Farms may be a long way from the people who will eat the food that they produce.
- Animal feed may be produced in a different part of the country, or even abroad.

These would all change if consumers lived nearer the farm and the traditional balance between animal and plant production on the individual farms was restored (Granstedt and Westberg, 1993). We've

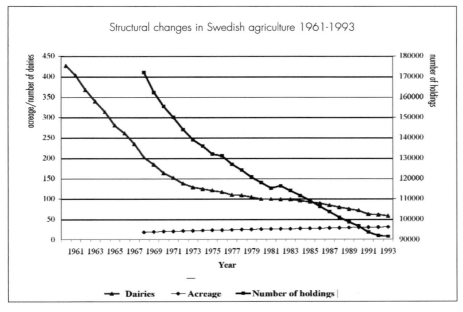

Figure 4 An increase in vulnerability can be expected as agricultural units become more specialised. This graph shows that as the size of Swedish farms increased, the number of dairies serving them fell.

also seen that about 10,000 kWh is used per person per year for food delivery. Is it unreasonable to think that this figure could be cut to 2,000 kWh if agriculture and human settlements were more closely integrated and there was a strategy for local food management? If this was possible for only 50% of the Swedish population, the amount of energy saved would be about 50 billion kWh annually, which is equal to the electricity produced by 10 nuclear reactors.

Naturally, energy use could also be cut by technological changes on the farm itself but since the total amount of fossil energy billion kWh (Hoffman, 1995), the scope for savings in this area is more limited, besides being beyond the scope of this article.

2. Increasing nutrient circulation

In modern agriculture, the replacements for nutrients lost by the export of pro-

duce from the land come from mineral ores (Phosphorus, Potassium), or from industrial processes (Nitrogen). The need for these replacements increases the vulnerability of the food system to breakdown because of the potential for problems in the mining and processing industries and because of the decline in resource availability and in the yield per energy effort we mentioned earlier.

Mature ecosystems meet their essential nutrient requirements in two ways: for elements that have volatile phases (e.g., Nitrogen, Carbon, Oxygen, Sulphur and Hydrogen) they are transported in the atmosphere and captured when needed; for elements that in practice have no volatile phase, repeated cycling solves the problem. Advanced ecosystems have the ability to eliminate the leakage and export of nutrients almost completely (Stark and Jordan, 1978; Odum, 1973, 1985; Kay, 1994).

Advanced self-organising systems are capable of homeostasis and exert a dynamic balance, a characteristic of open systems far from thermodynamic equilibrium. In such a system, material circulation is a necessary consequence of the structural changes associated with the increased capability to secure solar exergy in some form and convert it to low grade thermal radiation. This combined fulfilment of increased exergy degradation (Schneider and Kay, 1994) and material circulation is called the *regenerative cycle* (Günther and Folke, 1993; Günther, 1994b). This seems to be a general principle of any self-organising system. If the elements used for recharging exergy (embodied enegy) into the system are tapped off, the system will lose its power to recharge and eventually vanish. Examples of this are the bleeding of an animal or the constant export of nutrients from a farm.

In order to increase sustainability, it therefore seems a good idea to imitate the strategies of long-term surviving self-organising systems. One of the most important of those strategies seems to be the cyclic charging—discharging process of simple elements, the regenerative cycle referred to above. These elements are either volatile (Nitrogen, Carbon, Sulphur, Oxygen, Hydrogen) or non-volatile (Phosphorus, Potassium and trace metals). The limiting non-volatile elements and the volatile ones that carry a heavy energy investment, as the nitrogen oxides, are carefully recycled in such systems (Stark and Jordan, 1978; Odum 1973, 1985; Kay 1994). To do the equivalent on a modern farm, on, two changes are needed: (Figure 5).

Animal feed has to be produced on the same farm, or in the vicinity, allowing the manure to be returned to the land where the feed was produced. By this practice, 60-90% of the nutrients, at least the non-volatile ones, can be circu-

lated (Granstedt and Westberg, 1993). Nutrients with volatile phases, e.g. nitrogen, can be conserved by anaerobic storage or other means. When applied to farmland, they should be immediately covered with soil.

The nutrients actually exported as human food should be returned as uncontaminated as possible, preferably as human urine and (composted) faecal matter. With the use of source-separating toilets, which do not mix urine with faeces, the urine, containing most of the phosphorus and the nitrogen excreted (Günther, 1994) can be reclaimed easily. Faeces can be composted out of reach of flies to eliminate pathogens and then returned to the fields.

INTEGRATION OF AGRICULTURE AND SETTLEMENTS

Most of the problems pointed out in the first part of this paper can be ascribed to the unintentional separation of agriculture and settlements that has developed as a side-effect of the industrial revolution the last century. Re-integration of agriculture with settlements would be a way to solve the problems of increased vulnerability and decreased sustainability of the food system. Many of the environmental problems experienced today could also be alleviated by this strategy.

Micro-scale

Let's explore different scales of operation (Allen & Starr, 1982) to see how suitable each is solve the problems discussed earlier. We'll look first at a single agricultural unit and a small settlement of around 200 people.

1 *Elimination of dependency for feed and nutrients*

Assume that the farm produces both animal and vegetable products. Suppose too that all the feed for the animals is pro-

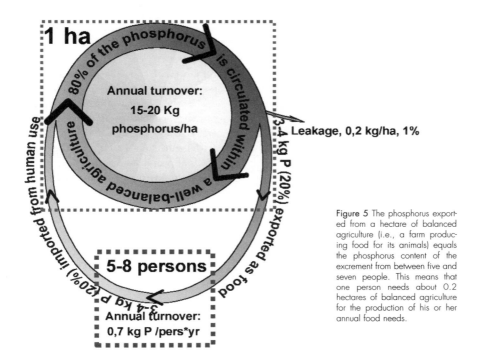

1 ha

80% of the phosphorus is circulated within a well-balanced agriculture

Annual turnover:
15-20 Kg
phosphorus/ha

3-4 kg P (20%) exported as food

Leakage, 0,2 kg/ha, 1%

80% of the phosphorus imported from human use

3-4 kg P (20%) imported

5-8 persons
Annual turnover:
0,7 kg P /pers*yr

Figure 5 The phosphorus export-ed from a hectare of balanced agriculture (i.e., a farm produc-ing food for its animals) equals the phosphorus content of the excrement from between five and seven people. This means that one person needs about 0.2 hectares of balanced agriculture for the production of his or her annual food needs.

duced in the area. This will reduce the need to import nutrients by 60—90 % (Granstedt and Westberg, 1993). However, the export of essential nutri-ents in food will still amount to 3-4 kg phosphorus/hectare/year. For the long-term survival of the system, this amount must be replaced. A human excretes 0.6—0.7 kg phosphorus/year in urine and faeces. This means that the phospho-rus content of the excrement from 5-7 persons equals the losses of phosphorus in food from a hectare of a balanced agricul-ture (Figure 5).

From these figures, the area of a bal-anced agriculture needed to support one person is obtained. This area is between 0.23 and 0.15 hectares, which is in agree-ment with the figure of 0.2 hectare per person calculated from a typical person's food needs and a conservative estimate of

the production capacity of an average Swedish farm (Günther, 1989). A 40 hectare agricultural holding can thus provide about 200 people with a large part of their needs.

Thus, if the farm's acute dependence on outside supplies of nutrients is to be cut, animal feed production and local human settlements must be integrated with the food producing system. This integration implies an increased diversity in local agriculture because of the increased diversity of products needed by the local population.

2 Elimination of leakage
The direct leakage of phosphorus from an agricultural unit is within the range of 0.2—0.4 kg/hectare/year (Brink & al., 1979). By planting buffer-strips beside streams, a large part of this leakage can

be captured (Mander & al., 1991, 1994) in the vegetation and reclaimed in the form of compost, biogas sludge or ash. Such buffer strips bring other advantages. The serve as windbreaks, increasing the yield 15—30% within 15 metres of the vegetation strip. They also increase the number of predators against insect pests (Andersson, 1990) and the number of bumble bees for pollination (Hasselrot, 1960).

3 Economy

The extensive handling and transporting system between the producer and consumer is not only energy demanding, but also appropriates more than 75% (calculated from the figures in LES, 1991, 1993a, b) of the price paid by the consumer for food. It is thus a factor in low farm incomes and the decreasing marginal returns in agriculture. Furthermore, most of the price paid to the farmer is swallowed up by the cost of the monetary and material inputs he or she has to buy. Calculations based on data from Augustsson and Andersson (1995) suggest that the proportion lost this way is about 85% (Figure 5). This means that the net income to the farmer is not more than 3.6% of the retail price in the shop

If farmers sold directly to consumers through the establishment of local markets where the farmer would be paid half the price for food that was paid by the consumer in the shop today, his or her income would quadruple despite the fact that the cost to the consumer has been sharply reduced. (Both figures assume the current product price to the farmer is 25% of the consumer price, which is somewhat high.) The calculation is set out in Fig. 6.

Medium scale

The implementation of the solutions proposed above is not incompatible with intermediate size settlements. Three or four settlements with their associated agriculture can form groups of 800—1200 persons and an associated agricultural area of 160—240 hectares. Such a population size is large enough for a good deal of the usual social infrastructure like primary schools, small service business etc. It could be argued that this size of settlement is not enough for the cultural needs of people, and for employment etc., and that this may generate an increased need for transportation. For the sake of discussion, however, imagine an area where such settlement types cover the land. In such an area, ignoring the incidence of lakes, mountains etc., everybody would have close to 18,000 neighbours within 3.5 km.

LARGE-SCALE IMPLEMENTATION OF THE PROPOSED SOLUTIONS: RURALISATION

Nutrient recycling becomes increasingly expensive with increasing distances (Günther, 1994). The energy requirements for distribution of food also tend to increase with quantum leaps when the distribution pathways require extensive packaging and preservation of the products. Providing this energy from fossil fuels is risky and unsustainable; so, if the goal is to provide this security, energy requirements have to be cut to a minimum and met from renewable sources. Also, the methods used to provide agriculture with its 'ultimate' raw material, phosphorus, must be changed. To maintain a linear flow of phosphorus through the society over a prolonged time is both wasteful and insecure.

Therefore, to attain nutrient circulation at the same time as energy support needs are diminished in large societies, a different societal structure strategy in should be applied: instead of the current trend towards increasing agricultural spe-

	TODAY		DIRECT SALE	
Consumer (4 person family)	60,000 kr	100 %	30,000 kr	50 %
Distribution and trade	45,000 kr	75 %	0 kr	0 %
Producer price	15, 000 kr	25 %	30, 000 kr	50 %
Producer expenses	12, 000 kr	20 %	18, 000 kr	30 %
Producer salary	3,000 kr	5 %	12,000 kr	20 %
Energy use, whole chain	40,000 kWh		8,000 kWh	

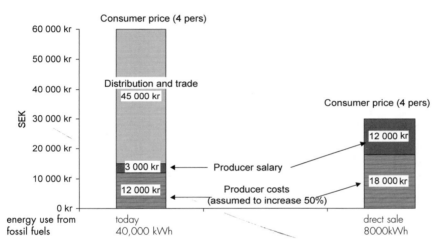

Figure 6 Direct co-operation between an agricultural unit and a near-by settlement would be economically beneficial to both the consumers and the farmer even if the production cost increased by 50%.

cialisation combined with urbanisation of the population, a closer integration of farms and settlements would be the goal.

A name for such a strategy is *ruralisation*, as opposed to urbanisation. This development strategy implies that instead of building a new house on the same site as one due for replacement or extensive repairs, small settlements integrated with agriculture as outlined above would be created in the hinterland of the urban area.

CONCLUSIONS
In this overview, I have argued that agri-

culture has a lot of problems that cannot be alleviated by better agricultural methods since they are due to the way the whole society has developed. Among these problems are

• its dependency on industrial energy support
• the need for constant inputs of nutrients and other materials
• the inescapable loss of nutrients, which is in turn caused by
• the linearity of the food handling system
• the alienation of farmers and farm workers from the rest of society.

These problems are aggravated by the following factors:
- the probable increase in fuel prices
- an increasing dependency of cheap energy
- the increasing specialisation of agricultural units
- the decreasing population working in agriculture
- urbanisation.

I argue that such problems, and others, as ecological and psychological ones, could be alleviated by *a closer integration of agriculture and settlements*, thereby:

- minimising industrial energy dependency
- increasing nutrient circulation
- increasing the integration between agricultural practice and other social activities
- increasing and supporting the ecosystem services received.

The economic returns from such systems seem likely to be better than those from the current type of agriculture in view of the latter's vulnerability and the near-certainty that its costs will rise sharply in the near future.

REFERENCES

Allen, T. F. H. and T. B. Starr, 1982. *Hierarchy, Perspectives for Ecological Complexity*. University of Chicago: Chicago and London.

Altieri, M.A., 1987. *Agroecology: The Scientific Basis of Alternative Agriculture*. Westview Press: Boulder. p. 227.

Andersson, L., 1990. *Florans inverkan på åkerns skadeinsekter och deras naturliga fiender*. Växtodling: 18. SLU: Uppsala.

Augustsson, L. and M. Johansson, 1995. *Sektorskalkyl för jordbruket*. Jordbruksverket 1995-03-16, Jönköping, Sverige.

Becker, W., 1992. *Befolkningens kostvanor och näringsintag (Food Habits and Nutrient Intake in Sweden, 1989)* Vår Föda 1992; 44:8. pp. 349–62.

Berkes, F. and C. Folke, 1994. 'Investing in Cultural Capital for a Sustainable Use of Natural Capital'. In: Jansson, A-M., M. Hammer, C. Folke and R. Costanza, eds. *Investing in Natural Capital: The Ecological Economics Approach to Sustainability*. Island press: Washington DC.

Booz, A., 1976. *Energy use in the food system*. Federal Energy Administration Washington DC 041-018-00109-3.

Brink, N., A. Gustavsson and G. Persson, 1979. *Förluster av kväve, fosfor och kalium från åker*. SLU publ. 181:4. Ekohydrologi 4. Sveriges Lantbruksuniversitet, Uppsala.

Brundenius, C., 1972. *Imperialismens ansikte: 400 år av underutveckling i Peru*. Stockholm: Prisma.

Cleveland, C.J., 1991. 'Natural Resource Scarcity And Economic Growth Revisited: Economic And Biophysical Perspectives'. In: R. Costanza, ed. *Ecological Economics: The Science And Management Of Sustainability*. Columbia University Press, New York, Oxford, pp. 289–318.

Costanza, R., 1987. *Social traps and Environmental Policy*. BioScience 37, pp. 407–12.

Diem, K. ed., 1960. *Documenta Geigy: Wissenschaflichen tabellen*. J.R. Geigy AG. Basel Schweiz

DOE—US Department of Energy, 1993. *International Energy Outlook* 0484(93).

Folke, C., 1990. *Evaluation of Ecosystem Life-Support*. Diss. Institution of Systems Ecology, Stockholm University.

— and Kautsky N., 1992. *Aquaculture with its Environment; Prospects for Sustainability*. Ocean and Coastal Management 17, pp. 5-24.

Giampietro, M., G. Cerretelli and D. Pimentel, 1992. *Energy Analysis of Agricultural Ecosystem Management: Human Return and Sustainability*. Agriculture, Ecosystems and Environment, 38, pp. 219–44

Goldemberg, J., T.B. Johansson, A.K.N. Reddy and R.H. Williams, 1987. *Energy for a Sustainable World*. World Resources Institute, Wiley-Eastern.

Goodland, R., H.E. Daly and S. El Serafy, 1992. *Population, Technology and Lifestyle: The Transition to Sustainability*. Island Press, Washington.

Gootas, H.B., 1956. *Composting Sanitary Disposal and Reclamation of Organic Wastes*. WHO,

Geneva.

Granstedt, A. and L. Westberg, 1993. *Flöden av växtnäring i jordbruk och samhälle.* SLU Info 1993, p. 416.

Günther, F., 1989. *Ekobyar, ekologiskt anpassad och resurssnål bebyggelse* (Eco-villages, ecologically adapted and resource-saving settlements). Ekokultur förlag, Borlänge.

— 1993. 'Phosphorus flux and Societal Structure'. In: *Proceedings from the Stockholm Water Symposium Aug. 11–14, 1992.* Stockholm Water Co. ISBN 91-971929-4-5, ISSN 1103-0127.

— 1994. *Self-organisation in systems far from thermodynamic equilibrium: Some clues to the structure and function of biological systems.* M.Sc. dissertation, Department of Systems Ecology, Stockholm University.

— 1994a. 'Cost Relations in Different Nutrient Retention Strategies'. Submitted to Waste Man. and Res. Denmark.

— 1994b. 'Converting Linear Flows into Cycles: The Phosphorus Flux in the Swedish Society as an Example'. Paper presented at the 2nd International Conference on Implications and Applications of Bioeconomics, Palma de Mallorca, Spain, 11–13 March 1994.

— 1994c. 'The HEAP trap: Phosphorus management and societal structure'. Accepted for publication in Ecological Economics, Elsevier, Amsterdam.

— and C. Folke, 1993. *Characteristics of Nested Living Systems.* J. Biol. Syst., 1, 3. pp. 257–74.

Günther, J., 1995. 'Interconnectedness between Ecosystem Health and Human Health'. In: Follér, M.L. and L. Hansson, eds. *Human Ecological Approaches to Health and Disease.* Gothenburg University, Gothenburg.

Gundersson. L., C.S. Holling and C.S. Light, 1995. *Barriers and Bridges to the Renewal of Ecosystems and Institutions.* Columbia University Press: New York.

Gutenberg, P., 1993. *Imaging development: Economic Ideas in Peru's Fictitious Prosperity, Guano 1840 –80.* University of California Press.

Hall, C.A.S., C.J. Cleveland and R. Kaufmann, 1986. *Energy and Resource Quality.* Wiley Interscience, New York.

Hasselrot, T. B., 1960. *Studies on Swedish Bumblebees (genus Bombus Latr.), their Domestication and Biology.* Opuscula Entomologica, Supplementum XVII. Lund.

Hoffman, R., 1995. *Jordbrukets energibalans—En analys av energiflöden i Svenskt jordbruk 1993*

och jämförelse med åren 1956 och 1972. KSLA Tidskrift. 'Lantbrukets energibalans— Energiflöden i Jord- och Skogsbruk'. Sammanfattning från seminarium 19/4/95, Stockholm.

Holling, C. S., 1973. *Resilience and stability of ecological systems. Annual Review of Ecological Systems* 4, pp. 1–23.

Holtan, H. and S. O. Astebøl, 1991. *Handbog i insamling av data om forurensingstilførsler til fjorder og vassdrag.* Revideret utgave. Statens foroerensingstilsyn. TA-774/1991 Oslo.

Huang, S-L., and Odum, H.T., 1991. *Ecology and Economy: Energy Synthesis and Public Policy in Taiwan.* J. Env. Management , Jun 1991 32:4 p. 313–34.

Hubendick, B., 1985. *Människoekologi* (Human Ecology). Gidlunds, Malmö.

Jordbruksverket, 1991. *Programplanen för funktionen Livsmedelsförsörjning* m.m. Bilaga A. Jordbruksverket. *Naturvårdsverket och Statens Livsmedelsverk.*

Kay, J.J., 1983. *Self-Organisation and the Thermodynamics of Living Systems: A Paradigm.* Department of Environmental and Res. studies, University of Waterloo, Ontario, Canada.

— 1984. 'Self-organization in Living Systems', PhD thesis, Univ. of Waterloo, Ontario.

— 1994. 'Some notes on "The ecosystem approach"; Ecosystems as Complex Systems' In: *Proceedings from the 1st International Conference on Ecosystem Health and Human Health.* Ottawa, Canada, June 19–23, 1994.

KEMI, 1994. Tvätt- disk- och rengöringsmedel. Rapport från Kemikalieinspektionen 5/94.

Kennedy, M., 1988. *Interest and inflation free money.* Permaculture Publications, Steyerberg.

Leach, G., 1976. *Energy and food production.* IPC Scientific and Technical Press, GB.

LES, Livsmedelsekonomiska samarbetsnämndens indexgrupp. 1991. *Analys av prisutvecklingen i olika led av livsmedelskedjan.* Jordbruksverket. Jönköping.

— 1993a. *Prisindex på jordbruksområdet. Beräkningsmetoder.* Jordbruksverket. Jönköping.

— 1993b. *Prisindex på jordbruksområdet, 1980-1992.* Jordbruksverket. Jönköping.

Mander, Ü, V. Kuusemets and M. Ivask, 1994. 'Nutrient Dynamics in Riparian Ecotones: A Case Study from the Porijõgi Catchment, Estonia'. Paper presented for publishing in *Landscape and Urban Planning.* Elsevier 1994. Proceedings from the European Congress of IALE Agricultural Landscapes in Europe, Rennes, France, 6-10 June 1993.

Mander, Ü., O. Matt and U. Nugin, 1991. 'Perspectives on Vegetated Shoal, Ponds and Ditches as Extensive Outdoor Systems of Wastewater Treatment in Estonia'. In: Etnier, C. and B. Guterstam: 1991. *Ecological Engineering For Wastewater Treatment.* Proceedings of the International Conference at Stensund Folk College, Sweden, 24–8 March.

Mitsch, W.I. and S.E. Jörgensen, 1989. *Ecological Engineering, an Introduction to Ecotechnology.* Wiley-Interscience, New York.

Norton, B. and B. Hannon, 1994. 'Democracy and Sense of Place Values'. *Journal of the American Planning Association.*

Odum, E.P., 1973. *Fundamentals of Ecology.* 3rd ed. Saunders, Philadelphia.

— 1985. *Trends to be Expected in Stressed Ecosystems. BioScience* 35: pp. 419–22.

Odum, H.T., 1971. *Environment, Power and Society.* Wiley-Interscience, New York.

Olsson, E., L. Karlgren, and V. Tullander, 1968. *Household and waste water.* Report 24:1968, The National Swedish Institute for Building Research. Stockholm.

Olsson, P., 1976. *Energianvändning i livsmedelsproduktionen.* SIK rapport 425/STU rapport 69:1978.

Pimentel, D. 1988. 'Industrialized Agriculture and Natural Resources'. In: Erlich, P.R. and J.P. Houldren, eds. *The Cassandra Conference: Resources and the Human Predicament.* Texas A&M University Press, College Station, Texas, phosphorus. pp. 53–74

— and C. Hall, eds, 1989. *Food and Natural Resources,* Academic Press INC, San Diego, California.

— T.W. Culliney, I.W. Butler, D.J. Reinemann and K.B. Beckmann, 1989. 'Ecological Resource Management for a Productive, Sustainable Agriculture'. In: Pimentel, D. and C. Hall., eds, 1989. *Food and Natural Resources,* Academic Press INC, San Diego, California.

Riely, P. J. and D. S. Warren, 1980. *Money Down the Drain—A Rational Approach to Sewage. The Ecologist* 10, p.10.

Rosser, J. B. Jr, C. Folke, F. Günther, H. Isomäki, C. Perrings, G. Peterson and T. Puu, 1993. *Discontinuous Changes in Multilevel Hierarchical Systems.* Systems Research Vol. 11, No. 3, ISSN 0731-7239, pp. 77–94.

Rydberg, T., 1991. *Energianalysperspektiv på dagens ekologiska lantbruk* (Energy Analysis Perspective of the Organic Farming of Today). *Ekologiskt lantbruk* 13, SLU, Uppsala.

SCB, 1993. *Naturmiljön i siffror* (The Natural Environment in Figures). Official Statistics of Sweden, Statistics Sweden; Stockholm.

SCB, 1994. *Jordbruksstatistisk årsbok 1994* (Yearbook of Agricultural Statistics 1994). Official Statistics of Sweden, Statistics Sweden. Stockholm.

Schneider, E.D. and J.J. Kay, 1993. 'Energy Degradation, Thermodynamics, and the Development of Ecosystems'. In: *Proceedings of the International conference on Energy Systems and Ecology.* The American Society of Mechanical Engineers, Advanced Energy Systems. Cracow, Poland, July 1993. p.10

— 1994. *Life As A Manifestation Of The Second Law Of Thermodynamics.* Mathl. Comput. Modelling 19, 6–8, pp. 25–48.

Smil, V., 1990. 'Nitrogen and Phosphorus'. In: Turner, B.L., ed. *The Earth as Transformed by Human Action.* Cambridge University Press, pp. 423–36.

Stark, N.M and C.F. Jordan, 1978. 'Nutrient retention by the root mat of an Amazonian Rain Forest'. In *Ecology* 59(3), pp. 434–7.

Svenska Kommunförbundet, 1991. *Det kommunala underhållsberget.* Delrapport: Vatten och avlopp. ISBN 91-7099-164-2.

Svensson, E., 1960. *Försök med vindskydd* (Experiments with Shelter). Statens jordbruksförsök. Meddelande nr 108. Uppsala.

Vollenwieder, R. and J. Kerekes, 1982. *Eutrophication of Waters: Monitoring, Measures and Control.* OECD 1982, p. 154.

Vråle, L., 1987. *Furorensingsmodell fra Avløpsvann fra Boliger,* NIVA publikation 60/87.

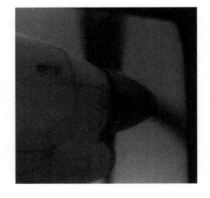

designing an economy with built-in sustainability

LOTHAR MAYER

The modern market economy creates a perfect environment for expanding financial capital at the expense of the biosphere at an exponential rate.

Human numbers are four times the level of a century ago, and the world economy is 17 times as large... Oceanic fisheries... are being pushed to their limits and beyond, water tables are falling on every continent, rangelands are deteriorating from overgrazing, many remaining tropical forests are on the verge of being wiped out, and carbon dioxide concentrations in the atmosphere have reached the highest level in 160,000 years. If these trends continue, they could make the turning of the millennium seem trivial as a historic moment, for they may be triggering the largest extinction of life since a meteorite wiped out the dinosaurs some 65 million years ago. As we look forward to the twenty-first century, it is clear that satisfying the projected needs of an ever larger world population with the economy we now have is simply not possible... We are entering a new century, then, with an economy that cannot take us where we want to go. The challenge is to design and build a new one that can sustain human progress without destroying its support systems—and that offers a better life to all.'

Worldwatch Institute, State of the World 1999.

The capitalist market economy is unrivalled in its capability to generate material growth at the expense of the biosphere. The further it shakes off any social and ecological fetters under the fierce competitive pressure of global markets, the more strongly its interconnected positive feedback cycles amplify and reinforce each other. Money begets more money, the rich become richer, the poor become poorer, large corporations grow and merge into global giants that determine economic and social conditions instead of governments who are losing their grip.

A system centred on making money out of money, the capitalist market economy came into its own with the industri-al revolution and has since increasingly come to control the human relationship with nature. Because of it, human demands on natural systems are no longer determined by human physiological needs but by the need to generate a return on capital. In such a system, corporations and economies grow rich by turning low-entropy natural resources into high-entropy waste. Part of the wealth they create this way is then invested to transform more natural assets into monetary value, and this cycle is repeated again and again. In this way, money/capital begets more and more money/capital, and the exponential growth of value creation translates into an exponential growth of the claims made on natural resources and life support systems.

Basically, importing low entropy (syntropy) and exporting high entropy is the process by which all self-organising systems create and maintain themselves. What, then, makes their man-made counterpart in the economic sphere such a ferocious, deadly competitor?

The difference at the level of self-organisation between organisms and ecosystems on the one hand and an industrial economy on the other, comes down to two essential points:

(1) Natural systems arise and have been extensively tested in co-evolution with other systems. The evolutionary process has knitted them into a network of sources and sinks, where every 'sink' for 'waste' is a source of food for other players, so that there is no way for noxious substances or poisons to accumulate in the biosphere. Their growth and replication is bounded by limiting factors like free energy or structural materials like nitrogen, sulphur, phosphorus or magnesium, which are not in unlimited supply. Incidentally, this limited availability of resources is one of the basic conditions for evolution to work.

Lothar Mayer is chairman of the German Schumacher Society. He studied economics at university in the 1960s but acquired his hands-on experience of how economics shapes the life of people, peoples and the Earth as a conference interpreter for international organisations, corporations and professional associations. After fifteeen years of ecological activism he turned to writing on the economy/ecology nexus in 1992, publishing the book **Ein System siegt sich zu Tode—Der Kapitalismus frißt seine Kinder**. His most recent book, from which this essay is adapted, is **Ausstieg aus dem Crash (Bailing out of the Crash)**. It appeared in 1999 and chapters in English can be downloaded from his website: www.Lothar-Mayer.de. His e-mail is LM@Lothar-Mayer.de.

By contrast, the industrial economy is a linear once-through system with a tendency to deplete sources and to fill up and congest sinks. Its processes are untested by evolution and can obviously be sustained only for a few seconds of evolutionary time. In the short run,

SYNTROPY & ENTROPY

Entropy describes the inevitable fate of all existing things: degradation, decline, dissolution, death. A simple, everyday example of how of entropy works is the way any concentrated energy form (like the heat contained in a cup of coffee) dissipates into a room over a period of time, becoming useless waste heat.

Syntropy is another word for low or negative entropy. In apparent contradiction to the second law of thermodynamics, islands of syntropy grow in an ocean of entropy through self-organisation of dynamic systems. Syntropy is the essence of life. Representing the temporary and localised suspension of entropy, it is at once created by life and enables life to flourish.

before its growth is checked by limiting factors, it behaves like a fire—it is characterised by unbounded self-reinforcement which will only be stopped by the exhaustion of its feed, the resources and life support systems of the planet.

(2) As a social system, industrial capitalism has gained an unbeatable competitive advantage by overlaying its physical process structure (exporting entropy, importing syntropy) with an abstract accounting structure which images the physical process symbolically and controls it by means of cultural conventions. In this accounting structure, earned syntropy turns into (monetary) income, and by the same token, money/capital is transformed into syntropy claims. Money which if invested turns into capital and generates a return or if made into a loan generates interest thus turns into a self-feeding generator of syntropy claims. In the short run it is a perpetual motion machine—so long as one disregards the pollution and exhaustion of its environment which is inseparably bound up with its functioning. As a concrete example, take the capital invested in the construction and maintenance of a coal mine. The investment results in generating many times the energy required in this process. The energy thus gained can be sold, i.e. be turned into money in the market. This extra money, combined with earnings from other enterprises, can be invested in another mine or an oil-field which, in its turn, will generate maybe five, maybe fifty times the energy used in the process, allowing the invested capital and the applied energy to grow continuously.

Economics is about using energy to transform useless matter into useful things. While the bottom line of a sucessful business enterprise is a *financial* surplus, the final result of the economic process and its interaction with the physical world is a decrease in syntropy and an increase in entropy, i.e. a loss of natural assets. In the capitalist market economy, the institution of money/capital with interest on money and returns on capital as its primary mission sits on top of and feeds on the physical process turning natural assets into monetary value (*verwertung*)* and, by the same token, into further claims for natural assets. This capital connection, the cultural construct of an unquestioned equivalence between capital and syntropy from which the system—pumped as it is from the symbolic level—derives its self organisational dynamics, is the heart of the capitalist market economy.

This capital/resources feedback loop turns into a hypercycle through being linked to human needs. The (human!) agents of the system who, from their own experience, know intimately the psychological profile of its customers have the capacity to invent a never-ending stream of new needs and wants. Moreover in a mature capitalist society there is a positive feedback loop connecting, on the one side, the gratification of essential human needs (for love, support and identity) with material *satisfiers* (impressive homes, cars, TV, clothes) and, on the other side, the deficits and needs that are created and sustained in the process. The cycle thus established displays classic features of addiction, maintaining and feeding on itself. The coldness of economic relationships creates an overwhelming craving for warmth—to which industry responds by offering an abundance of products promising to fulfil this need.

---

* The German word *Verwertung* which does not translate well into English described the process perfectly (*ver*-wert-*ung*) by referring both to the value creation and the concomitant disappearance or destruction of the substance which is being turned into monetary value.

The modern market economy based on industrial capitalism thus creates a perfect environment for expanding real and financial capital at the expense of the biosphere at an exponential rate. Let me recapitulate the necessary conditions for this process:

- in the physical world: on the one side, a source of low entropy from fossil fuels and raw material deposits amassed during the Earth's history, and their systematic exploitation, and on the other side, available sinks in the shape of entropy-exporting process structures, or 'syntropy generators' in the biosphere such as vegetation, the water cycle and the carbon cycle.
- at the cultural level: the construct of an unquestioned equivalence between capital and syntropy from which the system—pumped as it is from the symbolic level—derives its self-organisational dynamics.
- at the level of human nature: needs that supply an inexhaustible resource for creating value, enabling inexorable growth of the stream of money/capital.

By activating a whole new set of imaginary* needs, the rising real incomes in the productive sector can be absorbed and redistributed and transformed into a constantly growing demand. Without the suction effect of that demand, production would soon come to a standstill. At the same time, value creation in the imaginary sector develops a momentum of its own. Unlike the satisfaction of physical needs, it is not limited by inevitable saturation. In the realm of imaginary needs, value creation without limits is a possibility, at least as long as the purchasing power so generated is balanced by the production of enough goods and services so that inflation does not strip it of its value. In developed industrial societies, purchasing power and production are pushing each other along.

A mechanism has thus been created that permits unlimited value creation in the imaginary or notional sphere—the sphere beyond basic needs. Imaginary needs, however, are not always satisfied with imaginary goods—quite the contrary: there is nothing imaginary about silk bed-linen, a fifth pair of shoes, or a holiday in the Caribbean. What is imaginary is their value—it is derived from fantasies, from symbolic meanings, from prestige. Anything that exceeds the basic human needs becomes an inexhaustible resource the system can explore, use, exploit and turn into monetary value. Whenever some need or want or any little part of it is gratified, value is created through the payment made for this gratification. And, most importantly, any value created by gratifying notional or

---

* The term *imaginary* was used by J.G. Schlosser (1739–99), a contemporary and brother-in-law of Goethe. The monetary philosophy of Johann Schlosser is shown in greater detail in Binswanger (1991: 195). An even more appropriate term I should like to suggest is the word *notional* which denotes both the immaterial nature of the kind of needs in question and articles like buttons, buckles, mirrors and ribbons— the 'instrument of vanity and waste', as David Landes called them—as offered by peddlers at the doorstep in pre- and early industrial times. By *imaginary* or *notional* I am referring to all needs that go beyond subsistence. They are called *imaginary* or *notional* because they refer not to what human beings need for their survival but to what they would like beyond that, their wants. They are what humans desire, or require, to satisfy their feelings, their imagination, their social standing, their psychological or social deficits. One would call this a misfortune that was waiting to happen to humankind, with its ability to process symbols. This ability allows man to invest material objects like the cross, the car, palaces, clothes, medals, golden cutlery or red roses with meanings like divine power, male potency, social standing, personal values, a secure living or love, represemting an immaterial reality.

imaginary needs has the astonishing power of buying real resources—without any limitation.

This brings us straight to the core problem of the capitalist system. Our essential, organic, absolute or physiological needs are limited. They are subject to the principle of marginal utility: when you are hungry, one loaf of bread represents great utility, the second loaf less, and by the tenth loaf, utility moves towards zero. The same applies to jumpers or woollen blankets when you are cold, and to a roof over your head for protection from rain and snow. This limitation does not apply to the imaginary (non-essential, psychological, relative) needs. People will always crave status symbols such as big cars, beautiful houses, classy dogs and horses or famous works of art, because an individual's underlying psychological ('imaginary') needs like a craving for security, recognition, love or identification can be fulfilled—or rather unfulfilled—in a million ways. Another way of distinguishing between these two basic groups of needs is therefore to look at them as 'satisfiable/non-satisfiable.' (Zinn 1995)

> *We must be rid of this self-accelerating motor firmly locked to its own fuel pump.*

What this means is that the stuff from which the greater part of value creation in modern industrial societies is made can be reproduced at will. Provided the growth of the volume of money is carefully managed, the purchasing power resulting from this act of value creation in the imaginary sphere has the potential to grow beyond all limitations, all the time claiming its share of Nature's limited resources. And here we have it—the

fatal flaw in the design of the capitalist market economy. Things are bound to go badly wrong when money—whether it derives from fulfilling real, physically limited needs or imaginary, endlessly expandable wants—is allowed to claim real *and* imaginary goods.

The only conclusion that can be inferred from all this is that a solid line needs to be drawn between the world of real, essential goods and that of imaginary, superfluous ones. Money is not able to distinguish between the real and the imaginary. It is sheer madness to give it equal access to both. An economic system that allows this is bound to make such inroads on the real resources and on the life support systems of the biosphere—both naturally limited on a limited planet—that they will inevitably run out.

To stop this growth threatening the basis of life, first we must be rid of this self-accelerating motor firmly locked to its own fuel pump. One way of achieving this is to set an upper limit to the means of exchange for the acquisition of real resources by creating a strictly limited budget (which will in the first place be directed towards the supply of basics). Money in its traditional sense (as the means of exchange, of storage and of creation of value which can be replicated without limits) would then be confined to the sphere of endlessly reproducible luxury needs. There would be no convertibility between the two sectors.

So, on the one hand, the amount of syntropy consumed by human needs would remain limited to a sustainable level, and on the other hand, there would be an incentive to make a more intelligent and efficient use of a given budget without increasing demands made on the real resources—something that is inevitable in a capitalist market economy.

One possibility of creating such a 'resource' budget would be assign to every citizen a limited budget of CO_2 credits. Tying our consumption of natural resources and ecological services to a limited budget of CO_2 emissions builds an operational and verifiable concept of sustainability into the economy. Our use of resources and life support systems is then determined not by what we can set in motion by human labour, cleverness and capital, but by the budget set by our sustainable 'income' from natural assets.

Human economic activities depend very strongly on the deployment of energy for transforming existing matter into useful products. We could, therefore, in a rough approximation, take human energy use as a basis for outlining a 'legitimate' ecological space. As it is generated in all combustion processes, the greenhouse gas CO_2 is highly representative of energy consumption and, therefore, of industrial output. Logically, it therefore also roughly reflects the material flows, and the foreign substances and pollutants released during these processes, all of which put pressure on the natural systems. These kinds of pollution would be significantly reduced by a policy of limiting CO_2 emissions.

The principal argument for using CO_2 emissions as a standard for a sustainable economy is the fact that there is a high degree of consensus among scientists about the permissible global levels of CO_2 emissions that will not harm the planet's life support systems. These levels can be determined with some precision, and the IPCC (Intergovernmental Panel for Climate Control, a UN body), as well as the Enquiry Commission of the German Bundestag, have calculated that if global warming is to be prevented they must not exceed about 11 billion tonnes per year.

If we accept that long term sustainable development is possible only on a basis of fair distribution of wealth then, with a global population of six billion, our 11 billion tonne budget would allow two tonnes of CO_2 per person per year. The current per capita emissions of carbon dioxide in industrial countries stands at 11 to 13 tonnes. In the US this rises to 23 tonnes, while in most of the Southern countries it is much below two tonnes per year.

If we seriously want to make the sustainable use of natural resources and life support systems effective for the day-to-day and minute-to-minute behaviour of humans, the obvious way of doing so is to use this quota in the way of an annual income, as a basis of consumer spending, making it effectively into a second means of payment that is tied to a real resource. Just as the consumer nowadays automatically pays VAT with any purchase, he or she would in future be charged at the point of sale for all the carbon dioxide released during the manufacture of the goods or the provision of the services he or she is buying.

Carbon dioxide pollution charges could be assigned to the product like a value-added tax at each stage in production or the chain of value creation. Let's use a fridge as an example. The manufacturer undertakes to pay for the carbon dioxide pollution he is charged by the sheet steel supplier, who passes on the charges for CO_2 pollution arising from the rolling mill, the steelworks, the mining and the transport of the iron-ore that he in his turn has been charged for. Other items on this bill would be the CO_2 costs of the insulating material, of the compressor, of glass and plastic parts. By the time the fridge appears on sale in the retailer's shop, its CO_2 cost will also contain a surcharge for transport from the factory to the point of sale, as well as for the retailer's overhead costs such as heating and lighting.

When the consumer pays the aggregated pollution cost out of her CO_2 budget, the credits are passed all the way back down the value chain to firms that have used CO_2 rights for manufacturing in the first place. It goes without saying that, as with Value Added Tax, most of these transactions would take place in the accounts of the companies involved, and that the process, like the VAT system, would be closely monitored by a public body.

All the technical conditions for the practical implementation of a CO_2 budget are in place. Naturally, the individual's budget would not be reduced overnight to 2 tonnes, from its present 12 tonnes per year. It would happen gradually, over thirty or forty years.

The obvious objection that a CO_2 quota would throw us back to the post-war period with its ration cards misses the point. A CO_2 quota is not an allocation of individual articles, but it constitutes a completely freely disposable budget, albeit limited in size. War-time vouchers and ration cards represented a quantity of a particular article, half a pound of butter, or a pair of shoes, or two gallons of petrol. They were part of a centralist command economy with all its clumsy bureaucratic workings, its built-in unfairness and its absurd consequence of never giving people what they really need. Such a system can function only in tandem with a black market to balance out the deficiencies in the allocation by matching supply and production to demand.

CARBON DIOXIDE
already well

Plans for rationing CO_2 emissions broadly along the lines suggested by Lothar Mayer in this article are already well advanced. They were developed by David Fleming, whose article on the oil crisis is on p.98. Fleming calls his system Domestic Tradable Quotas, or DTQs. 'DTQs are an electronic system of rationing originally designed to enable national economies to reduce the greenhouse gases released by the combustion of fuels' Fleming says. 'They can also be used if fuel supplies are disrupted. I think they will be needed as a matter of urgency as severe increases in the price of oil take effect during the first decade of the century. '

DTQs are intended for application within an economy, not for trading between nations. A country setting up a DTQ system would set an overall greenhouse emissions budget that would be reduced year by year and 'carbon units' making the household sector's share of this budget (roughly 45%) would be issued free to all those resident in the country on an equal per capita basis. Firms and other organisations would have to buy their units—they would bid for them in an auction, just as happens with the issue of government debt. The money raised by this auction would go to the government.

All fuels would be rated for their greenhouse emissions and individuals and organisations purchasing them would have to surrender carbon units according to this rating in addition to paying cash. The price of various fuels in terms of carbon units is set out in the Box There would be a national market in carbon units in which low users could sell their surplus, and higher users could buy more.

'DTQs are a hands-off system' Fleming says. 'Virtually all transactions would be

RATIONING PROPOSALS
worked out

carried out electronically using the technologies and systems already in place for direct debit systems and credit cards. Initial research has indicated that the scheme is technologically feasible. The scheme has been designed to function efficiently not only for people who participate in it, but for those who do not—e.g. for overseas visitors, for the infirm and for those who refuse to cooperate.'

With their annual reduction in the carbon budget and equal per capita emissions entitlements, DTQs dovetail well with Contraction and Convergence, the global framework for limiting greenhouse gas emissions developed by Aubrey Meyer and his colleagues in the Global Commons Institute and described in more detail in the article beginning on p.158.

'The strong emphasis on equity—with all citizens becoming equal stakeholders in the environment—will, I believe, contribute substantially to the political acceptability of the scheme' Fleming says.

DTQs certainly meet the criteria established by Herman Daly for systems of this sort. In an article 'Allocation, distribution and scale: towards an economics that is efficient, just and sustainable' (**Ecological Economics 6**, 1992 p.188) Daly set these out as follows:

- First we must create a limited number of rights to pollute. The aggregated or total amount of pollution correspond-

ing to these rights is determined so that it falls within the absorptive capacity of the airshed or watershed in question, That is to say, the scale impact is limited to a level judged to be ecologically sustainable—an economic 'Plimsoll line' must be drawn as the very first step. Far from ignoring scale, this policy requires that the issue of sustainable or optimal scale be settled at the beginning...

- Second, the limited number of rights corresponding to the chosen scale must be distributed initially to different people. Perhaps equally to citizens, or to firms or perhaps collectively as pubic property then to be auctioned or sold by the government to individuals. But there must be an initial distribution before there can be any allocation and reallocation by trading.

- Only in the third place, after having made social decisions regarding an ecologically sustainable scale and an ethically just distribution, are we in a position to allow reallocation among individuals through markets in the interests of efficiency... Scale is... determined... by a social decision reflecting ecological limits. Distribution... by a social decision reflecting a just distribution of the newly created assets. Subject to these social decisions, individualistic trading in the market is then able to allocate the scarce rights efficiently.

—Editors

TRANSLATING EMISSIONS INTO FUELS' CARBON-UNIT COST
Estimates of the global warming potential (GWP) of gases released by production and combustion of fuels.
1 kg carbon dioxide = 1 carbon unit. The GWP of methane and nitrous oxide is measured as carbon dioxide equivalents.

FUEL	Natural gas	Petrol	Diesel	Coal	Grid electricity (night, UK)	Grid electricity (day, UK)
PRICE IN CARBON UNITS	0.2 per kWh	2.3 per litre	2.4 per litre	2.9 per kg	0.6 per kWh	0.7 per kWh

The 'price' is the number of carbon units you would have to give up to get, say, a litre of petrol.

HOW THE CO2 ECONOMY

By tying the use of natural resources to a limited CO_2 budget, the CO_2 economy would come with a built-in operational and verifiable standard of sustainability. Our use of resources and life support systems would be determined by real natural resources that can be used on a sustainable basis rather than by our earning capacity or by the amount of capital we can mobilise at any given moment. A resources-based budget activates a feedback and control mechanism that enables us to react directly to any indications of scarcity or to signs of stress which, if left uncontrolled, might take on a massive and life-threatening form.

The budget allocated to each individual would be stored on the magnetic strip of a charge card or on the chip of a smart card. Laser scanners in the supermarket or at the petrol stations would read one bar code for the price and one for CO_2 content from the price label, and the card terminal would charge the card accordingly. A new chip card charged with the new reduced CO_2 allowance would be issued every year. If someone used up their allowance before the year was over they would have the choice of earning more by carrying out environmental restoration such as planting trees, taking care of threatened biotopes or re-naturalising the beds of rivers and streams. Alternatively, they would be able to buy extra credits from people who did not need all their theirs. Naturally, as each person's CO_2 quota shrinks, the price of emission rights will go up steeply.

1 Separating needs from wants
In a CO_2-bounded economy, the distinction between survival and luxury goods would emerge as a matter of course and of personal choice as opposed to a distinction decreed by an authority.

2 Long-term planning and structural change
Bringing in a CO_2 economy over a time span of 40 years would provide industry with the security of long-term planning it often demands. It would enable individuals to change their personal lifestyles, their energy consumption, the way they use their cars, their culinary and leisure habits.

3 Industry, the world of work, the world we live in would be radically changed by re-defining what is economical or cost-effective
Whereas conventional cost-effectiveness is expressed as the ratio of money revenues over money invested or spent, *real cost effectiveness* is achieved only when needs are satisfied using the minimum amount of real resources such as labour, raw material, syntropy potential.

4 The effect on the character and the meaning of work, on workplaces and unemployment
The focus would shift from producing exchange value for sale on the market, i.e. for money—to the production of useful goods. There would be little point in producing exchange value money because only very few useful things can now be purchased with it. It will make more sense to produce utility values for yourself or your immediate environment, such as

- to grow food—fruit, vegetables, potatoes—in the garden or an allotment
- to repair bicycles and toys instead of buying new ones
- to make your own furniture and household articles
- to sew, repair and alter your clothes. In other words, do all those things that are completely pointless under the current definition of what is economic (cf. point 3)
- to create a LETS system or some other type of mutual neighbourhood support using vouchers for real goods and services based on an exchange system.

WOULD WORK IN PRACTICE

5 A new standard for technical best performance

In a society which functions on a limited resource budget, the idea of best performance will be applied to the much higher level of the needs to be satisfied, rather than to the level of the product (heating, car, house, TV set, long-distance flight). The aim is to find the method that uses as little material and energy as possible in meeting such needs as

- comfortable room temperature
- mobility
- protection, privacy, peace and security
- entertainment and leisure pursuits.

For engineers and designers, the higher degree of efficiency has always been something like a Holy Grail. Nothing could be worse than a steam engine that needs nearly as much coal as it extracts from the mine. But corporate calculations soon degraded their noble striving towards energy and material efficiency to mere cost efficiency.

6 A solar society

A CO_2-bounded economy would allow all types of renewable forms of energy to develop and find the niche they are best suited for:

- solar collectors on the roofs and walls of buildings for interior heating and hot water
- photovoltaic panels for generating electricity also on walls and roofs
- wind power stations
- bio-gas plants producing fuel for cars with gas-powered engines and for supplementing the supply of electricity and heating from direct solar energy.
- cars powered by fuel cells running on hydrogen produced with electricity generated by windmills.
- small scale co-generation plants based on bio-gas and plant oil to supplement direct solar power during periods of little sunlight.

7 Foreign trade, the local and regional economies

The limitation represented by a CO_2 allocation would add the full cost of transport to imported products—the further they have to travel, the greater the CO_2 'cost'. It would not be long before this affected the massive flow of goods between countries and continents. World trade has multi-

plied by a factor of ten since 1945, and it is not impossible to imagine it shrinking to 1945 levels or further.

A resources-based currency would, over the next few decades, bring the international division of labour back to manageable levels. Charging transport costs in full (in CO_2) could be the first step towards making many of today's imports and exports economically non-viable. Taking environmental pollution into account at the production stage would cause products that are able to compete in the market solely because they are produced with total disregard to ecological conditions or by over-exploitation of natural resources to drop out of the import statistics. A reduction both of global trade and of the extreme division of labour, both of which have resulted in an unbearable volume of air and road transport, would bring economic activity back to the local and regional level. As for imports from far-away countries, people would tend to apply their limited CO_2 budget to a few luxury goods where, due to their small bulk transport costs are minimal, like tea, coffee, spices and silk—i.e. the exotic products which were imported at the beginning of long-distance trade.

8 CO_2 budget and CO_2 account as a means of information

Even short of its introduction as a parallel currency, a simple CO_2 index summarising the environmental impact of products and services would serve as a useful guide and incentive. In regard to motivation and behaviour, a CO_2 quota would have the advantage of saving the individual from all the negative emotions that environmentally conscious people experience in all their lifestyle and consumer choices. No more uncertainty, guilt, resignation, no more feeling like a fool, fearing that whatever you do will not be enough. If marketed properly, the CO_2 quota could make us feel contented about doing the right thing, saving the planet for our children, not taking more than is our due, to be united in something worthwhile, to feel that we are all in the same boat: none of us want it to sink, so we all have to limit our baggage!

9 CO_2 currency as a pure means of exchange

The CO_2 budget would be a testing ground for a currency which is designed to be a pure means of exchange—uncontaminated by the runaway effects of money-as-capital, i.e. money for making money for making money.

A budget based on CO_2 and resources has only one thing in common with the war-time ration coupons: both limit the amount of resources available. In every other way the CO_2 budget would be able to be used as if it was money, and like money it would have an impact on supply and demand in the market. It would also influence the allocation of resources, favouring the conservation of energy and raw materials, recycling, re-use, zero-emission cycles and renewable energies because these are the areas where people would concentrate their spending because they would be soft on their CO_2 budgets. A resource-based budget would ensure that after one or two decades there would be an abundant supply of goods and services which were not only produced with a minimum of resources but which also consumed a minimum in use.

As I said, a sustainable CO_2 budget could not be achieved overnight. Systems would need time to adjust but German emissions could shrink from twelve to two tonnes per head over a span of, say, 40 years, i.e. by a quarter tonne per year. Right from the start, it would have to be clear that in the year 2020 they would have shrunk to seven tonnes. This would create the certainty required to bring about long-term structural changes. Without such certainty it would be very difficult and often impossible for an individual to change his or her personal lifestyle, energy consumption, car use, eating habits, leisure time pursuits and holiday patterns.

The transition to a CO_2 economy is an emergency brake to stop the rapid course into self-destruction. It creates the material conditions which support and promote sustainable use of the life support systems—rather than penalising it as an unbounded capitalist market economy does.

A CO_2 budget would also set us on the road to greater distributive equity worldwide. The concept of a CO_2 economy determines the upper limits of individual consumption out of a fund of essential resources defined as a commons. By the same token, it makes available the 'environmental space' which the countries of the South need to achieve the level of economic development necessary to satisfy their basic needs. The claims of one half of humanity must be limited in order to preserve a living space for the other half. Rationing CO_2 would stop human beings appropriating resources they want but don't need and by doing so, excluding others and depriving them of their livelihoods.

REFERENCES

Binswanger 1994: H.C. Binswanger und Paschen von Flotow, *Geld und Wachstum*, Stuttgart 1994.

Binswanger 1991: Hans Christoph Binswanger, *Geld und Natur*, Stuttgart 1991.

Braudel 1979: Fernand Braudel, *Civilisation matérielle, Economie et Capitalisme, XVe–VIIIe Siècle*, Paris 1979.

Cobb/Daly 1994: Cobb, J.B., Cobb, C.W. and Daly, H.E, *For the Common Good*, Second edition, Boston 1994.

Daly 1999: Herman Daly, *Wirtschaft jenseits von Wachstum*, 1999.

Ebeling 1991: Werner Ebeling, *Chaos—Ordnung —Information*, Thun 1991.

Worldwatch Institute 1999: *Worldwatch Institute, State of the World 1999*, 1999.

Zinn 1995: Karl Georg Zinn, 'Wie umweltverträglich sind unsere Bedürfnisse', in: Sigmund Martin Daecke (Hg), *Ökonomie contra Ökologie? Wirtschaftsethische Beiträge zu Umweltfragen*, 1995.

what next for slowing climate change ?

AUBREY MEYER

US opposition to meaningful steps to curtail greenhouse gas emissions is putting the whole world in jeopardy. Feasta is helping to develop an approach which might break the American veto.

If humanity's reaction to the threat of global warming is not fast and effective, we might as well not bother to respond at all because the only thing slow and grudging actions would achieve would be to delay the onset of whatever is to happen by a few years. The choice we face is therefore between making determined, drastic changes now, or doing nothing. There is no middle road.

This is because, if we allow the warming to proceed too far—and we've no idea how much warming is safe—powerful feedback mechanisms will kick in and there will be no clawing back from where they take us. We don't even know whether these feedbacks will be positive or negative, whether they will lead to another ice age or to a runaway warming, as the panel explains. But they will happen. They've happened before and they work very quickly, as the ice-core and pollen records show.

It doesn't really matter whether a rapid warming or an ice age occurs—either would be equally catastrophic. So the message is clear: greenhouse gas concentrations in the atmosphere have to be stabilised within the next ten or twenty years

if we are to have a decent chance of avoiding the one or the other. This in turn means that we don't have the luxury of waiting until the most economically powerful countries on the planet decide to attempt to solve the problem. That might be too late. A structure has to be found within which those countries that recognise the seriousness of the problem and are prepared to act can do so without waiting for the others, who can always join the effort later. After all, it would have been impossible to establish the EU if it had been necessary to get all 15 countries to sign up at once. Why should action to halt climate change be any different?

One part of that structure is Contraction and Convergence, the method of controlling greenhouse gas emissions I've developed over the past ten years with colleagues at the Global Commons Institute in London and about which I spoke at a Feasta conference in March 2000.

So what is C&C and how might it help slow, or even halt, the warming process that is making people so concerned? Essentially, it involves three steps:

1. An international agreement is reached on how much further the level of

carbon dioxide (CO_2) in the atmosphere can be allowed to rise before the changes in climate it produces become totally unacceptable. Fixing this target level is very difficult as the concentrations are too high already.

2. Once the ultimate overall limit to CO_2 concentrations as been agreed, it is a simple matter to use an estimate of the proportion of the gas released which is retained in the atmosphere to work out how quickly we need to cut back on current global emissions in order to reach the target. This cutting back is the Contraction part of Contraction and Convergence.

3. Once we know by what percentage the world has to cut its CO_2 emissions each year to avoid a build-up of CO_2 in the atmosphere above the agreed concentration target, we have to decide how to allocate the fossil fuel consumption that those emissions represent.

Should it be left to the market to do so?—If it did, we would effectively allow the industrialised nations, which have caused the warming problem and have become rich through their overuse of fossil fuel, to continue to use the lion's share. Or should we say, as the Americans once did, that all countries should cut back by the same percentage? This proposal would, of course, mean that those countries which use most fossil fuel now would continue to use most in the future. That would scarcely command world-wide support. Or should we say, as the C&C approach does, that the right to emit carbon dioxide is a human right which should be allocated on an equal basis to all of humankind? This might appeal to a majority of the countries of the world but the overconsuming countries would have to be allowed an adjustment period in which to bring their emissions down before the Convergence on the universal level. So C&C has a period for that built in.

AUBREY MEYER is a violinist and composer who was once the principle viola player in the BBC Ulster Orchestra. He was born in Bradford, grew up in South Africa and studied music at the University of Cape Town. He was a founder of the Global Commons Institute and largely responsible for the development and promotion of the 'Contraction & Convergence' approach to halting global warming. In 1998 he won the Andrew Lees Memorial Award with the following citation: 'Aubrey Meyer, almost single-handedly and with minimal resources, has made an extraordinary impact on the negotiations on the Climate Change Treaty, one of the most important of our time, through his campaign for a goal of equal per capita emissions, which is now the official negotiating position of many governments and is gaining acceptance in developed and developing countries alike.' He works full-time on climate change issues and lives in North London.

After convergence, each country would receive the same allocation of CO_2 emissions permits per head of its population at some agreed base year. Those countries which were unable to live within their allocation would be able to buy more permits from countries which ran their economies in a more energy-frugal way. This feature would lead to a steady flow of purchasing power from the countries which have used fossil energy to become rich to ones which are currently poor. It would thus not only shrink the gap between rich and poor but also encourage the South to develop along a low-fossil-energy path.

'The paleoclimate record shouts out to us that, far from being self-stabilising, the Earth's climate system is an ornery beast which overreacts to even small nudges.' Wallace Broecker, a paleoclimatologist at Columbia University, says.[1]

Broecker personally believes that the reaction he fears will be strongly negative and that the climate in the northern hemisphere will cool by as much as 10ºC in as little as ten years if the Gulf Stream halted. This would give Dublin a climate equivalent to that of Spitzbergen. How might this happen? Well, at present the large volumes of warm water that flow from the Gulf of Mexico across the Atlantic to Europe lose heat and freshwater to the air by evaporation along the way. This makes the water cooler (its temperature drops from 12-13ºC to 2-4ºC), saltier and thus more dense until, somewhere off the coast of Iceland, it becomes heavier than the surrounding sea, sinks and flows south along the seabed. Much of it then rounds Africa, joining the Southern Ocean's circumpolar current.

Broecker calls this flow 'The Conveyor' and says that it is equal to that of 100 Amazon Rivers. 'It's similar in magnitude to all the planet's rainfall. The amount of heat carried by the Conveyor's northward-flowing upper limb and released to the atmosphere is equal to about 25% of the solar energy reaching the surface of the Atlantic north of the Straits of Gibraltar' he says. Hence its massive effect on Europe's climate.

If global warming prevented the Gulf Stream from cooling sufficiently to sink, its flow would stop. This seems to have happened about 8000 years ago when, it is suspected, fresh water from melting ice in Canada flowed into the Atlantic and, by making the water in the Gulf Stream less salty for about 400 years, caused a mini ice age.

Certainly, the last Ice Age proper started so suddenly it was almost as if something had been turned off. An analysis of pollen deposits in France shows that the switch from a warm inter-glacial climate to tundra conditions in which it was too cold for fruit and nut trees to grow took less than twenty years. The end of that Ice Age was very rapid too. Ice core samples from Greenland show that there was a 5-10ºC rise in temperature in the space of twenty years. Was this the Gulf Stream starting up again?

While they accept that the Earth's climate can flip in a matter of years from one stable regime to another, very different one, most authorities fear that, rather than cooling, the flip might take the form of a rapid warming which would continue until some new balance between heat inflow from the sun and outflow to space was reached. In November 1998 the British Government's Hadley Centre for Climate Prediction and Research issued a set of projections[2] which showed that if nothing was done to restrict fossil fuel consumption, the rate at which the world warmed would accelerate. Average world land temperatures, which have risen by almost 20C since 1900 would soar by a further 3°C over the next fifty years, the report said. This would be the most significant change in the global climate since the end of the last ice age.[3]

The warming would not be uniform, however. Increases around the poles would be much greater than at the Equator, with northern Russia, northern Canada and Greenland acquiring average temperatures some 6-8° C above their current level. Naturally, a lot of snow and ice would melt and the resulting water, coupled with the thermal expansion of the warming seas, would cause sea levels to rise by four inches. Unless massive defences were built, this rise would put

TO SUDDEN, RAPID CHANGE

some 78 million people at risk of annual flooding compared with 10 million in 1990. Indeed, this figure is almost certainly a gross underestimate because the model which produced it does not allow for any increase in the number or ferocity of storms.

Although the warming would allow trees in the northern hemisphere to grow closer to the pole and thus take in extra carbon dioxide from the air, forests would contract elsewhere and release greenhouse gases as they rotted or burned. Quite soon, the rate at which forests in one place were releasing CO_2 would outweigh the rate of CO_2 absorption in others. 'Tropical forests will die back in many areas of northern Brazil. In other areas of the world, tropical grasslands will be transformed into desert or temperate grassland' the Hadley report said. 'After 2050, as a result of vegetation dieback and change, the terrestrial land surface becomes a source of carbon releasing approximately [10 billion tonnes of CO_2] into the atmosphere [each year].' Although this release rate is equivalent to a third of current emission levels and would consequently accelerate warming, the report says that the feedback 'is not yet included in climate models.'

A second positive feedback was also left out of the Hadley model because too little is known about it. Huge quantities of methane—a much more powerful greenhouse gas than CO_2—are stored on the seabed and in permafrost, the permanently frozen earth which covers at least a fifth of the planet. The gas is combined with water or ice to form a solid called methane gas hydrate. 'Rising temperatures destabilise the hydrate and cause the emission of methane' Euan Nisbet of Royal Holloway College, University of London, writes in his book[4] **Leaving Eden**.

'One of the nightmares of climatologists is that the liberation of methane from permafrost will enhance the Arctic warming because of the greenhouse effect of the methane, and so induce further release of methane and thus increased warming, in a runaway feedback cycle.' He fears that warming will also release methane from hydrate in shallow Arctic seas. 'Any slight warming of the Arctic water will release hydrate from the sea floor sediments almost immediately' he writes.[5] 'The danger of a thermal runaway caused by methane release from permafrost is minor but real... The social implications are profound.'

Several other potentially damaging feedbacks were also omitted from the Hadley study. One is that as oceans warm, they become less capable of absorbing carbon dioxide which therefore builds up in the air more rapidly. A second is that changes in the chemistry of the upper air will affect the rate at which methane—which is relatively short-lived in the atmosphere at present—gets broken down. Taken together, these four effects can only mean that there is a significant risk that warming will spiral out of control during the next half-century unless greenhouse emissions are drastically reduced before then.

NOTES
1 **Science**, no.278: pp.1582-8, 1997
2 A summary of the results is available at http://www.meto.govt.uk/sec5/CR_div/Broc hure98/index.html
3 Background Brief, Conference of the Parties 4, UN Framework Convention on Climate Change, Buenos Aires, November 2, 1998.
4 E.G. Nisbet, **Leaving Eden: To protect and manage the Earth**, Cambridge University Press, Cambridge, 1991, pp.65-6.
5 E. Nisbet, Climate change and methane, **Nature**, vol. 347, September 1990, p.23.

But what currency would the fossil-fuel-hungry countries use to buy their extra emissions permits? I put this question to Richard Douthwaite on the telephone about three years ago and he immediately said that, if reserve currencies like US dollars, Euros, Sterling and Yen were used, the countries which issued those currencies would get their extra permits at a discount. This was because a proportion of the money they paid over would not be returned to them in payment for their exports but would be used instead as if it was a world currency to finance international trade. Obviously, this would give these countries an unfair advantage over the rest of the world. Consequently, if C&C was to work fairly and well, it had to become even more radical. We had to extend it into the area of international monetary reform.

Richard put forward proposals for doing so in his Schumacher Briefing, *The Ecology of Money* which was published in October 1999. He suggested that an international agency be set up to handle two things. One was the allocation and issue of greenhouse gas emissions permits he called Special Emission Rights or SERs according to the C&C formula. The other was a new global currency which would be used for trading SERs internationally. This he called the ebcu, an acronym for emissions-backed currency unit.

Ebcus would get into circulation by being distributed, free, to the nations of the world on the basis of their populations, just as everyone gets the same allocation of cash when they start a game of Monopoly. Richard wants ebcus to be used for all international trade, not just the purchase of SERs, and thinks that a majority of countries might be prepared to insist on payment in ebcu to avoid giving the countries with reserve currencies a permanent trading advantage. If, after

trading with ebcus began, the price of an SER in ebcu rose above a certain figure, the issuing agency (IA) would sell more SERs for ebcus, thus putting a ceiling on their price. The ebcus the IA received for the sale would be permanently removed from circulation. This would reduce the number in use, restricting the amount of international trade it was possible to carry on, and thus the world demand for fossil fuels. In other words, the system automatically restricts the level of international economic activity to one which is compatible with bringing greenhouse gas emissions down along the internationally-agreed trajectory so as to keep the atmospheric concentration below the agreed target. On the other hand, if humanity learns to manage with less fossil energy, there's no barrier to the amount of trade going up.

The next step came in October 2000 when I spent ten days in Westport with Richard working on my Schumacher Briefing on C&C. A lot of our time was spent discussing the apparent impossibility of getting the US actually to make even the totally-inadequate emissions reductions it had pledged under the Kyoto Protocol, let alone the savage cuts urgently required to reduce the risk of a catastrophic climate change. It was vitally important that the US should not be allowed to block action by other countries.

The inclusion of the ebcu proposals in the C&C package would make it very attractive to most nations in the Majority World (MW) as it would give them emissions permits to sell each year and also an initial allocation of the new world currency which would go a long way to clearing their debts. However, it would be very unpopular with the US, which would not only have to buy emissions permits every year but which would also lose the advantages given it by the power of the dollar. The main OPEC countries would oppose the system too, as making it necessary for oil companies to buy emissions permits before they could take delivery of oil or gas would mean that they could afford to pay less for the fuel. The cost of the emissions permits would come straight out of the fossil energy producers' pockets. Some fossil energy-producing countries might be in an intermediate position, though—they might lose oil revenue but gain from the sale of permits. Overall, it might be possible to get a majority of countries to give their support for going ahead.

This idea that a part-world, let's-ignore-the-US-and-go-ahead-anyway solution might be practical developed quickly. The Dutch alternative news-magazine *Ode* had called a conference on international monetary reform in early December, billing it as an attempt to produce a Bretton Woods agreement (the agreement under which the World Bank and the IMF were set up) for the twenty-

first century. It had even booked a five-star hotel at Noordwijk aan Zee with the same style and ambience as the hotel on the other side of the Atlantic used in 1944 by the original Bretton Woods negotiators. Richard had been invited to speak, others in the Feasta network were going to be involved and he thought the organisers would invite me too. It seemed a great chance to give the C&C plus monetary reform package an airing.

As over two years' preparatory work preceded the original Bretton Woods agreement, Richard thought we'd better prepare a draft treaty to take with us. I was tied up in the climate negotiations at The Hague, so, with the help of other Feasta members and particularly John Jopling and James Bruges, he drew up the following document which spells out in some detail how a more sustainable climate and monetary regime might be achieved. The explanatory comments are part of the original paper.

the treaty of Noordwijk

FEASTA'S DISCUSSION DRAFT

Preamble

The world economy is not working well. Its over-use of the Earth's resources threatens the stability of the climate and is causing the fastest rate of species extinction since the disappearance of the dinosaurs. Moreover, fisheries and forests are being destroyed by over-exploitation, aquifers pumped out and soils eroded with little thought for the consequences. The natural capital on which future generations will depend is being rapidly lost.

Yet despite the economy's profligate and increasing rate of resource use, the majority of humanity still lives in dire poverty and the gap between rich and poor is growing. In 1997, the richest fifth of the world's population enjoyed 74 times the income of the poorest fifth, up from 60 times in 1990 and 30 times in 1960.

The poverty has serious consequences. Dirty water and bad sanitation enable cholera and diarrhoea to kill three million of the poor a year. Indoor air pollution, mainly from cooking stoves, causes two million deaths. Vector-borne diseases such as malaria kill another 800,000. And urban air pollution and agri-chemicals, the results of the way our economic system has developed, are also major killers. In all, roughly a fifth of all disease in poor countries is caused by factors which could be readily changed if a relatively small amount of resources were switched from other uses.

Even if we were to disregard its damaging effects on the environment and on the lives of millions of people, the world economy has to be considered dysfunctional in its own terms because of its fundamental instability. It is widely accepted that something as simple as a stock market crash could cause it to break down catastrophically and plunge the world into a depression comparable or worse than that in the 1930s. Moreover, a national economy can be ruined almost overnight by speculative money flows, as Mexico's was in 1994.

All these problems are due in large part to faults built into the present global economic system when it was set up at Bretton Woods in 1944. At that time, in response to overwhelming pressure from the United States, mechanisms designed to redress the balance between countries with trade surpluses and those with trade deficits were left out. Consequently, the problems the system produces cannot be solved until it is replaced or radically changed.

Designed to allow the world economy to move towards the goals of sustainability, stability and equity, the Treaty of Noordwijk would, if ratified on behalf of a majority of the world's people, bring about most of the reforms required to alleviate the above problems. In particular it would:

- Put a genuine world currency into circulation for the first time.
- Limit the level of global economic activity to the maximum compatible with the Earth's environmental health.
- Bring about a fairer distribution of the Earth's resources.
- End most Third World debt.
- Provide annual funding for improved health, educational and social services.
- Give national governments more power over international investors and speculative currency movements.
- Remove the necessity for countries to achieve economic growth purely to avoid financial collapse in circumstances in which the growth is known to be environmentally and socially damaging.
- Make national economies much more stable.
- Allow countries to move towards sustainability as rapidly as they would wish rather than the pace of the slowest.
- Remove the unfair built-in advantages enjoyed by countries issuing 'hard' currencies in the present global financial system.

CLAUSE 1 We, the parties hereinafter subscribed, resolve to set up a new international institution, the Issuing Authority, to issue and manage a global currency on behalf of us all.

Comment: A world currency is necessary in the interests of international equity. Because there is no global currency at present, the countries which issue 'hard' currencies such as the dollar, the pound sterling, the Euro, the yen and the Swiss franc all benefit very considerably from having their monies used as global money substitutes. Their benefits arise because the central banks in third countries keep their currencies in their foreign exchange reserves, effectively giving them an interest-free loan of the goods and services which were supplied to earn the money in the first place. The US is the major beneficiary—at the end of 1999, the dollar accounted for 66% of global foreign exchange reserves according to the IMF. In addition, billions of dollars are held offshore by non-US banks and lent as Eurodollars to non-US customers. In addition, many billions are used for international trade transactions not involving the US, for purchases in 'dollar shops' or are hoarded by their holders for fear their national currency will collapse or civil disturbances will break out. These vast holdings explain in part why the US has been able to run a balance of payments deficit on its current account for many years. What this means is that the US has been able to purchase a much greater value of goods and services from the rest of the world than it has supplied.

CLAUSE 2 The Issuing Authority will be controlled by a board of directors elected by a representative of each of the subscribing states. Each representative will be deemed to hold a proxy on behalf of each citizen of the country he or she represents.

Comment: This clause means that populous countries will have a greater say in choosing the members of the board of the IA than countries with small populations. Once elected, the directors will be able to act independently of the countries which voted for them—they will not represent any specific bloc or part of the world. This will be quite unlike the situation in the World Bank and the IMF in which almost half of all the votes are controlled by the seven leading Western industrial countries with the result that the institutions are run to further the industrialised countries' interests.

CLAUSE 3 We further resolve that the Issuing Authority be responsible for issuing carbon dioxide emission rights to an Approved Organisation in each subscribing state in accordance with the broad principles of Contraction and Convergence.

Comment: If global warming is to be curtailed, the international community is going to have to agree a generally-acceptable framework for doing so. The only framework being widely discussed at present is Contraction and Convergence. This involves setting a target for the maximum level of greenhouse gases such as CO_2 in the atmosphere and then working out by how much the current level of emissions needs to be cut annually so that the target is kept. Then, having set each year's emissions quota in this way, the current year's allocation is shared out among the nations of the world according to the size of their population in a base year— say 1990. Those countries which don't receive enough emissions permits to be able to consume as much fossil energy as they would like can then purchase permits to emit more greenhouse gases from countries such as India which currently use very little fossil energy per inhabitant. Every year there would be a new issue of emissions permits in line with the pre-determined, declining quota for that year. This system would not only ensure that the target level of greenhouse gases in the atmosphere was not exceeded but would also shift purchasing power from countries which have become rich by their over-use of fossil energy to poorer parts of the world.

CLAUSE 4 At the same time as the first year's issue of carbon dioxide emission permits is made, the Issuing Authority will distribute the new global currency to the central banks of the subscribing states on the same population-related basis as the permits. The subscribing states undertake to use the new money for trading in emissions permits and for all other international transactions.

Comment: For the reasons already explained, if those countries with widely-acceptable currencies were able to use them to buy extra emissions permits, they would effectively be getting a discount on their purchases because a large fraction of the money they paid over would go into circulation as if it was world currency and not be presented back to the wealthy issuing country in payment for goods and services bought by the poorer country.

The new currency is intended to be used for all international transactions, not just those involving emissions permits. The IA will not be able to stop private traders using, say, dollars, for a transaction not involving the US, but all countries should be encouraged to feel that it is wrong to continue to use another country's currency for transactions not involving that country as it gives an unfair international advantage to the country whose currency is used.

The issue of the global currency will mean that countries which hold dollars and other convertible currencies will no longer need them in their foreign exchange reserves, for general international trading and for hoarding—the new money will be available for these jobs instead.. They will consequently be able to use their hard currency holdings to pay off their foreign debts. If they have too little hard currency to get out of debt entirely, they will be able to buy additional hard currency with part of their global currency allocation.. This is likely to release most poor countries from all their external debt problems. Any surplus global currency should be regarded as capital and used for development projects.

CLAUSE 5 The Issuing Authority will undertake to sell more emissions permits whenever their price in terms of the world currency, which is to be called the ebcu (Emissions-Backed Currency Unit), rises above a specified level. Equally, if the price of permits falls below the specified level having once achieved it, the IA will either put more ebcus into circulation on the same per capita basis as they were originally issued or reduce the supply of emissions permits in the next annual allocation.

Comment: This mechanism fixes the value of the global currency in terms of emissions permits. It also controls the total amount of activity that it is possible to carry on within the world economy. The Quantity Theory of Money states that the amount of money available determines the number of transactions it is possible to carry out in an economic system at any given price level if the speed at which money passes from hand to hand stays constant. Thus, if the level of economic activity in the world economy is so high that additional fossil energy is required to fuel it and the demand for this extra fuel drives the price of emissions permits up above the specified level, the IA will sell additional permits and remove the ebcus it receives in payment for them from circulation. This reduction in the world's money supply would reduce the level of activity in the global economy and thus the demand for fossil energy, causing the price of permits to fall back. Similarly, if the price of permits fell, either the level of activity in the world economy would be too low (in which case mass unemployment would be evident) or humanity would have been so successful in developing non-fossil energy sources that the demand for fossil fuel had dropped. In the latter case, the IA should reduce the quota of permits it distributes the following year in order to accelerate the fall in greenhouse emissions and achieve a lower, safer maximum concentration of greenhouse gases in the atmosphere. In the former case, just enough extra ebcus should be issued to alleviate extreme hardship.

CLAUSE 6 The Approved Organisations to which the IA will issue emissions permits will be independent national trusts set up specifically to handle emissions permits on behalf of the individuals entitled to them. Each subscribing state undertakes to submit for the IA's approval proposals for the means by which the trustees of its trust will be chosen. We understand that no trust will become an Approved Organisation unless it is clear that its trustees are independent of government and can act independently of it. Subscribing states grant the IA the power to cease to issue permits to any AO which it believes has not handled previous issues of permits and/or the revenue from them in the best interests of the beneficiaries.

Comment: One of the problems with any system which involves the flow of a great deal of valuable property to any country is that the ruling élite may take most of it for itself, or use it to further its political or military ambitions. Consequently, just as the World Bank and the IMF have the power to refuse to lend to governments with policies they dislike, so the IA must have the power to see that each person in whose name an emissions allowance has been issued actually benefits from it. Generally, each trust will auction its allocation of permits and then decide how to spend the national currency it receives for them in the best interests of the people of the country concerned.

For example, as transport, water and sanitary services, health care and education are more effectively provided on a collective rather than an individual basis, a trust might choose to allocate part of its income to those directly, rather than giving all the money to the people in whose name they hold it so that they can buy these services independently. A trust might also favour operating old age pensions and children's allowances rather than giving a flat basic income to everyone, as everyone would be able to benefit from these at some time in their lives. Trusts might also make funds available for the rapid development of renewable energy sources, in order to prevent general hardship by keeping energy prices down. However, as cost structures will change considerably as the use of fossil fuel becomes much more expensive, the first duty of most trusts will be to ensure that the very poor do not suffer from the changes. They will consequently have to distribute a proportion of their income directly to those in whose name they hold it, possibly as a citizens' income.

While the trusts will sell their allocations of emissions permits for their national currency, they need not necessarily (and perhaps should not because of the risk of corruption) restrict the bidders to their own citizens. Foreigners whose bids are accepted will have to pay in ebcu, and these sales will fix the exchange rate between the ebcu and the national currency.

CLAUSE 7 The subscribing states undertake to have two national currencies, one for trading and the other for savings, in operation within five years from the date of ratification of this treaty. They agree to set each currency up so that it has its own external exchange rate which they will allow to move in such a way that inflows and outflows to and from the relevant account balance from month to month.

Comment: The reason that speculative and/or investment capital flows can be so damaging is that they alter the exchange rate which applies to imports and exports. This is because when investment funds, foreign loans or hot money flow into a country, their conversion out of foreign currency into the national one increases the demand for the national currency above what it would otherwise be and thus lifts its value in terms of the foreign currency. This, in turn, makes imports cheaper and means that exporters earn less. In other words, inward capital flows damage domestic producers and favour foreign ones. This means that if capital subsequently begins to flow in the other direction, the country is less able to manage on its home production and its export earnings than it would have been if the capital inflow had not taken place because its home producers and exporters have been undermined. Moreover, if interest rates are raised to try to stem the outflow—as happened in Mexico—every company with any debts at all will see its profits fall because of the additional interest it has to pay on its borrowings. Some companies may be driven out of business altogether.

The solution to this problem is to keep capital flows and import-and-export money flows completely apart. This was the usual practice in most countries until the Bretton Woods system was destroyed by President Nixon in 1971 when he removed its basis by unilaterally deciding that the US would no longer sell gold at $35 an ounce. In the aftermath, when countries abandoned the fixed exchange rates they had had with the dollar and allowed the value of their currencies to float, they mistakenly saw no need to keep current and capital flows separate.

The maintenance of separate exchange rates for the two types of money flow means that the value of a country's exports will always equal the value of its imports and also that there will be no net flow of capital into or out of the country. It will, of course, be possible for people to move their capital abroad, but only by exchanging it, through the market, with people wishing to move their capital the other way. This provision would completely halt short-term speculative flows and remove the need for a Tobin-type tax. It would also give governments much more power as, if the markets did not like their policies, the only effect would be to alter the exchange rate on the capital account. There would be no crisis. The system would be very stable.

Separating the two flows and having differing exchange rates for each essentially means that a country gets two types of money, each with a different function. One would be exchange money, used solely for buying and selling. This would be the money to be spent into circulation by the government as described in Clause 8. The other type would be the money in which one's savings were kept. This second currency would be expected to keep, or increase, its value relative to the exchange currency over the years. Its existence would mean that a government would not have to worry too much if the exchange currency lost a little of its value each year from inflation because it had chosen to keep plenty of exchange money in circulation to ensure that there was plenty of work.

The two currencies would be linked as follows: Supposing you wanted to buy a capital asset, such as a block of shares or a house. You would take your exchange money, the sort in which you would get your pay, and buy savings money to use for the asset purchases. This savings money would come, via a broker, from someone who had sold some of their capital assets and was wanting to get hold of exchange money to pay for living expenses. The exchange rate between exchange money and savings money would be fixed by the market. If a lot of people wanted to save and fewer people wanted to cash in their savings, then more exchange money would have to be offered for the savings money.

If you wished to buy shares or a house overseas, you would buy savings money with your exchange money, and then use your savings money to buy savings money in the country in which you wanted to invest. If ever you wanted to sell up abroad, the steps would be reversed.

All this might sound very complex the first time it is encountered. In practice, however, it would be easy to carry out and, by ensuring stability and enabling national economies to run at their maximum capacity consistent with keeping greenhouse gas emissions below the global target, bring many benefits.

CLAUSE 8 For reasons of national and international financial stability, the sub-scribing states undertake to issue their national trading currencies by spending them into circulation themselves rather than by allowing their commercial banks to create these currencies by lending them into use.

Comment: Of all the money we use, only the notes and coins are issued by the government through its central bank. The rest—the money we transfer when we write a cheque, authorise a direct debit or use a credit or debit card—is created by the commercial banking system and only exists because someone has borrowed it and is paying interest on it. As notes and coins are now mostly used just for minor transactions, 97% of the money in use in a typical industrialised country has been created by someone going into debt. This makes the financial system very unstable because, if people begin to feel a little uncertain about their economic future, they will not be prepared to take out as many new loans as they did, in total, in the equivalent period the previous year. As the earlier loans are being repaid, the fact that the total value of new loans has fallen means that less money is being put into circulation than is being taken out by the repayment of loans and the payment of the interest due on them. In other words, the amount of money in circulation will contract and, as we have already seen, the Quantity Theory of Money suggests that, unless prices fall or the smaller amount of money is passed from hand to hand faster, the amount of trading carried out in the economy will contract.

The lower level of trading will cut business profits and these will be further reduced because the stock of money available to be divided up amongst firms at the end of a year is lower. The lower profits and tougher business conditions will make people even more reluctant to borrow, causing a further contraction in the money supply, which in turn will deter more borrowing. The economy will enter a downward spiral and end in a severe depression. This explains why governments are so keen to ensure that economic growth continues year after year, even though it might be damaging the environment and society. In the present system, growth is necessary to ensure that enough borrowing goes on to prevent the money supply contracting and causing a slump.

Allowing the commercial banks to create most of a country's money and charge interest on it gives a massive, distorting subsidy to this part of the financial system. The alternative is for the

PROPOSED WORLD CURRENCY SYSTEM

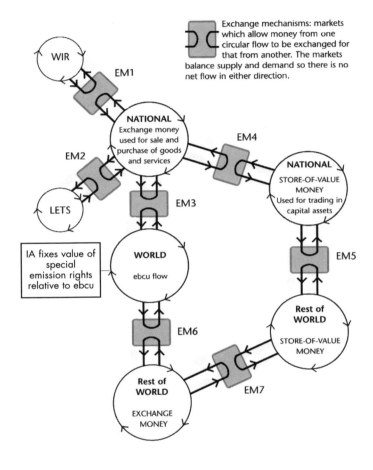

Exchange mechanisms: markets which allow money from one circular flow to be exchanged for that from another. The markets balance supply and demand so there is no net flow in either direction.

WIR

EM1

NATIONAL
Exchange money used for sale and purchase of goods and services

EM2

EM4

LETS

EM3

NATIONAL
STORE-OF-VALUE MONEY
Used for trading in capital assets

IA fixes value of special emission rights relative to ebcu

WORLD
ebcu flow

EM5

EM6

Rest of WORLD
STORE-OF-VALUE MONEY

Rest of WORLD
EXCHANGE MONEY

EM7

EM1: Allows people with earnings in a Wirtschaftsring-type system to exchange them for the national exchange currency, and vice-versa

EM2: Allows members of a LETS to exchange their units for the national exchange currency, and vice versa.

EM3: Ensures that flows of money from imports and exports balance each other. Ebcus from exports and the sale of SERs are exchanged for units of the national exchange currency which people provide in payment for imports and the purchase of SERs.

EM4: Allows people with exchange money they wish to save to swap it for store of value money provided by people who need to spend their savings or who have taken out a loan repayable in over twelve months.

EM5: Balances capital flows (which are in the store-of-value currency) into and out of the country.

EM6: is a composite of all the EM3-type exchanges operated by the rest of the world.

EM7: Balances the flow of money into savings with the flow of money out of savings for the rest of the world.

IA: The Issuing Authority provides the only fixed point in the system. If ever the price of an SER in terms of ebcu rises beyond a certain point as a result of exchanges between countries, the IA will supply SERs and reduce the world's ebcu stock.

This is how the multi-currency system proposed in the Feasta Noordwijk Treaty would work. All seven exchange mechanisms balance supply and demand by altering the relative price of the pair of currencies being exchanged through them. There is therefore no net movement of currency from one circular flow to another.

government to spend the required amount of money into circulation itself. In an expanding economy, this would allow taxes to be reduced or the level of government services increased. More importantly, by making the amount of money in circulation much more stable, it would make the level of economic activity much more stable too. If the government found that the economy was slowing down and unemployment was developing, it could issue more money to itself and spend it into use. This spending would create additional jobs not only directly but also because the additional money supply would enable an increased amount of trading to go on. On the other hand, if it put too much money into circulation so that a rapid inflation developed, it could easily correct the situation by putting up taxes and withdrawing the money from use. This would be a much more effective way of controlling the money supply than the present one which involves increasing the interest rate so that people are deterred from borrowing. The drawback with this as a control method is that raising the rate of interest raises the price of the money which businesses have already borrowed. This is itself inflationary as it adds to business costs and, naturally, firms try to recover their higher costs by charging higher prices. As a result, quite high, and therefore damaging, increases in interest rates are often required to keep prices steady under the present regime.

CLAUSE 9 Subscribing states undertake not to trade with, lend to, or borrow from, non-subscriber states except on terms approved by the IA. They grant the IA the right to suspend the issue of emissions permits to Approved Organisations if the state which the AO serves allows trading with non-subscriber states without the consent of the IA or, if IA consent has been given, on terms not approved by the IA. In cases in which a subscribing state's actions are seriously undermining the interests of other subscribers, they grant the IA the right to delete the state's name from the list of subscribers.

Comment: This clause is to deter Free Riders. A few industrial countries are likely to consider staying outside the global currency/ghg emissions control system in order to subsidise their production of goods and service by using fossil fuel for which emissions permits have not been purchased. This would give their exports a cost advantage over countries inside the global system if they were allowed to trade freely with them. Consequently, in order to prevent the global system from being undermined, countries within it have to be able to protect themselves against this type of unfair competition. If these powers enable the IA to stop subscribing states from trading with non-subscribers except on terms which it approves, the risks of the system failing are much reduced.

In practice, the IA is likely to require those importing goods from non-subscribing states to buy emissions permits to cover the emissions the production of the imports generated. The same system would work in reverse—exporters to non-subscribers would be given emissions permits to cover the fossil energy their products required to make. However, exports to non-subscribing states are likely to be small in the early years of the system as the importing countries will be required to pay in ebcus for them and they will be earning very few ebcus because the policy of the subscribing states will be to spend their stocks of now-redundant dollars and other convertible currencies for their imports and only use ebcus once these have gone.

CLAUSE 10 Subscribing states undertake to allow their national trading currencies to be supplemented by regional and local trading currencies. They agree to encourage regional and local governments to accept the payment of regional and local taxes in supplementary currencies which meet specified standards.

Comment: Under the Noordwijk system, governments will cease to have their economies' rate of economic growth as their primary concern. Instead, they will give priority to ensuring that as much economic activity is carried on as is possible within the greenhouse gas emissions allocation. If they put a lot of exchange money into circulation in an attempt to reduce unemployment in peripheral or rural areas, they are likely to find that an excessive amount of money gets into circulation in the more prosperous areas and that this raises the demand for energy there, causing the exchange rate of their exchange currency to fall in relation to the ebcu. Consequently, a better way of ensuring that all areas of a country are as economically active as their inhabitants wish to be is to encourage the development of regional and local currencies in the poorer areas as these would allow local trading to be carried on even if the national currency was scarce. The local currencies would have their own variable exchange rates with the national currency. As a result, their issue and circulation would not affect the exchange rate of the national currency with the ebcu except to the extent that more fossil energy was used by the extra activity they generated..

It has frequently been pointed out that if the North of England had had its own currency in the 1980s rather than using sterling, its shipyards, factories and mines would not have been as badly affected as they were by the high value of the pound brought about by the flow of money from North Sea oil and the earnings of the City of London. Similarly, the former East Germany was badly affected by the one-for-one exchange rate chosen for the Ost mark against the Deutschmark. The introduction of regional currencies would prevent these problems and end the social hardship which results from the one-currency-suits-all approach to money matters.

CLAUSE 11 This Treaty will come into force when it has been ratified by subscribing states whose total population comprises more than half the population of the world.

SUMMARY
The Treaty of Noordwijk will bring an end to an extraordinary period in the his-

tory of humanity in which groups of people, their productivity enhanced by their excessive use of fossil fuel, used the wealth that their high productivity brought them to purchase whatever they wanted from the rest of the world without regard for the sustainability of what they were doing or for the effect they were having on those living in a more sustainable way.

In addition, the Treaty will end a period in which economic growth had to be generated without regard for whether or not it was proving beneficial purely to keep the economic system from immediate collapse. Such growth puts unnecessary pressure on the environment and denies resources to people whose need for them is acute.

The Treaty will bring about circumstances in which each nation, released from most international and internal debt, will have the freedom to work towards environmental and social sustainability as rapidly as it wishes without regard for international investors or its competitive situation and without having to limit itself either to the pace of the slowest country or the maximum made possible by international negotiations.

In short, the Treaty, if ratified, will bring about a more equitable, stable and sustainable future for all of humankind.

The *Ode* conference itself was a wash-out although the company was enjoyable and the hotel was fine. The problem was that only six or seven people of the 150-plus present actually knew anything about money systems and the way they work, let alone the climate crisis. Consequently, the first draft of the 'official' statement of what had been agreed at the meeting had no mention of money at all. Richard and Bernard Lietaer, the former Belgian cen-

tral banker and currency reformer, protested about this (I'd gone up to my room to play my violin out of sheer frustration) but were fiercely opposed by Mickey Huibregsten of McKinsey Netherlands, the international consultants, who, for some reason we failed to discover, had been made responsible for assembling the statement. 'We have to leave specific techniques out of this', 'We can't sign something we don't understand' and 'There's uncertainty about climate change' are some of the phrases I'm told Huibregsten used. The document he produced was so bland and toothless as to be a complete waste of time.

Nevertheless, the effort put into assembling the draft 'treaty' wasn't wasted. It has been widely circulated and discussed on the internet where it is called 'The Feasta Noordwijk Treaty' to distinguish it from Huibregsten's work.

The challenge now is to assemble a group of nations which will put it, or something very similar, into effect. It matters very much which countries join the system and which don't. If only those countries which expect to have a surplus of permits to sell in the first few years join, the system won't work as there will be no 'over-consumers' in the market to buy permits although a small demand could be created by requiring firms importing from the over-consuming bloc to buy permits to cover the amount of fossil energy used to make whatever goods and services they are bringing in.

To make the market for permits work properly in the absence of an all-world membership, the number of permits issued by the IA would have to be reduced by the number the non-participants could have been expected to buy had they joined. Obviously, this cuts the benefits to those with permits to sell, so it is crucial to get some overconsumers— the Europeans, for example—to join the system too, perhaps on the understanding that a lot of the orders currently going to the US and other countries which stay out will be switched to them. The more overconsumers joining, the greater the financial flow to the Majority World (MW) and the bigger the market the MW will be able to provide for industrialised country exporters.

If the MW refused to sell raw materials and manufactures to overconsumers

unless they joined the system, it would put irresistible pressure on many to do so. The MW states would have the freedom to refuse to sell as most of their debts to the overconsuming bloc would have been cut sharply when ebcus began to be used for all inter-MW trade and freed up the reserve currencies currently used for inter-MW trading for debt repayment. Moreover, the MW could make the threat without causing itself unemployment to the extent that demand in the MW rose because more money was in circulation and the MW countries needed more resources themselves.

If the MW were unhappy about a total refusal to sell to over-consuming non-members, they could merely say to the US and similar countries: 'We don't need your dollars any more. We'll only sell to you if you pay us in ebcu'. This would mean that the US had to earn ebcu before it could import. It could only do this by exporting to the MW and, before its exports could clear customs, the importers would have to buy emissions permits to cover the energy taken to make them so that the US did not gain a competitive advantage from being outside the system.

So where do we go from here? As the last few paragraphs show, the feasibility of introducing the C&C plus monetary reform package on a piecemeal basis depends entirely on which countries sign up for it and the policies they adopt towards non-participants. It would be very nice to produce a model which predicted the outcomes for each country according to whatever other countries were involved, and I'm currently looking for volunteers to undertake that work.

The modelling results will be essential for the other strand I'm following. This is to talk to various MW governments to try to interest them in the idea of not only attempting to avert a damaging change in the world's climate but also bringing about a more equitable distribution of the world's wealth. If some charismatic MW leader—perhaps Dr. Mahatir of Malaysia, who, during the Asian Crisis, saved his country from economic ruin by going against the West's advice and introducing currency controls—took up the C&C plus monetary reform package and promoted it, the chances of building a more sustainable world would soar.

I'm confident that I'll find some government to take on the idea given the reaction of the 99 nations who met in Shanghai in January 2001 to consider *Climate Change 2001: The Scientific Basis*, the scientific part of the Intergovernmental Panel on Climate Change's latest assessment of the climate crisis. The sig-

nificance of *Climate Change 2001* is that whereas five years ago the same scientific group forecast a rise in temperatures of between 1 and 3.5°C over the next 100 years, its latest forecast is for a rise of between 1.4 and 5.8°C. The group now expects sea levels to rise anywhere between 3.5 and 34 inches in the same period. The difference between the high and low temperature and sea-level estimates represents uncertainty about the pace of the changes, which the report calls 'potentially devastating'.

So how did the 99 nations react to the report after a line-by-line consideration? They accepted it unanimously. This gives me hope that it might be possible to build a consortium of countries prepared to take determined action in the near future.

BOOK REVIEWS

misleading us or deluding themselves ?

MALCOLM SLESSER

Natural Capitalism–the next industrial revolution
Paul Hawken, Amory B. Lovins, L. Hunter Lovins
Earthscan, London, 1999
ISBN 1-85383461-0, £18.99 (hb), £12.99 (pb) in UK.

Perhaps the most widely discussed recent book on the transition from a wasteful, unsustainable economic system to a more sustainable one is **Natural Capitalism**. Unfortunately, the book is deeply flawed because, like most US books of its type, it pretends that the transition will be so highly profitable that the market alone will bring it about and that government regulation and legislation are unnecessary. Moreover, it maintains this position despite an excellent chapter on the ways in which markets can fail.

According to the authors, David Brower, the American environmentalist and mountaineer, once proposed a user's manual for those buying an Earth. 'This planet has been delivered in perfect working condition, and cannot be replaced. Please don't adjust the thermostat or the atmosphere'. Those of us who do our environmental and resource sums know our Earth cannot continue along its present path of wasteful growth. This book lays out the upcoming problems in simple, accessible language. But so do many others. The difference is the claim that solutions are round the corner if we but adopt what the authors call 'Natural Capitalism– *the next industrial revolution*'. The question is whether this vision is real or imaginary.

This stimulating, informative and visionary book should be widely read. Regretfully, however, their faith in technology and social engineering should be taken with a pinch of salt, if not indeed with a health warning. The Lovins' (husband and ex-wife), if not co-author Paul Hawken, are well known for the optimism with which they propound solutions to environmental and resource issues. No one is more welcome at business seminars on the environment. They are Pangloss to Rabelais' cynicism.

The book is a vast, well-documented tapestry of anecdotes of how more service can be (or could be) got from less materials and energy. Like the star-studded night sky the book is a constellation of options that twinkle beguilingly at the reader, beautiful to behold, but without a clear structure. Much of the thesis in this book has already been expounded in an earlier work, *Factor Four*, written with Ernst von Weizsacher of the Wuppertal Institute in Germany.

In *Natural Capitalism* the authors expand the range of anecdotal information, gloss them with science, and extrapolate diminishing dollar costs into the distant future. In this rosy future there will be so much energy saving that oil will scarcely sell for $5 a barrel. To arrive at this state of affairs they make some heroic assumptions, and incur some thermodynamic howlers. How is the reader to interpret hyperbole like '*92% less energy use*' or '*100% saving*', or the claim that electricity from photo-voltaic devices is of '*higher quality*' (p. 97), or that '*combined cycle gas turbines are not subject to Carnot's Law*', or phrases like '*useful work extracted ... to more than 90% of the original fuel energy*'? One should not lightly buck the second law of thermodynamics, for no-one has yet succeeded. Amory Lovins has a degree in physics. He should know better.

Their technique is simple. Some recent technological developments are reported which can cut the energy and materials needs by (say) half. Then new ways of doing things can cut the need for that energy by a further half (half of a half equals a quarter). Then, since we have cut some inputs to a quarter, other economies follow in their train. This a very dangerous argument.

Over the next half-century, even if global economy expanded by 6—8 fold, the rate of releasing carbon by burning of fossil fuels could simultaneously decrease by anywhere from one third to nine-tenths below current rate. This is because of the multiplicative effect of four kinds of actions. Switching to natural gas and renewable energy, as fast as Shell Oil planners consider likely, would cut by one half to three quarters the fossil-fuel carbon in each unit of energy consumed. ... The efficiency of converting that energy into delivered forms, notably electricity, could meanwhile rise by at least half, thanks to modern power plants and recapturing waste heat. The efficiency of converting delivered energy into desired services would also increase by about 4-6 fold. [Why?, How?] Finally the amount of satisfaction derived from each unit of energy might perhaps be doubled by delivering higher-quality services and fewer unwanted ones.

The allure of this argument is indeed compelling for it banishes the doom and gloom merchants to their dismal cellars; but it is misleading, for there is one thing they have over-looked: human greed. The evidence is that when you get more from less, you just take advantage of the slack. Economists call this the 'rebound effect', and it is well documented. Is it significant that neither 'rebound effect' nor 'thermodynamics' appear in the index of a book that is astonishingly rich in allusions to energy?

This critique may seem churlish when the environmental problem is so well put and where there are undeniable options for better material and energy use and waste recycle. Are the authors simply deceiving themselves? I think so, and in two ways. Firstly by using monetary measures to extrapolate into the future. Money is an abstraction that does not lend itself to longer term mensuration. Secondly, every single energy- and materials-reducing possibility impacts on the entire economy somewhere, somehow. These options needed to be tested through the medium of a holistic physically-based model of the economy. Only in this way can we get a feeling for the extent of the possibilities. Just to give an example: this reviewer was one of a team developing such a model for the European Union with members of the Wuppertal Institute who espoused not merely factor 4 but factor 10. However hard we tried, using their data, we could never achieve more than about a factor 2 reduction in input per unit output.

Let me close on some of the best aspects of this book. The authors offer an excellent critique of market and economic theory. The chapter 'Making Markets Work' lists 18 assumptions implicit in the theory of perfect markets, the cornerstone of economic modelling (p. 263). They deftly destroy them on the

in his own words...
AMORY LOVINS

Natural Capitalism describes what capitalism could be like if it behaved as if natural capital were properly valued. Natural capital is the living world that provides resources and ecosystem services, which we can neither replace nor live without. Ecosystem services are extremely valuable, but they're not on anyone's balance sheet, and they get inadvertently liquidated in pursuit of resources whose market value is recognized. But rather than spending decades arguing about how much money ecosystem services are worth, I think it makes more sense to behave as if we were properly valuing them, through operational principles that are profitable even now when natural capital is valued at zero. Our book explores, through hundreds of examples, four such principles that strongly reinforce each other.

The first principle is to use resources with radically greater productivity; to get ten to a hundred times as much work out of them through better technologies that provide the same or better services with more brains but less money. This substitution can dramatically reduce the half-trillion-ton-a-year flow of resources, from depletion to pollution, that is at the root of the degradation of natural systems.

New methods and designs often enable you to 'tunnel through the cost barrier' and make very large resource savings. Resource productivity can often achieve not diminishing but expanding returns. That's a surprise, but it's now well demonstrated in a wide range of technical systems and economic sectors.

The logic of increasing resource productivity is familiar because it's the same logic that led the first Industrial Revolution to make people a hundred times more productive. Economics teaches that you should economize on your scarcest resource because that's what limits progress. In those days, some 230 years ago, the relative scarcity of people was limiting progress in exploiting seemingly boundless nature. Today we have the opposite pattern of scarcity: we have abundant people and scarce nature. So it now makes sense to substitute abundant people for scarce nature—not the reverse, as we still seem prone to doing.

The second principle is to redesign production on biological lines with closed loops, no waste, and no toxicity. It is to design out anything that shouldn't be there, anything that isn't benign and valuable, any unsaleable production. This will yield better products at lower cost. It will transform everything that we produce into either a natural nutrient that goes to compost or a 'technical nutrient' that goes back to remanufacturing.

When you redesign production on biological principles you rely for raw materials less on what is dug up and more on what is grown. We should also be mimicking nature's very effective and life-friendly way of making things. Janine Benyus's book Biomimicry gives some great examples. That tree we're seeing outside the window turns sunlight, air, soil and water into a sugar called cellulose, as strong as nylon but several-fold lighter, and then it embeds the cellulose into a natural composite called wood, which is stiffer and stronger than steel, aluminium alloy or concrete. Yet the tree doesn't require smelters, blast furnaces or cement kilns. It works at ambient temperature in an elegantly frugal and beautiful way.

The third principle is to change the business model by switching from selling goods to delivering a continuous flow of service and value. And this should be done in a relationship that rewards both the provider and the customer for resource-saving and loop-closing. It's one of those radically simple ideas that, once you see it, makes a great deal of sense. For example, Ray Anderson, Chairman of Interface Corporation, realized that people don't want to own the carpet in their office; they just want to walk on it and look at it. So he started to lease a floor-covering service. His company owns what's on your floor. They're responsible for keeping it always fresh by replacing one-square-metre carpet tiles in the worn spots, which are only one-fifth of the whole carpet area. Interface can thus provide a better service with lower cost, higher profit, and more employment. Now the firm has designed a new product called Solenium that uses 35% less material per square metre and lasts for following page. They make a good argument for transferring taxes from labour to resources. It is a pity they don't record the pioneer work done here by the English engineer, Farel Bradbury, who invented the name UNITAX for this proposition, and who has led thinking in this area for the last twenty years.

The authors make the important point that economics does not and cannot value natural capital. But unfortunately they side-step the resolution of this important issue.

It is not the aim of this book to assess how to determine value for such unaccounted-for forms of capital. It is clear, however, that behaving as though they were valueless has brought us to the verge of disaster... Capital-

ism as practised, is a financially profitable, unsustainable aberration of human development. What might be called 'industrial capitalism' does not fully conform to its own accounting principles. It liquidates capital and calls it income. It neglects to assign any value to the largest stocks of capital it employs—natural resources...

We can but agree. Their preface states:

We believe the world stands at the threshold of basic changes in the conditions of business. Companies that ignore the message of natural capitalism do so at their peril....(We) show that the move towards radical resource produc-

tivity and natural capitalism is beginning to feel inevitable rather than merely possible... If at times we lean more to enthusiasm than reportage, it is because we can see the tremendous array of possibilities for healing the most intransigent problems of our time.

Well, this trend is inevitable, but let's be realistic about it.

MALCOLM SLESSER is the author of several books on environment, development and resources. He is the architect of the Natural Capital Accounting approach to macro-economic scenario analysis. He trained as a chemical engineer and set up the Energy Studies unit at the University of Strathclyde and became its first professor. He lives in Edinburgh.

---

twice as long. It is better in all respects for the customer, costs less to produce, has nothing toxic in it and can be completely remanufactured into an identical product. So when you combine that seven-fold reduction in material needs within the five-fold material-saving from the service leaser's replacing only the worn bits, you've got a 97% reduction in the flow of materials to maintain a superior floor-covering service at lower cost.

Such a business model as this is going to be very difficult to compete with. By switching to a service model and systematically wringing out waste even before the new product was released, Interface had doubled its revenue, trebled its profits and nearly doubled its employment. Its goal is to take nothing from the Earth and to put nothing harmful back into the environment. The new product cuts off the flow to the rubbish-tip by remanufacturing, and can even cut off the initial flow from the oil well by making the Solenium from a renewable carbohydrate. All that waste turns into profit. Interface does very well by doing good.

Other firms are excited and envious that Interface got there first. In one business after another we see the service-leasing model taking over. But remember, what's important here is not so much the form of the transaction—leasing a service instead of selling a product—but that the provider of the service and the customer for the service both get rewarded for doing more and better with less.

For example, if you lease a 'dissolving service' from Dow and they then repurify the solvent through more trips, their costs go down, their profits go up and they can also charge you less to get more market share. If they figure out a better way to degrease your parts in your factory, like not putting the grease on them in the first place, so that they need less or no solvent to yield clean parts, that's even better.

Similarly, if Carrier is leasing you a comfort service which makes its air-conditioners more efficient or more durable, they make more profit by providing better service at lower cost. If they then team up with other firms that can fix your building so that it needs little or no air-conditioning to provide better comfort, that's even better, because what you want is better comfort at lower cost. If they don't meet that need, their competitors will and they're out of the air-conditioning business. This way they're evolving toward continuously meeting your shifting value needs in the best way at the least cost. That's exactly where any business ought to be—shifting saved resources from a reduced revenue to a reduced cost. James Womack calls this concept, the 'Solutions Economy'.

The fourth principle is reinvesting in restoring, sustaining and expanding the stock of natural capital, as any prudent capitalist would do. That's the easiest step because God does the production; we just need to get out of the way and allow life to flourish wherever it can. As

more people choose fewer resources, this creates increasing business value.

Many ranchers in the American West are finding that new techniques of grazing management can yield a much richer and more diverse grass community and turn the range from desert back to real fertility. They graze more animals but in a different way that mimics the way that grass and grazers have historically coevolved.

This is why we are excited about Wes Jackson's work at the Land Institute. He is turning Great Plains agriculture back into something that looks very like a prairie. It's a perennial polyculture that needs no ploughing, feeding or spraying. You sit there and watch it grow and once in a while you harvest it, either mechanically or with ungulates, to taste. It's at least as productive as the very input-intensive hybrid cereals—and so it should be, because during 3.8 billion years of selection and experimentation whatever didn't work was recalled by the Manufacturer! The prairie is the most efficient way of durably using the sunlight available in that place. If there were a better way to do it, it would have been there already.

From an interview with Satish Kumar printed in **Resurgence** 198, January /February 2000. The full interview is at http://www.resurgence.org/.

three tiger sightings, but its stripes are in dispute

PEADAR KIRBY

The Making of the Celtic Tiger: The Inside Story of Ireland's Boom Economy
Ray Mac Sharry and Padraic White
Mercier, Cork, 2000
ISBN 1-856353-36-2, IR£12.99

The Celtic Tiger: Ireland's Continuing Economic Miracle
Paul Sweeney
Oak Tree Press, second edition, 1999
ISBN 1-860761-48-8, £14.95 in UK

Inside the Celtic Tiger: The Irish Economy and the Asian Model
Denis O'Hearn
Pluto Press, London, 1998
ISBN 0-745312-83-7, £13.99 in UK

Judging from the three books under review here, the battle for the meaning of the Celtic Tiger is well and truly under way. The most recent of the three, *The Making of the Celtic Tiger* by Ray Mac Sharry and Padraic White is, as one might expect from the Minister of Finance who introduced the austerity package in March 1987 from which the beginnings of Ireland's economic recovery is usually dated, and from the managing director of the Industrial Development Authority in 1981–90, a paean of praise to 'an economic transformation that none had predicted'. Paul Sweeney's *The Celtic Tiger*, in its second edition, acknowledges an apprehension that economic growth would falter or even crash as soon as the first edition was published in 1997 and seems more convinced than ever that the Irish economy entered a virtuous circle from 1987. He does, however, admit to 'unfinished business', most notably in tackling poverty and the housing crisis. Denis O'Hearn, alone among the three, casts a more critical eye on the Celtic Tiger phenomenon, and through a careful comparison with the East Asian Tigers, particularly

Singapore, raises some fundamental questions about its sustainability and its social impact.

The three books therefore are situated along a spectrum of meaning, from the uncritical, self-adulatory account of Mac Sharry and White at one end, to the highly critical analysis of O'Hearn at the other. Sweeney lies somewhere in between, seeing some of the darker sides of contemporary Ireland's development as challenges still to be met by the Celtic Tiger. A review of them therefore offers an opportunity to evaluate the meaning of this contested phenomenon and, in particular, to highlight and examine some of the major criticisms being raised.

Mac Sharry and White's account is by now a very familiar one. It sees recent Irish economic growth as marking 'a permanent structural shift in the level of Ireland's economic performance' (p.361) and marshals all the well-known reasons to explain it—consistent macro-economic management of the economy, investment in education, social partnership, EU structural funds combined with the fiscal discipline imposed by the Maastricht criteria and, of

course, very high levels of inward US investment. These are described at length without the slightest hint of any critical evaluation. The only valuable addition to what we already know only too well from dominant economistic accounts of the Celtic Tiger are the chapters on the IDA written by White. But again these are purely descriptive and it appears that the author has never allowed a doubt to enter his mind that the multinational route to industrialisation might have some drawbacks to it. This, then, is official Ireland's view of itself, which was clearly evident in the extensive and uncritical media attention which the book was given when published (including an adulatory full-page review in *The Irish Times* by the paper's editor).

Sweeney's account, while displaying an almost naïve sense of wonder at the high levels of economic growth achieved by Ireland since the early 1990s, does at least raise some critical questions. Central to these are questions about its sustainability and its social impact. Sweeney seems unsure whether poverty has increased or not during the period of economic growth (he makes both claims between pages 170 and 180 without apparently realising the contradiction) but he does admit that there has been 'no assault on poverty in the 1990s' (p.180). His remedy is to urge that 'the radical reduction of poverty and unemployment must become the priority to complete the Irish success story' (p.205) and believes that, with large budget surpluses, there has never been a better time to do this. Essentially, he seems to believe that poverty and inequality could be eradicated within Ireland's current economic model, if only the political will existed to do it.

Sweeney devotes chapter 8 to answering the question 'Will the Boom Continue?' and does so by examining what he sees as the eight main threats to the boom, such issues as the break-up of social partnership, bottlenecks in the economy, overdependency on a few products, disinvestment by the multinationals and a general downturn in the world economy. His conclusion, however, is optimistic; as he puts it:

Even a slowdown from the high rates of growth of recent years is likely to still be high by international standards [sic]. Many of the potential problems can be dealt with by the Irish themselves. Ireland's future looks good, for the first time in a very long time' (p 226).

Addressing specifically the question that Ireland's extreme dependence on multinational companies leaves it very vulnerable to these companies simply pulling out, Sweeney again takes an optimistic view arguing that state policy has succeeded in rooting the multinationals here. He also believes that the state's industrial policy is finally showing success in developing strong Irish companies, able to compete on international markets.

The problem with Sweeney is that his examination of the main

problems he identifies is far from thorough. In all cases, he seems to jump to optimistic conclusions on the basis of wishful thinking rather than marshalling any convincing evidence for his position. In some cases, the evidence he marshals seems to contradict his case. For example, he dismisses the view that states have been rendered more powerless in a globalised world economy and offers, by way of evidence, a table (Table 5.1, p.133) which he says illustrates the growing power of states since it shows that state spending as a percentage of GDP has grown since 1960. Yet, what is striking about the table is the evidence it shows that state spending has declined between 1996 and 1999, in some cases quite dramatically (in the Irish case from 37 to 29.9%). On the face of it, this table seems to present worrying evidence to support the case he is arguing against, but this he ignores.

In facing squarely both the issue of sustainability and the question of the social impact of economic growth, O'Hearn's book is by far the best. Drawing on extensive knowledge of the East Asian Tigers, he examines in some detail the differences between their industrial policy and that of Ireland. Instead of depending on foreign direct investment (FDI), he shows that the East Asian Tigers fostered strong indigenous companies through active state involvement. He finds Singapore to be closest to the Irish case since it depended more than the other East Asian Tigers on attracting in FDI (indeed, Padraic White in his account names the Economic Development Board of Singapore as being, together with the IDA, 'one of a small number of national investment-promotion organisations which have been demonstrably successful in promoting foreign investment to the benefit of their country' (p.309)). However, unlike

Ireland O'Hearn finds that the Singaporean state intervenes quite heavily in the economy with government control and directives replacing market price mechanisms in three areas: the labour market, state-owned enterprises and forced private saving (p.28). From this, O'Hearn concludes:

I have considered the present basis of Irish growth to be unsustainable because it depends on a continuous increase in exports by foreign corporations, a factor over which the Irish state has no control, apart from the IDA's ability to attract and hold TNC projects. The IDA has been very successful in this regard during the 1990s, but ultimately will be unable to maintain its success rate as the expanding EU periphery increases competition for foreign investment, as key skills become scarce in Ireland, and as global contractions and shake-outs inevitably hit TNC operations in Ireland. (p. 161).

Instead, he regards the central lesson of the East Asian experience, including that of Singapore, as being that reliance on FDI must be balanced by 'strategic government intervention to help create more sustainable indigenous technological capabilities' (p.161). In the light of O'Hearn's emphasis, it is interesting that Padraic White argues in his book that the IDA must maintain its effort to keep attracting new multinationals to Ireland since 'the nature of industry keeps changing—there is a continuous process of decline in some sectors (for example, textiles and mechanical engineering) and growth in others (software and e-commerce). So we can assume that a fair share of the industries we have today will decline and decay in coming years' (p.313).

The second major issue to which O'Hearn turns his critical scrutiny is the social impact of economic growth. While the picture he paints of growing poverty and inequality accompanying the Celtic Tiger may not be disputed by Sweeney, where O'Hearn clearly parts company is in his argument that Ireland's model of economic growth is a cause of this inequitable social outcome. This is so because he identifies in the Irish success story a rationale 'which pits economic growth *against* social prosperity' (p.165; emphasis in original). Thus, Ireland needs to maintain low corporate taxation to attract in multinationals and adopts a 'hands off' approach to issues like low pay. He concludes: 'Despite the warning signs of increasing inequality and poverty, Irish governments have consciously chosen growth and exclusion over prosperity and inclusion' (p.165). The implication of this is that further economic growth of the Irish kind will only exacerbate social inequality; Sweeney, by contrast, regards further economic growth as holding the best prospect for eliminating poverty.

In addressing the sustainability of the Celtic Tiger, none of the authors of these books addresses its

environmental impact as has been done recently, for example, in the Environmental Protection Agency's millennium report on Ireland's environment. The only mention of these issues, is the brief description given by Padraic White of some conflicts between pharmaceutical companies and local communities on environmental pollution (pp. 277–9). He seems to believe, however, that the setting up of the EPA with its 'strong licensing powers' has resolved the causes that led to these conflicts.

What distinguishes these books, however, is the understanding shown and the assessment made of the wider forces that are shaping our economy and, thus, our livelihoods and social life. Mac Sharry and White's view is limited to advocating a subservient marketled insertion into the global economy with the state shaping Irish society to serve the needs of multinational companies. Sweeney displays a superficial acquaintance with issues such as globalisation and the social impact of economic growth but shows little capacity to examine them thoroughly; he thus

resorts to wishful thinking instead of drawing conclusions from a careful assessment of evidence. O'Hearn, alone among these three books, draws on a fuller and more grounded knowledge of the world order and the enormous challenges it poses for peripheral states interested in achieving benefits not just for élites but for their societies. This leads him to draw more pessimistic conclusions about the prospects for the Irish economy and Irish society. Though, in places, the book gives the impression of assembling evidence to suit a pre-conceived theoretical position, the broad thrust of his conclusions seems to be solidly based. Among these three books, it alone alerts us to the need for more thorough critical examination of this phase of Ireland's development.

PEADAR KIRBY is a lecturer in the School of Communications in Dublin City University. He has recently been awarded a PhD by the London School of Economics for a study entitled 'Growth with Inequality: The International Political Economy of Ireland's Development.'

... *and sparing the workers too*

ROSHEEN CALLENDER

Sharing the Work, Sparing the Planet
Anders Hayden
Zed Books, London, 2000
ISBN 1856498182, £15.95 in UK

This is a very fine book: thought-provoking, fact-filled, useful and readable too! It's about the worldwide movement for Work-Time Reduction—referred to throughout as WTR. Its author, Anders Hayden, is Research and Policy Co-ordinator for 32 Hours: Action for Full Employment in Toronto.

He has done us all a great service by marshalling so much information and analysis about this important topic in just under 200 pages.

Hayden's main thesis is that WTR will help to sustain the environment and increase employment, social justice and the quality of people's lives. He presents various

social, economic, environmental, ecological and gender equality arguments for WTR and is basically urging all of us—men, women, employed, unemployed, unions, governments, environmentalists, ecologists, greens, reds, whatever—to join the world-wide campaign.

Hayden also presents a fascinating account of that campaign and the developments that have been taking place in many countries, including Canada, the United States, Japan, China, South Korea, Brazil, France, Germany, Denmark, the Netherlands and others. What's particularly interesting is that in each country the emphasis, motivation and experience has been quite different.

For example: working hours have been increasing in the US, whereas they have been falling in Japan. France took the statutory route and legislated for a 35 hour week in 1998; whereas in Germany, the trade unions used collective bargaining to reduce working hours, in the face of considerable employer anger; and for them the emphasis was very much on job maintenance and creation. In the Netherlands, which is now probably the industrial country with the shortest average annual working hours (less than 1,400 a year), WTR was achieved both through collective reductions of standard hours and an increase in individualised part-time options; and it was achieved fairly harmoniously, in contrast to the experience in countries like France and Italy.

The Dutch experience is particularly interesting for Ireland not only because WTR has been achieved through social partnership, but also because, along the way, the debate about it has changed significantly. The emphasis has shifted from collective reductions towards greater individual flexibility; and, with unemployment falling, the reasons for WTR have also shifted from job creation to personal choice, quality-of-life and gender equality arguments. And, after many years of women calling for men to work fewer hours on a paid basis—to share the paid work—as well as to share more equally in the unpaid work of the family, household,

community, or society generally, this has actually started to happen. (Well, *some* of it has started to happen … Dutch men are working shorter hours for employers—one in five now works part-time—but Dutch women, like women everywhere, are still doing most of the unpaid household work!)

However, at least in the Netherlands it's becoming 'fashionable' for men to spend more time at home and play a bigger role in raising their children! The Dutch trade unions ran a big campaign in the early 1990s to encourage men to work part-time and these efforts seem to have succeeded in breaking the stigma that's generally attached to male part-time work. In this regard, Hayden quotes a Dutch doctor with three children who, when interviewed about working a 4-day week, was asked if part-time work and less money made him 'less of a man'. 'No', he replied, '*not less of a man, but maybe more human.*'

Hayden also mentions the fact that in 1997, the Dutch Minister for the Economy 'took pains to excuse himself from a parliamentary debate to get home for his daughter's birthday' (a bit of a first, at the time: since then, a Finnish Prime Minister took a week's parental leave and UK Prime Minister, Tony Blair, took a little parental leave on the birth of his son last year). Also, in 1997, the Dutch government introduced a new Career Breaks Bill—similar to some of the paid leave provisions pioneered in Denmark—giving Dutch workers the equivalent of Unemployment Benefit when taking leave for caring or for studying (on condition that the employer consented and hired an unemployed person for the same period).

Another proposal before the Dutch parliament at that time was a 'Work and Care Bill' that included the right to 10-days paid leave for the care of family members. It was

expected to become law by 2000 but Hayden's book went to print in 1999 so we'll have to find out what happened from some other source. As far as I know, we in Ireland have actually beaten the Dutch to it, thereby becoming only the second country in the EU (after Germany) to introduce a statutory right to Carer's Leave. It took effect in October 2000, accompanied by a social welfare payment—Carer's Benefit—for those who meet the Pay-Related Social Insurance requirements; and it gives people the right to take up to 15 months' leave.

Our new Carer's Leave legislation is a real advance, but what relevance does WTR have in general for a country like Ireland today? We currently have one of the highest growth rates in the world. Our income per head is just starting to reach European norms. For the first time, most people are able to get jobs; indeed there are skills shortages in some sectors. But although our working hours are supposed to be reducing, as a result of both collective agreements and national legislation (implementing the EU Working Time Directive), no-one's showing much sign of actually reducing the number of hours worked per week. The national average remains firmly around 40-41; less for women, more for men. British and Irish workers still work among the longest hours in Europe and have the shortest holidays, no payment during parental leave, very short paid maternity leave and no study leave worth speaking of, for most workers. And the one breakthrough, the new paid Carer's Leave legislation—first mooted by former Minister for Social Welfare, Proinsias De Rossa, in 1996, and campaigned for by SIPTU and the ICTU since that time—has barely been noticed by most people, never mind being hailed as progressive or even significant.

Generally speaking, the 'official' reduction to a 39-hour week in Ireland has simply meant more time being paid at overtime rates, rather than less time being worked. Because, of course, the grossly inflated price of necessities such as accommodation, childcare and transport to work has been putting huge pressure on people— particularly young couples—to work longer and longer hours, if they can benefit financially from doing so.

Which, of course, makes the issue of WTR all the more relevant, though not necessarily more popular. What young worker, nowadays, can contemplate WTR—to study, be with children, or elderly relatives, or do something else of particular interest—if they have to pay a mortgage and/or heat their house or flat and/or pay for childcare and/or meet the rising cost of transport to and from their work?

Hayden's book doesn't cover WTR developments in Ireland, which is probably just as well because—apart from the Carer's Leave breakthrough—we wouldn't look too good on any international league table. North-European countries like Denmark, Finland, and the Netherlands are very much the 'leaders' in this field and the information Hayden provides on them, including many interesting quotes and anecdotes, are invaluable to all of us arguing for similar rights here.

For example, since 1994, all workers in Denmark have been able to take educational, parental and sabbatical leaves of up to one year (subject to their employers' agreement) during which they get 100% of unemployment benefit if it's educational leave or 60% if it's parental or sabbatical. This is in addition to fairly generous maternity and paternity leave.

Not content with all this paid time off, Danish workers went on a nation-wide general strike, in spring 1998, for a sixth week's paid holidays. The strike lasted 11 days and ended when each worker was granted an extra two days' leave per year; while those with children under 14 got an additional two days in 1998 and one more in 1999. Of course, there were mixed views about this strike— some labelling the demand for a sixth week's paid holidays as excessive; others seeing it as not only a justifiable attempt to share in Denmark's economic success, but also, as Hayden puts it, 'an enlightened choice of putting time over money as the way to take that share'. Women trade unionists in Denmark were a major force behind the demand for more free time in the 1998 strikes. The KAD—an all-female union with 100,000 members—had wanted to strike for an extra twenty days, not just an extra week! For them, the demand for more free time was 'an absolute priority'.

And for us in Ireland? It's probably true here, as well, that women in the unions have been the main proponents of WTR—indeed, some of us have been on about it for the past 20 years and more, with varying degrees of support, at different times, from our colleagues and friends!

I remember a seminar in 1982, run by the Trade Union Women's Forum in the North Star Hotel in Dublin, on just this topic (and others). WTR featured prominently in my own paper to that seminar, entitled *Time versus Money—the need for re-organisation of work* in which I argued the case for WTR on grounds of 'women's equality … economic efficiency, social necessity and human development in general', elaborating on each of these in turn. In my paper, which was later published by the TUWF as part of a pamphlet *Topical Issues for Women at Work*', I argued that there had to be national legislation, or at least coherent national policy, on

WTR; plus a host of other changes including reforming and greater integration of the tax and welfare systems, legislation to introduce a national minimum wage, an end to discrimination against part-time workers, more childcare facilities, greater working-time flexibility, better leave arrangements, including paid educational leave and restructuring of pension arrangements to suit women and part-time workers better.

Progress on all these fronts has been slow over the past 20 years but just recently there have been spurts of activity—arising partly from EU Directives, partly from collective bargaining and partly from commitments secured by the unions in the context of national agreements—on tax, social welfare and pension reforms, on better rights for part-time workers and on better leave and greater work-time flexibility (if not reduction).

We in Ireland have a long way to go to catch up with countries like Denmark, but at least WTR is firmly on the trade union agenda, in the form of our demands for paid parental leave, longer paid maternity leave and the introduction of paternity leave on a statutory basis; and our current insistence that the two Framework Agreements (on Family-Friendly Policies and Developing Equal Opportunities at the level of the Enterprise) contained in the Programme for Prosperity and Fairness be used effectively by employers and employees to make working hours more flexible and shorter wherever possible.

As regards Hayden's thesis that WTR is about 'Sharing the Work and Saving the Planet': my own view is that it's very much about 'saving the workers' too. Today's workforce in Ireland—men and women alike, are stressed out working long hours to pay for over-priced accommodation, high transport costs and hugely expensive childcare (if indeed they can find any). Working parents, especially, are generally exhausted from juggling the competing demands of work and family life—never mind dreaming about other quality-of-life issues. Of course it makes sense to reduce working hours, but only if everyone does so, or has an equal opportunity to do so, without loss of essential income.

The vital instruments and ingredients now exist in Ireland for squaring the circle and solving the problem: very high labour productivity, a statutory minimum wage, legal limits on working hours, fiscal instruments, welfare policies, anti-poverty strategies and a huge Exchequer surplus. Not forgetting the needs of children, older people, those with disabilities or special needs—who want us to spend time with them, as well as earning enough money to support them and also produce the goods and services that people want and need. We have both the reasons and the resources to make major progress towards a more human and humane working environment. But will we?—that's another day's work!

Meanwhile, Hayden's book should be read, or at least kept as a reference, by everyone who already believes in WTR and everyone who doesn't. It will convert the sceptics and energise, or perhaps re-energise, the converts.

ROSHEEN CALLENDER is an economist who works for SIPTU, Ireland's largest trade union. She has specialised in social policy, pensions, company and employment law and equality issues; and is currently the union's National Equality Secretary. Prior to that, she worked in the union's Research Department from 1973. She was seconded to the Department of Social Welfare between January 1995 to June 1997 to work as Special Advisor to the then Minister for Social Welfare.

IN HIS OWN WORDS... ANDERS HAYDEN

An extract from **Sharing the Work, Sparing the Planet.**

Work-time reduction can be more than a defensive response to the disappearance of jobs. It can be linked, and has been so historically, with a different vision of progress. 'Progress' is by now largely associated with the expansion of GDP and increases in material living standards. At the root of such progress is the continued increase in labour productivity, that is, hourly labour output. While technological advances, more effective forms of work organization, and improvements to worker skill levels will most likely bring continued improvements in productivity, there is no inherent reason why they must also lead to increased production. WTR can instead channel productivity gains towards the non-material benefits of more free time. This argument is perhaps the most significant way in which WTR fits into an ecological vision, standing as it does at the crossroads of a utopian vision and a pragmatic recognition of what is achievable in the not-so-distant future.

This vision combines a sense of both necessity and possibility. According to French Green economist Alain Lipietz, 'Creating a society which gauges progress by the growth of free time more than by the accumulation of wealth is an imperative stemming from responsibility'— that is, the responsibility of sparing the planet from the effects of an indefinite growth of mass consumption. In return for fulfilling this responsibility, the people of the North stand to benefit. If labour productivity continued to rise at a normal rate, and the resulting gains went exclusively towards increased free time rather than increased incomes, it would take only a few short decades to cut the work hours of the 'consumer class' of the North in half.

Breaking out of the 'work and spend' cycle would create abundant time for a wide variety of self-directed activities. (...)

A positive vision of 'working less and living more,' a vision that aims to create 'an advanced lifestyle appropriate for a post-industrial era,' is extremely important for green politics, which has suffered from the general impression that it involves an embrace of Malthusian austerity and dour asceticism. A vision of progress centred on reducing work time gives substance to the green claim that life can be better in a less materialistic society. According to Juliet Schor, 'The centrality of growth in our political and economic culture means that moral or pragmatic environmentally-motivated appeals may not be successful. But, with widespread perceptions of cultural and economic decline; the promise of a higher 'quality of life' may be.'

can democracy deliver ?

JOHN BRUTON TD

The Local Politics of Global Sustainability
Thomas Prugh, Robert Constanza and Herman Daly
Island Press, Washington, 2000
ISBN 1559637447, £14.95 in UK

The problem tackled by this book could not be more fundamental. How best can we organise politics so that economic forces do not propel us towards environmental disaster?

The authors argue that environmentalist tactics such as obstruction and fearmongering do not amount to a strategy. The effect of individual protests wears off quickly. Consumers do not integrate lessons from them into their daily spending and waste-generating activities.

In any event, there is so much scientific uncertainty about environmental and ecological issues that neither environmentalists nor their opponents will ever disprove one another's case conclusively on technical grounds. The issue remains political.

The authors argue that sustainability is primarily a local issue, rather than global one. If everyone acted sustainably at local level, this would look after the global ecosystem. Every human act affects the environment, so every human being should develop habits that are environmentally sensitive.

The authors argue that the global ecosystem is finite and fixed, and that the economy can only grow at the expense of the ecosystem. They argue that almost all economic activity transforms high quality matter (natural products), in low quality wastes which nature must then absorb. Nature's capacity to absorb wastes is now being pushed to, and in some cases well beyond, its limits.

The authors make the very reasonable point that it would be quite impossible for 10 billion people in the world to live the lifestyle of the average American. The average American consumes five times as much grain products and sixty times as much fuel as the average Indian. It does not require much imagination to see what would happen if one billion Indians demanded and got as much grain and fuel products as Americans already have. Americans consume 30 per cent of the world's non-renewable resources, with only 6 per cent of its population.

8 per cent of the world's population has a car. Affluent societies demand more and bigger cars. What on earth would happen if 20 per cent of the world's population had a car?

Status goods are the drivers of modern consumerism. It is not need, but comparison with peers, that makes people buy them. Needs can eventually be satisfied, but demand for status goods is literally insatiable. The authors remark, with justification, that popular environmentalism is a mile wide and an inch deep. We may make gestures to the environment, but we are unwilling to radically alter our lifestyle.

The authors claim that conventional professional politics, as in liberal democracies like Ireland and the United States, is unlikely ever to deliver the lifestyle changes needed to create a sustainable world. It is adversarial, partisan, bureaucratic, dominated by interest groups and run by an élite. Voters act like consumers. They make their voting decisions in an uninvolved way. Politically speaking, they know the price of everything and the value of nothing. As a result, neither voters nor politicians engage with long term issues like sustainability. Observing Irish politics today, it is hard to disagree with this critique.

The authors, to their credit, then attempt to come up with a solution. They argue for what they call 'Strong Democracy'. By this they mean a localised system whereby every citizen would be involved in every political decision. Town meetings, interactive electronic discussions and local referenda would be the preferred means of reaching consensus and a decision. Professional elected public representatives would see their role diminished, and much of their work done by panels of citizens selected by lot.

The authors would argue that a citizenry which was directly involved in difficult political decisions, for example, in deciding on waste disposal options, would learn, through that process, to create less waste in their own daily lives. Strong democracy would make people less selfish.

The authors, having made this reasonable argument, display a great lack of confidence in its practicality. They do not show how nations, or global organisations could be run on the basis of Strong

Democracy. They admit that 'it would be ridiculous' to contemplate a citizen assembly for the whole country'. They even say of their proposal 'whether it would work better than the system now in place, or work at all, is a matter of speculation'. After 123 pages, one would have expected something a bit firmer than this!

In any event, the experience of citizen's assemblies during the French revolution does not suggest that they necessarily take mature or long-sighted decisions. The experience of popular referenda in California and Switzerland shows that they can be captured by vested interests, like property owners and male voters.

My own view is that institutional solutions, like those advanced in this book, will not suffice to give us a sustainable world. Individual consumer decisions need to be directly influenced. A shift of the taxation away from income towards spending would damp down consumerism. This is mentioned in the book, but not developed. Consumer decisions are also influenced by people's value systems. Value systems are shaped by factors outside politics—by secular public morality and by religion.

The Enlightenment of the eighteenth century gave man a misplaced self-confidence—a confident belief in inevitable progress, in free markets, and in the superiority of man-made science over all natural phenomena. The decline of traditional religion flowed from this.

Sustainability requires us to meet the present generation's needs without compromising the ability of future ones to meet theirs. This is a moral, not an institutional issue.

The world is facing an environmental crisis because men and women, as profit maximisers and as consumers, have lost their sense of responsibility to pass on the earth undamaged to great grandchildren. A religious sense, that puts present needs back into proportion with eternal ones, is necessary for us to feel a sense of responsibility to future generations of people we have never met.

That sense of proportion comes from a belief in something outside, and greater, than oneself. That transcendental sense is missing in the modern world, and its absence contributes directly to mindless, environment-destroying, consumerism.

JOHN BRUTON was leader of Fine Gael until February 2001. He first entered the Dáil in 1969 at the age of 22 and became leader of his party in 1990. He was Taoiseach between December 1994 and June 1997.

building the new Jerusalem

CIARÁN CUFFE

London Pathways to the Future—Thinking Differently
John Jopling
Sustainable London Trust, 2000
ISBN 0953768007, £9.99 in UK

Creating enthusiasm for local government is not an easy task. However, John Jopling succeeds in generating interest in the challenges that Mayor Livingstone and the Assembly face in London over the next four years. He sets out the issues and threats that must be addressed, ranging from traffic congestion to air quality and suggests that full citizen participation in the democratic process is necessary in order for London to become a sustainable city. This contrasts with the spin doctoring and manipulation that has characterised many recent political campaigns. He identifies methods of empowering community groups, using a vision-led approach, and ensuring that all stakeholders are involved. He also identifies the opportunity to implement Local Agenda 21 with the re-emergence of a London-wide local authority.

Jopling suggests that an economic strategy that addresses global inequality is required for London, citing the powerful effect of financial decisions emanating from the City. He distinguishes carefully between growth and development, pointing out the pitfalls that lie in wait for those who worship growth as an end in itself. The second part of *Pathways to the Future* addresses the challenges of participatory government. Best practice models such as the city of Curitiba in Brazil are profiled.

This is a seminal resource that should be on the reading list of all those wishing to influence the future direction of their communities. The book is well referenced and an evocative series of colour photographs reinforces the text.

As a city councillor in Dublin, I found the discussion of sustainability and city planning highly useful. Planning systems are outdated in both Britain and Ireland and fail to incorporate sustainability as an integral part of the development system. Tinkering with the existing legislation does not go far enough. What is needed is nothing

less than an entire sea change and re-evaluation of what we wish to achieve.

Jopling's book lays the groundwork for this task. He gives an excellent background to the developments in sustainability since the Earth Summit in Rio, and provides a toolkit of resources that will be of use to those involved in active campaigning. Involving communities directly in the planning process is one of the methods that Jopling advocates. So, having helped inner city communities to

prevent the excesses of high-rise development, I was interested in the way Jopling showed how we can learn from previous mistakes in urban planning and work in partnership to provide sustainable mixed-use development in our towns and cities.

CIARÁN CUFFE is an architect and urban planner. He was first elected to Dublin City Council in 1991 and is the Green Party's Dáil candidate in Dún Laoghaire.

making money, yet growing poor

DAVID O'KELLY

The Post-Corporate World—Life After Capitalism
David C. Korten
Kumarian Press, West Hartford, Conn., 1998
ISBN 1-576750-51-5, $27.95 in US

Those who have read *When Corporations Rule the World* will not need me to introduce David Korten's latest book *The Post Corporate World*. However the title could discourage those who don't have a business or economics background. Don't be misled. This is a very readable book because essentially David Korten is a good story teller. Too often very radical and important books (and this *is* an important book) do not reach the readership they deserve because the reader can be forgotten in the rush to deliver new insights. Not so in this case.

David Korten shares with the reader his own journey of discovery. Reading this book one is intrigued and excited in a way that is rare in non-fiction. The intrigue comes from watching Korten unravel the mystery of how we have been so smart and yet so dumb in the way we have organ-

ised our world. The excitement comes from exploring truths that we instinctively recognise yet are never explored by our homogeneous mass media that feeds us the same diet of pap every day—*globalisation blah blah sustainable growth blah blah competitiveness blah blah new economy blah blah.*

David Korten started life (like many of us) as a firm believer in the values of the Western industrialised world. He was inspired with missionary zeal by his history tutor to forego a business career and instead go out extolling the benefits of *economic development* to our less educated brethren in the 'Third World'.

Having spent over thirty years as a development worker in Africa, Asia and South America he has learned at first hand the true impact of this development process not just in the 'Third World' but

also in western industrialised countries. The relentless pursuit of economic growth at the expense of people and the environment. The confusion between money and real natural wealth and the way it distorts life itself. These were the starting points for Korten's journey.

The book is, however, much more than a simple rant against the forces of globalisation and capitalism. It is a powerful and thoughtful analysis that makes the break with the *mechanistic* view of the earth that dominates western culture and uses the *organic* model for our society that offers many useful examples and lessons for the future.

One of the most powerful of these lessons is the analogy of capitalism as a cancer within the global body. Like cancer cells, capitalism overcomes the body's natural rejection mechanisms by disguising itself as being a normal and integral part of the body. So nobody questions the money system. We accept our money system as being normal when, as Korten explains, it is far from normal, natural or even very effective. The other feature of cancer/capitalism of course is that it ultimately destroys its host.

The book is neatly segmented into four parts. The first part *The Deadly Tale* describes in very clear terms the way we have been seduced by the most powerful communicators in the world into believing the capitalist's story. That money above all else is the defining measure of human ambition and of wealth. Hence the institutions of money take precedence over the truly productive human activities.

Yet as King Midas discovered you can't eat it and you can't use it as a substitute for a loved one. We have been fooled into confusing money with the true wealth of the world such as clean air and water and the mineral and natural resources that have been laid down over aeons of creation.

Yet Korten makes a very clear distinction between the market and capitalism. This is quite refreshing as very often anti-capitalist authors do tend to confuse the two. Korten goes back to the father of modern market theory, Adam Smith, the man most often mis-quoted by Celtic tiger cubs. He discovers that Smith believed that markets, to be efficient and effective, should be based around small, locally-owned enterprises. He would almost certainly not have been in favour of the monopolistic, global mega-corporations that currently control our lives.

The distinction he makes is stark. Capitalism is the use of money for the benefit of those that have money. Healthy markets are life-based and have as their purpose the employment of available

resources to meet the basic needs of humanity.

The second part of the book is titled *Life's Story*. The story is literally the story of life on our planet and it puts our presence into the context of 15 billion years of evolution and charts the development of life on Earth and of the true natural wealth of our planet, mineral deposits and bio-diversity. This a helpful preamble to the development of the organic paradigm that is so useful in exploring how we relate to the world. In the West we have operated on the materialistic, rational model propounded by Descartes and Newton that has dominated our approach to nature, medicine and of course, money.

Korten tells us that we have much to learn from the way that healthy organisms operate. Human society is not a machine. When we try to operate as machines things go badly wrong. When we use the organic model we are much more likely to have healthy relationships and societies. Korten draws a number of lessons from life's wisdom. They are very familiar and will resonate equally with the community worker, the priest, the businessman and the farmer. It is worth quoting them here:

1 Life favours self-organisation
2 Life is frugal and sharing
3 Life depends on inclusive, place-based communities
4 Life rewards co-operation
5 Life depends on boundaries
6 Life banks on diversity, creative individuality and shared learning

The third part of the book is called *Envisioning a Post Corporate World*. The question usually asked of anyone attacking the status quo is 'Well what's the alternative?', the implication being there is none. Korten (if I can use one of his favourite words) is mindful of this fact and he draws a very clear pic-

ture of the alternative. (This will be very useful as many observers already feel that we might need an alternative quite soon if/when the American stock market goes 'pop'.)

Again the organic view of society is developed and shapes Korten's vision of how politics, finance, business and community can and must work in the future. A key factor of this vision is how markets work. Korten talks about the *'Mindful Market'* and how capitalists traditionally escape responsibility for the consequences of their actions. 'So land is poisoned for years to come, so what? So people are thrown out of work and have to emigrate, so what? So we are damaging the global environment, so what? We have only one responsibility, to our shareholders. We cannot afford ethics or morality.'

The capitalist cannot afford morals. That is why it is much easier for large corporations with no physical or emotional ties to people or place to create such havoc and human misery. It is not even efficient by their own standards.

So again drawing on the work of Adam Smith, Korten has formulated a set of rules for mindful markets that could make an excellent mission statement for any business with an eye to the future. Fundamentally these rules are life-based rather than money based. It's amazing how common sense always sounds so obvious when you hear it but then you hear it so rarely. It is a sign of how far we have strayed that books like this are so essential. We have to explain to ourselves that really we are all born with a shareholding in this world and that this should not be denied us.

The fourth and final part of the book is called *Coming Home to Life*. Rather than leaving us angry and helpless Korten gives us a chart for how we must change our way of thinking and our way of being if we are to survive as a species. The process of globalisation is already far advanced and with its inherent instability, somebody needs to be planning for the future. Without giving it all away it won't come as a surprise if I tell you that the architects of the EU, EMU, GATT, NAFTA, WTO and the World Bank would not be charmed.

The mere fact that a book such as this has been written at all may be a sign that we are coming out of the dark age of capitalism. It is

doubtful if such an analysis could have taken place even ten years ago. Frijtof Capra (who is also quoted in the book) would have come closest with his seminal work *Turning Point*.

You certainly don't have to be an economist to read this book but it should be on the curriculum of every economics degree course and every business studies course.

But you should read it. Get it now. It will cheer you up and it might even change your life.

DAVID O'KELLY is a member of the FEASTA committee. He is currently researching the links between the money system and what he describes as 'the many cracks apparent in the fabric of modern society due to unbridled economic growth.' After holding a number of senior management positions in industry, he now works as a management consultant. He has been active in local politics and community development for 30 years and has served as a local councillor. He lives in Co. Wicklow.

restraining the four horsemen

FRANCES HUTCHINSON

The Lugano Report: on Preserving Capitalism in the Twenty-first Century
Susan George
Pluto Press, London, 1999
ISBN 0-745315-32-1, £9.99 in UK

'A brilliant, terrifying book which should be on the bedside table of every policy maker in the West' (Victoria Brittain). Susan George's latest masterpiece represents the culmination of her twenty-five-year battle to document the causes of hunger, famine, debt and structural adjustment. Titles such as *How the Other Half Dies* (1976), *Faith and Credit* (1994), *The Debt Boomerang* (1992) and *Fate Worse than Debt* (1987) have become best sellers. Now *The Lugano Report* presents a message which is at once stark and powerful. If Western 'civilisation' is to continue far into the twenty-first century, global corporations will need to take positive steps to preserve free market capitalism in the light of the disintegrating global environment.

The book is set out in the form of a report commissioned by 'one or two prominent, though informal groups'. Setting aside ethical considerations, the highly paid but

anonymous working party of 'policy intellectuals' identify potential threats to the free-market capitalist system, examine the likely course of the world economy, and make recommendations of strategies necessary to ensure survival of the system. In her conclusion, the author states: '*The Lugano Report* is as accurate, sober and detached an assessment as serious research could make it... Aside from the basic conceit, nothing is made up and I would not be in the least surprised to learn that a similar document has actually been produced by a real-life Working Party.' Thoroughly researched, the Report is presented with clarity and perception.

The facts documented throughout the Report build a picture of rising populations, increasing ecological degradation accompanied by a sharp divergence between the interests of the affluent élites and the vast masses of 'losers' mainly,

but not exclusively in the countries of the South. Although economic growth has heretofore been regarded as a 'good thing', unmanaged growth will give rise to unmanageable pressures on the environment, leading to economic chaos which would impact on rich and poor alike. The Working Party concludes that free-market capitalism can only survive if present population trends are reversed, and the world population is reduced by one third, from its present 6 billion to around 4 billion.

Deliberate mass exterminations would carry negative impacts on the economy and the environment, while being costly and politically unacceptable. The Working Party therefore advocates in meticulous detail the judicious management of naturally occurring 'Population Reduction Strategies' such that losers self-select or appear to be accidental victims of naturally occurring phenomena. Historically, population reduction has occurred through conquest, war, famine and pestilence, represented by the Four Horsemen of the Apocalypse. The scope for building a consensus in favour of population reduction in the basis of ethical, economic, political and psychological strategies using the Four Horsemen is alarmingly realistic.

As George deftly demonstrates, leaders of global corporations and their transnational structures—the World Trade Organisation, European Round Table of Industrialists and the like—have the potential capacity to restrain the power of the Four Horsemen to their own ends. However, in my view it is most improbable that they would use it. They might conceivably limit the force of destruction by conquest, war, famine and pestilence to the 'illiterate, unemployable, superfluous' and 'degenerate' losers. This might be done in order to maximise the numbers of surviving 'winners'. However, the quest to maintain 'business-as-usual' for future generations would necessitate the evolution of a form of corporate altruism hitherto virtually unknown. Short-term self-interest in the thrill of a vast gamble on the world's markets forms an unlikely precondition for development of a mature concern for the future of the wider community and its natural resource base.

This leaves the future in some degree of uncertainty. George's fascinating yet all-too-brief 'Annexe' rehearses the main arguments for taking immediate individual and collective responsibility for reweaving 'the social fabric that neo-liberalism is rending'. Realistically, George advocates withdrawal of economic activities from the transnational orbit to local small business enterprises, but within a national and global framework capable of over-riding the divisions of identity politics based on national, religious, political, gender, class, racial and other differences. At present, these divisions serve to perpetuate a system that is 'a universal machine for ravaging the environment and for producing losers that no one has a clue what to do with', providing excellent fodder for the Four Horsemen. The message emerging from George's excellent work is that the true enemy lies in the myriad divisions created by identity politics. While energies are directed towards single, divisive issues, corporate power remains unrestrained.

The fact remains we are all policy makers. George concludes: 'Left-leaning foundations have in my view shown stupidity bordering on the criminal in not defending—that is, putting money into—progressive ideas. The Working Party understands the importance of creating and using ideology.' Time to abandon the luxury of apportioning blame, in favour of shouldering the burden of collective responsibility.

FRANCES HUTCHINSON is a former secondary schoolteacher who now lectures in economics at Bradford University. She is the author of two books which played an important part in getting the nature of debt-based money into the public domain. These are The Political Economy of Social Credit and Guild Socialism (1997) and What Everybody Really Wants to Know About Money (1998).

here's hoping the corporate reformers will be left behind

NADIA JOHANISOVA

Vanishing Borders
Hilary French
Earthscan, 2000
ISBN 1-853836-93-1, £12.95 in UK

Between 1950 and 1998, world exports of goods increased 17-fold—from $311 billion to $5,400 billion. The number of transnational corporations grew from 7,000 to 53,600 between 1970 and 1998, the number of international refugees went up 16-fold between 1961 and 1998 (from 1.4 million to 22.4 million), and the average cost of a three-minute phone call from New York to London fell from $245 in 1930 to $3 in 1990.

In *Vanishing Borders*, Hilary French, the vice-president of the Washington-based Worldwatch Institute, uses these and other data to imply that globalisation, which she defines as 'a broad process of social transformation' involving growth in trade, investment, travel and communications as well as transboundary pollution and infection, is here to stay. She does not try to analyse how the process came about. Instead she focuses on its impact on natural systems.

As might be expected, this does not make encouraging reading. In chapters devoted to the timber trade, mining, atmospheric pollution, toxic chemicals, agriculture, infectious diseases and biodiversity decline, she gives us very carefully researched and clearly presented information on the often complex environmental and social problems connected with growing international trade and investment, and the movement of people and goods.

The chapter on pesticide trade is especially disturbing. We use fifty times more pesticides than we did fifty years ago, and the types we use now are ten times as toxic as those used then.. Exports of pesticides have risen nearly ninefold since the 1950s. Many shipments to the Third World are of pesticides banned in their country of origin and, on arrival, they are often applied by farm workers with little knowledge of the products' hazards and without any adequate protective gear. According to WHO statistics, the result is that each year 25 million people in the Third World suffer at least one incident of pesticide poisoning and 20,000 of these die.

While the description of the environmental and social impacts of globalisation in *Vanishing Borders* is convincing and well-informed, the passages which describe and suggest solutions to the problems appear curiously pale and superficial. We learn about environmental treaties and green investment funds, emission limits and certification programs, the need for better technology for Third World countries, voluntary agreements between commercial companies, governments and NGOs. Although the author does worry about the fact that the World Trade Organisation (WTO) can strike down certification programmes, national environmental legislation and even international agreements on grounds of 'unfair trade barriers', she suggests only minor changes to both the WTO and the IMF and World Bank. Essentially, she accepts the status quo.

The whole book is permeated by the assumption that globalisation is irreversible and the most promising solution to the problems it causes is a firm world government, aided and supported by enlightened businesspeople and international NGOs. Absent or almost absent from the suggested solutions are the development of local economies, limiting the power of transnational corporations and of advertising, the abolition or radical reform of the World Bank and IMF, the support of local traditions and commons and land reform in the Third World, regulation of economic speculation by the Tobin tax or otherwise, nor yet trying to limit economic growth or international trade itself. The main roots of the problems are thus not addressed, and the author´s position is in a way similar to that of reform Communists in Eastern Europe before the democratic revolutions who knew that many things were going wrong in their countries but wanted to correct them within the framework of the system which had caused them.

Despite such shortcomings, this is a very useful book for anybody who needs to get an overview of the current international environmental situation. It is well-researched and clearly and concisely written in the best tradition of Worldwatch Institute publications. Its target audience is obviously those in power and businesspeople who are interested in the environment but who might find a more radical analysis too threatening. The book will serve such people well. To go back to our analogy: in the Communist era in Eastern Europe, it was this group who started the reforms which then gained their own momentum and left their original protagonists behind.

NADIA JOHANISOVA translated Schumacher's **Small is Beautiful** into Czech. She teaches human ecology at the University of South Bohemia in the Czech Republic and helped found Rosa, an environmental organisation based in Ceske Budejovice.

what happens when the wells run dry?

JAMES BRUGES

Cadillac Desert
Mark Reisner
Pimlico, London, March 2001 (first published in the US in 1986, updated 1993)
ISBN 0-712667-17-2, £14 in UK

Fly over the prairie states of America and you will see clusters of dark circles like tiny coins on the ground far below. Each circle is a field of crops, half a mile in diameter, irrigated by a rotating arm from a single well. In the past the land's thin grass fed wandering herds of buffalo. Now the grain exports from this area are vital for financing America's imports and are a major contributor to feeding the growing world population. The transformation is a miracle of modern agriculture.

Underneath seven states lies the biggest aquifer in the world. It was created when water from melting glaciers seeped into gravel at the end of the last ice age and has been there ever since. It was found in the 1920s but water extraction only really got under way in the 1960s. Four to six feet are now pumped out each year and nature puts back just half an inch. For how long can this go on? It could last five years, it could last thirty, no one knows.

The farmers of the area once believed that the breadbasket they had developed was too valuable for the country to lose and the government would come to their aid when the waters dried up—the government had, after all, provided many massive water projects elsewhere. So they did nothing to economise when 'putting water to good use'. But their hopes are fading. The dust bowl that devastated the area in the 1930s is likely to return.

While Mark Reisner's authoritative book deals with exploitation

of the aquifer, it is largely a detailed history of water projects in the American West. River water that was once lost to the ocean now provides electricity, municipal water for cities and irrigation for agriculture. Desert states like California are habitable only because of these projects. He points out, however, that all but one of the great civilisations of the past which depended on irrigation were ultimately destroyed by salination. Egypt was the sole exception because the Nile's annual flood washed surface salts out to sea— but the Aswan dam has changed that.

No natural water source is entirely pure and if an impervious substrate prevents irrigation water from draining away, the salts it contains will accumulate around the roots of the plants. If, on the other hand, the land is drained, the salts will accumulate in rivers where they are liable to be concentrated by evaporation, especially in dams. This is the reason that the salinity of the Colorado River where it crosses the border into Mexico's most fertile region had become so great by 1973 that it was liquid death to plants and caused an international incident.

80,000 dams were constructed in the US in the twentieth century; so many that there is hardly a free-flowing stretch of river left. 2,000 of them are among the biggest engineering projects in the world. Despite the fact that the dams were built with over-capacity, so that the build-up of silt would not seri-

ously reduce water retention during the first 50 to 100 years; some have already been abandoned. In due course the majority of the rest will have to be abandoned too leaving a country of artificial waterfalls in place of rivers.

The construction achievements in the 'can-do' years from 1940s to 1980s were so great that many Americans came to believe that their technology and enterprise could solve all their problems. Having tapped most of their own water, they seriously considered diverting the Yukon river from Alaska or building a massive lake filling much of Canada's uplands. But Canada was not so keen to lose its salmon and white-water rafting!

This eminently readable book is full of fascinating stories and gives an insight into American politics. The two national organisations responsible for water development repeatedly deceived the public, Congress and the Senate. They ignored presidential directives and they frequently acted outside the law. Congressmen voted for political reasons, not through conviction. Many of their projects had little, or negative, value and provided breathtaking examples of creative accounting.

The consequences were dire: salmon, previously a staple food, has been largely eliminated; some of the worst and most predictable ecological disasters the world has ever seen were perpetrated; sustainable farms were flooded and replaced with unsustainable irrigated areas; minority communities were dispossessed with derisory compensation. The staggering cost of the federal water projects means that US agriculture is subsidised on a massive scale—the richest farmers with the richest farmland are in California and 70% of their profits come from water subsidies. Small farmers (and Third World farmers) are undercut and put out of business.

The book shows how big construction and agribusiness controls Congress, milking the federal budget for centralised projects that would have been the envy of any communist dictatorship to the detriment of social programmes. While reading the history of these two organisations with their blinkered interest in water projects, I kept finding parallels with the powerful world organisations which are similarly allied to commercial interests: the IMF, the WTO and the World Bank. Will their myopic interest in free trade also leave a legacy of crippled agriculture, ecology and culture?

The book is a detailed study of how one country is drifting towards a water crisis. It does not suggest solutions, or analyse the consequences to the world of the loss of one of its main grain-growing areas, or suggest how the most powerful country in the world will react.

Mark Reisner, who died in 2000 aged only 51, researched the story for over a decade. Some parts are difficult for those unfamiliar with the US and its history, and this may be why the book has not been published on this side of the Atlantic before. But the detail only makes the conclusions more alarming. There is currently much talk about climate change but at least the extent of that can possibly be contained by a switch to renewable energy sources. Can anything be done about emptied or poisoned aquifers, about silt-filled dams, or about salt-laden soil?

JAMES BRUGES is an architect living in Bristol where he is concerned with issues of urban sustainability. His Little Earth Book, a wide-ranging guide to the global sustainability crisis and the solutions to it, is reviewed below.

a small book that packs a big punch

MARY-LOU O'KENNEDY

The Little Earth Book
James Bruges
Alastair Sawday Publishing, Bristol, 2000
ISBN 1-901970-23-X, £4.99 in UK

The Little Earth Book is certainly little—it is the size of a CD case—but its message is powerful and very thought provoking. It consists of fifty chapters on as many topics. Each is between two and four pages long and imparts condensed information and an evocative message on an aspect of the environment, the economy or the life sciences. Anyone who wishes to follow up any of these topics can then turn to the rich reference guide.

The early chapters emphasise the importance of approaching sustainability systematically by respecting four key principles:
- We must not extract more toxic minerals from the Earth than can be safely contained or reabsorbed;
- We must not allow any new, stable and persistent molecules we make to increase in nature;
- We must not diminish the world's life-support system by disrupting its natural cycles; and
- We must recognise that all people in the world need the benefits of nature—equally.

These rules of sustainability are set by nature, not by man, the book emphatically states.

The author then presents several chapters each offering startling examples of the damage done to natural systems in the name of economic growth and 'progress'. Again and again the reader is struck by the extent to which human activity has arrogantly and irresponsibly disregarded nature. For example, in the last thirty years human activity has destroyed a third of the planet's natural wealth. The global freshwater fish catch was 45% lower in 1995 than in 1970. Cod are now on the Endangered Species list. Reading these, one is left with a solid understanding of the interconnectedness of our world and, more importantly, of the means of achieving its sustainability.

Westerners cannot but feel shame for the indulgent abuse our system has perpetrated on the global environment and the disastrous consequences that this has had in the form of climate change, pollution, poverty and hunger. The real shame, however, comes from knowing that through organisations like the World Bank, the IMF, the World Trade Organisation and the United Nations we had the power to put things right but chose not to do so.

Little Earth discusses a number of ways in which things could be improved now, such as the cancellation of Third World debt and the control of greenhouse gas emissions by trading in pollution quotas. It also explores proposals developed by economists and activists for reforming economics so that the transition from growth economics to sustainable economics might be made.

Bruges' message about the problems facing the global community is uncompromising. He believes it needs to respond to three threats with unprecedented urgency. These are climate change, genetically modified organisms and persistant

organic pollutants, all of which are discussed by him throughout the book. He keeps the issue of action foremost in one's mind but, although he highlights the need for participative structures and decision-making, many of the actions he discusses have to be taken on a national and international stage. I suggest his next book should explore the positive actions which individuals and communities can involve themselves in to help bring sustainability about.

Bruges believes that scientists have a special responsibility 'to widen their imagination to encompass the interconnectedness of all life' and to 'work out how we can share the world without harm to its other creatures'. However, he calls upon us all to consider how we can achieve 'a stable and sustainable economy for all humanity'.

Little Earth provides a broad, very accessible overview for anyone

seeking to understand current issues concerning ecology, the environment, climate change, world debt, genetic engineering etc. It is an invaluable handbook on questions of sustainability. And, while it frequently makes points with which some people will disagree or argue, it will certainly stimulate readers to react urgently. They can scarcely fail to do so when presented with its snapshots of the many interrelated factors destroying our world at such an alarming rate.

MARY-LOU O'KENNEDY is a member of the Feasta Committee. She is manager of the County Wexford Partnership, a local development company which addresses social exclusion and marginalisation in County Wexford. She is currently working with the Partnership and local community groups to create a 'model' for the development of sustainable rural communities.

modern money, debt slavery and destructive economics

JOSEPH GLYNN

The Grip of Death
Michael Rowbotham
Jon Carpenter Publishing, Oxford, 2000
ISBN 1-897766-40-8, £15 in UK

'Fascinating' ... 'lucid and original' ... 'an essential self-education tool' ... 'well researched' ... 'one of the best'; these are some of the very favourable comments this book has received from people like Herman E. Daly, Richard Douthwaite, Bryan Gould and Ed Mayo. Their views should be enough to persuade anyone interested in creating

a better world that it is essential reading. As David Korten puts it, Rowbotham 'fearlessly reveals deeply disturbing truths about our debt-based money system that befuddle bankers, economists and politicians'.

So don't let the title, the grim cover illustration, the reference to debt-slavery or even the price put

you off. This is a very relevant, well-written and empowering book. Asking your library to obtain a copy would be a service to your local community.

The truths it reveals are at times shocking. It is, for example, frightening to learn the extent to which our collective indebtedness has grown in recent years. The book also explodes more than a few widely accepted myths and it is not just a powerful indictment of bankers, economists and the money system. *The Grip of Death* may well be the best book ever written on how we can move towards a money system for a sustainable and inclusive world.

First, Rowbotham shows the reader how our present type of money is created; almost entirely by private banks and other lending institutions. Although the power to issue, manage and control the supply of something so vital to us all as money should be under democratic or government control, unfortunately it's not.

In the UK for example, 1997 Bank of England statistics show that the total amount of money created by the Treasury on behalf of the UK government is a mere £25 billion in notes and coins. Banks and building societies created the remaining £655 billion—that is, 97% of all money in use in the UK— by lending it into existence in the form of mortgages, personal loans and overdrafts. Consequently, borrowed money makes up almost the entire UK money stock. The same is true elsewhere. In the US well over 90% of the money supply has been lent into existence.

Traditionally, the amount of money banks could create and lend into circulation was controlled by governments setting liquidity and reserve/asset ratios for the institutions to meet. By the 1980s, however, the liquidity ratio had become functionally meaningless because, as Rowbotham explains, the banking system had found ways around it by investing in short-term government securities.

The reserve/asset ratio governed the amount of their own money banks were required to set aside as a standby in case large numbers of depositors wanted to withdraw all their money simultaneously. A reserve/asset ratio of 10% meant that if a bank made a loan of £10,000,000 it must have £1,000,000 of its own capital in cash or on deposit in the central bank to back it. This ratio has since been replaced by the capital adequacy ratio, which also links a bank's lending to the amount of its own capital it has. It is set at around 8% by international agreement. However, instead of being an effective restriction on banking and money creation, Rowbotham shows in practice it helps perpetuate the problem of escalating debt and forced growth.

Rowbotham contends that conventional banking theory and these supposed restraints allow economists to present the institutionalised usury of the system as something that operates under control. He shows emphatically that these controls are inadequate.

In regard to the ownership of money, bankers and economists claim that it is created as a 'service to the borrower'. Like the myth that banks are merely lending out their depositor's money, this suggestion is false. Rowbotham shows that bankers create money for themselves, because as borrowers repay the loans which created the money initially, their payments are accounted as assets of the bank.

On monetary policy, the author shows that raising interest rates, the economist's standard response to inflation, certainly works but in much the same way as a lump-hammer works to carve a chicken! Higher rates do curtail new borrowing, but previous borrowers suffer too by having to pay extra interest. As a result, debt escalates, businesses go bankrupt, homes are repossessed and millions of workers are laid off as the economy sinks into recession or worse.

The term mortgage refers to the medieval 'death pledge', a form of borrowing where the owner pledges his house to another 'until death'. This form of usury was forbidden under Christian law. The book's title derives from that term and the evidence Rowbotham outlines justifies his use of the equally grim term, 'debt slavery'. The distinguishing characteristic of a slave he argues is not that he is badly treated. Rather, it is that he has no say over important aspects of his life.

The statistics presented on British and American mortgage borrowing are indeed shocking. He reports that in 1996 the total value of the UK housing stock was approximately £1100 billion, against which mortgages totalling £409 billion (i.e.; 37%) were registered. In the US in 1997, a massive $4.2 trillion, (i.e. around IR£3500 billion) was outstanding on mortgages, including, 48% of the value of the all US residential property.

Rising indebtedness has also been highlighted by some of the contrarian market analysts in recent years. One of them, Robert Prechter, estimated the total debt registered against US citizens, companies and agencies was close to $20 trillion. Some say that if US citizens stopped buying what they cannot afford, their economy would collapse.

Rowbotham illustrates clearly the central role played by bank credit in economic life and how debt-based money is at the root of destructive economic trends. He shows why most people, businesses and governments get so heavily into debt. Exploring the broader impact of debt-finance he shows how it engenders a pronounced bias toward unsustainable growth.

By analysing money in action, the flows and tensions, he enables the reader to see the role and responsibility of the financial system for the nature of modern growth. Forced economic growth is shown to derive from intense competition for money, lack of purchasing power and near total wage dependency. He thus demolishes the suggestion that growth is responsive to the aggregate desires of people either as consumers or workers. His analysis is revealing and complements Herman Daly's perspective on decadent growth and Douthwaite's 'Growth Illusion' which he shows, 'enriches the few, impoverishes the many and endangers the planet.'

It is not consumers, but the debt-based financial system which makes a techno-marvel, disposable, wasteful, junk-product 'consumer' economy inevitable, he states. The consumer is 'completely subordinated to the process.' Industry and consumers are also completely subservient to the regular booms and slumps of the business cycle which he contends is entirely monetary in origin, shape and effect.

Historically both the landed and financial aristocracies have wielded formidable power but Rowbotham does not acknowledge the central role of inequitable land distribution in determining socioeconomic evolution. Land still provides the collateral for the largest portion of lending and neither aristocracy could have succeeded or prospered to the same extent without the partnership of the other. He could perhaps have included landlessness, homelessness and housing / rent inflation among the factors contributing to forced economic growth.

Although the role of land and property speculation is omitted from his explanation of the boom-bust cycle, his analysis is full of insights and does not seem incompatible with this reviewer's neo-Georgist viewpoint. Land/property

owners and banks each benefit greatly from the rampant land price inflation and spatial squeeze so characteristic of the 'boom' economy. It was Winston Churchill who described land as the greatest monopoly, a perennial monopoly and the mother of all other monopolies.

Rowbotham's exposé of the debt-based financial system offers us original and valuable perspectives upon agriculture, centralisation, export trade and the competitive inefficiency of food distribution. He argues that the financial system so dominated agriculture and food production that it forced them to supply people with what they expressly do not want. Transport has become a competitive device which he shows has led to futile waste.

However, the most appalling effects of our debt-based financial system are, he contends, felt in the Third World. The success of the multinationals he attributes not to their efficiency but to the conditions, advantages and pressures created by the debt-based financial system. Countries are locked in trade warfare, desperate to secure the export revenues to service loans which Rowbotham insists are of a fraudulent nature; 'The full horror and iniquity of Third World debt is that the under-developed and indebted countries of the world are acting as part of the money supply to developed nations'. He shows how this money is created as debt registered to impoverished nations but bound up in the economies of the wealthy nations.

Rowbotham talks about disarming the financial system, about the 'temporary tigers' and the manipulated consensus. He considers in detail the suppressed alternatives put forward by Abraham Lin-

coln, C.H. Douglas and others. Lincoln's *Monetary Policy*, a literary gem, is included in full. Thus Rowbotham covers the background in detail before outlining his prescription.

In the final chapters Rowbotham shows that the opportunity for evolutionary, as opposed to revolutionary change, is within reach. He outlines a 'spectrum of opportunity' available through the creation and phased introduction of government-issued debt-free money. This 'compensating money supply' is part of a cautious and realistic strategy of reform. Its key objective, it would appear, is to attempt to find the right balance between a stable debt-free money supply and a useful level of bank credit. He provides an outline and statistics on how this strategy could be implemented over two decades in the UK.

The author concludes by stressing that monetary reform is not primarily a technical matter but a political one. He shows convincingly that bank-produced money is neither a neutral nor accurate medium and that money should be created instead by governments answerable to their peoples to whom the right to issue money properly belongs.

This is an excellent book and a catalyst for public debate on money and debt-finance. Rowbotham has done us all a service. This is a book which deserves a very wide readership.

JOE GLYNN is a market research consultant and land tax advocate. He campaigned actively with Raymond Crotty in defence of Ireland's sovereignty in the 1980s. He later became active within the Green Party and now works with Earthwatch—Friends of the Earth Ireland.

different monies bring different results

LOTHAR LÜKEN

The Ecology of Money
Richard Douthwaite
Green Books, Devon, 1999
ISBN 1-870098-81-1, £5 in UK

'... *due to the way money is put into circulation, we have an economic system that needs to grow or inflate constantly. This is a major cause of our system's continuous and insatiable need for economic growth, a need that must be satisfied regardless of whether the growth is proving beneficial.*'

Money makes the world go round—but in a downward spiral it would appear. Poor countries are bled dry while banks can 'create' more money out of nothing. Life savings are devoured by inflation while speculators 'earn' billions. Whole regions are thrown into decline while multinationals shift plants around the globe in a real time game of 'Monopoly'. All this is facilitated through our monetary system.

"Then it's agreed. Until the dollar firms up, we let the clamshell float."

Drawing by Ed Fisher, © 1971, The New Yorker Magazine, Inc., reproduced in **The Ecology of Money**.

But: 'There are, potentially at least, many different types of money, and each type can affect the economy, human society and the natural environment in a different way.' So says Richard Douthwaite in his book *The Ecology of Money*. It came out as No. 4 in the new series of 'Schumacher Briefings'—and that's what it does: briefs us on where money comes from, where it goes and what it does on its way.

'Certainly, if we wish to live more ecologically, it would make sense to adopt monetary systems that make it easier for us to do so.' It is the purpose of the book to explore these alternatives. After looking into the pros and cons of money produced by banks or states or people, Douthwaite arrives at a system of four different currencies for four different purposes: a LETS-type system for local trading; national/regional exchange currencies; 'store of value' currencies for savings; and *ebcus* (energy-backed currency units) as the international currency. This sounds complicated—and it is. But the 'Briefing' goes a long way to explain it—and anyway 'Readers should not feel that they need to understand every paragraph completely before moving on...'

Interesting to note is maybe how Richard's enthusiasm for LETS systems is a bit more muted here, compared to his 1996 book *Short Circuit*. The 'Celtic Tiger' has lowered the importance of local safety nets—for the time being... The emphasis here is more on the international system and 'ebcus' based on SERs (Special Emission Rights for CO_2)—this would link the value of money to something tangible, the release of greenhouse gases, and thus help to meet one of humankind's biggest ecological challenges. This idea (first aired in Ireland by Douthwaite in *Earthwatch* issue no. 43) seems to be gaining momentum now.

Of particular interest for Irish readers will be the special two pages on Gerry McGarry's 'Roma' local currency-system that operates in Ballyhaunis—with the participation of 92 of the 95 local traders. It isn't just all theory—it's happening! But whatever the details— *The Ecology of Money* will show you that it is not just *how much* money we've got but maybe more so *what kind* of money.

LOTHAR LÜKEN is editor of **Earthwatch magazine** where this review first appeared. He lives in West Cork.

196

FEASTA *review* 1

an intriguing suggestion… but would it work?

DAVID CRONIN

Creating New Money: a Monetary Reform for the Information Age
Joseph Huber and James Robertson
New Economics Foundation, 2000
ISBN 1-899407-29-4, £7.95 in UK

In this new book, Joseph Huber and James Robertson propose a significant reform of the monetary system as it now exists. At present, there are two issuers of money in the economy. One is the central bank, which issues notes and coin (or 'cash'), and the other is the commercial banking sector which creates deposits (or what the authors call 'non-cash' money). Huber and Robertson's proposal essentially is for the central bank alone to become the sole supplier of both forms of money.

Their proposal would effect a radical reordering of the monetary system. As they see it, the key benefit of this reform is that it will recapture seigniorage (or the profits of money issue) from commercial banks and provide an additional source of funds to government for using either to increase public expenditure or to reduce tax rates. They also argue (pp.41–2) that their seigniorage reform proposal will have environmental benefits by removing the creation of new money as debt that is seen as a contributory factor to unsustainable development (as argued in greater detail by Douthwaite in *The Ecology of Money*).

Huber and Robertson's proposal is a stimulating and intriguing one. The study of money is arguably the most difficult area of economics, in what to many is already a complex, even esoteric, subject. Yet, because Huber and Robertson's basic proposal is a straightforward one (that by restricting the issue of both cash money and non-cash money to central banks, monetary and economic performance can be improved), they have written a book that is accessible to those with little background but an interest in economics, without compromising on the need to outline and defend rigorously their proposals to an economist audience. The latter group will be particularly glad that the authors anchor their proposal on its ability to minimise inflation and to provide viable media of exchange and stores of value.

Could the 'plain money' proposal, as the authors term it, succeed today or in the future? Having noted the authors' promotion of the scheme as a monetary reform for the Information Age, my reaction to this particularly important question is to query whether it would succeed in the Information Age. It may not do so because the Information Age is delivering technologies that make control and regulation of money markets difficult (just as it is proving difficult to regulate other related areas, such as the Internet).

Because the 'plain money' proposal appears to rely heavily on government control of media of exchange issue, the very nature of technological developments at this time may make such monetary control (or any other form of centralised control) increasingly difficult. (See, for example, F.X. Browne and David Cronin, 'Payments Technologies, Financial Innovation, and Laissez-Faire Banking: A Further Discussion of the Issues', in J.A. Dorn (ed.) *The Future of Money in the Information Age*, Cato Institute, Washington D.C., 1997). At the same time, it may be that this new electronic technology, by allowing rates of interest to be paid on money issue that equate with the interest earned by commercial banks on their loans, can in itself succeed in minimising or effectively eliminating seigniorage within the economy.

Recognising that all publications ultimately represent work- or thought-in-progress, this may provide an interesting next avenue for Huber and Robertson to carry their research forward. In the meantime, they are to be complemented for providing a detailed monetary reform proposal and for engaging in a policy debate that is likely to become of greater importance to academics and policy-makers alike.

DAVID CRONIN is an economist with an interest in the impact of technological developments on money and finance. The views expressed in this review are his own responsibility. He lives in Dublin.

from individualistic to social economics

BEN WHELAN

Economics for the Common Good
Mark A. Lutz
Routledge, London, 1998
ISBN 0-415143-13-6, £18.99 in UK

What do Gandhi, Herman Daly and the author of *Small is Beautiful*, E.F. Schumacher, have in common? All three tried (or in Daly's case, is trying) to move economic thought away from the dehumanised, mathematical, and amoral stance that has formed the basis of conventional economics since the Industrial Revolution. They are consequently qualified to be called social or humanistic economists, the terms now used to describe thinkers who place human—and more recently environmental—welfare at the centre of their discipline.

The main problem with conventional economics is that it has an abstracted version of humanity, *Homo Oekonomicus*, or Rational Economic Man, at its heart. J.S. Mill contrived this creature in the belief that it was human nature always to prefer more wealth to less. While Mill himself was aware of the limitations of his abstraction, he promoted it in an effort to provide a theoretical basis for a science of political economy. Today this greedy, self-seeking creature has become the unquestioned 'truth' that has led to many of today's social and environmental problems.

Real-life situations never conform exactly to Mill's simplifying assumptions. As the desire for more wealth clearly does not define our every action, the humanist critique of modern economics includes the assertion that 'what is economically rational is often socially or morally unreasonable'. In all aspects of life we face choices

that could lead to many different outcomes. It is exactly this human choice that is ignored in economic rationality, which is only about satisfying self-interest.

In *Economics for the Common Good*, Mark Lutz traces the history of social economic thought over the past two hundred years. He sees his work as an 'introduction to economics in terms of human rather than material welfare in the light of community decay and inequality'. Throughout the book Lutz makes the case for a 'broader more sensitive economic science' that goes beyond the paradigm that produced conventional economics.

The ideas that support conventional economics were developed at a time when the industrial revolution had increased the availability of mass-produce goods. A presumption developed that the machine revolution would release humanity from its dependence on nature and allow rational economic man to fulfil his endless desire for increased wealth. However a Swiss economist, Jean Sismondi, was unconvinced and questioned the assumptions underlying present-day economics at the time they were being laid down.

Sismondi travelled to industrialising England and was not impressed: 'I have seen production increasing whilst enjoyments were diminishing...I sought for happiness in every class, and could nowhere find it'. He was particularly aware of the impact that machinery had on job availability and workplace conditions. He

noticed that when more money was available to business, jobs ended up being lost as the companies replaced their workers with machines. This ran contrary to the traditional stance that said increased income would increase wages and job numbers.

It was clear to Sismondi that the preoccupation of economics with wealth had blinded it to its implications for society and the natural world. He saw that the economics that was emerging would perpetuate the unequal division of wealth and lead to a poor standard of living for many people. He therefore favoured an economics that measured its success against what was happening to real people, rather than in terms of monetary accumulation. 'We lose ourselves whenever we attempt to consider wealth abstractly' he wrote. 'Wealth is a modification of the state of Man: it is only by referring it to man that we can form a clear idea of it.'

Lutz says that the real indicators of prosperity should not be 'exclusively related to the fulfilment of preferences' as the 'common good' is often in conflict with individual desires. The ultimate aim of social economics is, he says, 'to lay down principles of economic policy to guide the policy maker in ascertaining what is conducive to social welfare and what is not.'

Sismondi's legacy is evident in the work of John Ruskin who in turn inspired Gandhi. Although not an economist, Ruskin saw that the economic system had degraded society's aesthetic sensibilities. He held that the working class were forced, through a system that contained no value judgements and was practically amoral, to ignore any hope of reaching above their designation as 'covetous machines'.

Gandhi read Ruskin's book *Unto this Last* while he was in South Africa. It cast a 'magic spell' over him and changed the course of his life. He became committed to putting Ruskin's principles into practice. Lutz points out that, following Ruskin, 'Gandhi saw economics as meaningful only if it pursued the right end: an economic system providing the basic necessities while incorporating the social values of human dignity, non-violence and creative labour.' His goal was therefore to create viable local economies free from dependence on the machine and factory system of the industrialised world.

More recently, the problem of environmental sustainability has begun to preoccupy social economists such as Herman Daly and E.F. Schumacher and has led to the formation of groups such as Feasta. Daly has sought to get his discipline to see that the economy is a subset of the natural ecosystem and that its expansion is threatening to overwhelm the ecosystem's ability to regenerate the resources we use and to absorb the wastes we produce, Daly proposes that 'the path of economic progress must shift from growth (quantitative expansion) to development (qualitative improvement)'. Schumacher also warned of environmental depletion and, like Gandhi, emphasised the need for appropriate technology, village economies and an ethical economics as a way to restore people to their position as the point of the economic system and 'not merely a factor in production'.

Today the good work done by the social economists needs to be expanded and deepened into a deeply ecological economics and Lutz cites the familiar portents of environmental collapse in order to renew our commitment to the task. A respectful, caring attitude is needed toward the Earth if it is to flourish. We must avoid the trap of preserving only those things known to be beneficial to man. Here lies real danger, as our limited knowledge of ecological systems seen through selfish human-centred lenses is the biggest threat to biodiversity and therefore sustainability.

Lutz realises that there are both moral and natural limits to growth. He says that 'clearly social justice and ecological sustainability are two sides of the same coin' and that we have a duty to social fairness to maintain the planet's liveability. Standard economics tries to avoid the ecological dimension by believing that if something gets scarce, a substitute can be found for it. This is the 'myth of substitutability' and is without foundation as Herman Daly has shown. We can't ignore the diminishment of nature just because we have a lot of machines and factories. Manmade capital cannot be substituted for natural capital. They are complementary—both are needed for the production of goods.

Besides tracing the intellectual line of development of humanistic economics from Sismondi to E.F. Schumacher, Lutz presents it as a real alternative to mainstream economics. Moreover, throughout the book he exposes the various pseudo-religions within economics, such as those of efficiency and unregulated international competition. He clearly reveals the flaws inherent in individualistic economics and offers solutions to current global problems through the eyes of the social economists.

Even though the book is quite dense it is not heavy going. *Economics for the Common Good* works as both an introduction to economics in general and as a specialist study in social economics providing both general and academic readership with much to think about. It paves the way for social economic thought to become an important force in the ever-shortening race to save the planet.

BEN WHELAN is a member of the Feasta Committee. He studied Theology in Trinity College Dublin and took an MA at the Naropa Institute in California studying Sustainability, Economics, Cosmology, Mystical Religion and Indigenous Wisdom with Stuart Cowan and Matthew Fox. After returning to Ireland he worked as assistant editor for the Sustainable Ireland Source Book 2000 and helped found the Sustainable Ireland Co-operative which organises the annual Convergence Festival in Dublin. He writes on permaculture, bioregionalism, altered states of consciousness, Maya cosmology and ancient mathematics.

the world according to George Soros

DAVID C. KORTEN

Open Society: Reforming Global Capitlism
George Soros
Little, Brown & Company, London, 2000
ISBN 0316855-98-7, £12.99 in UK

No man can serve two masters: for either he will hate the one, and love the other; or else he will hold to the one, and despise the other. Ye cannot serve God and Mammon.   Matthew 6:24

George Soros, high-stakes financial speculator, international philanthropist, and a man of grand contradictions, tells us in his final paragraph of *Open Society: Reforming Global Capitalism,* that writing it clarified his thinking on his plan for the world and led him to a clear sense of mission for his foundation network. He closes with an ominous sentence.

I shall not spell it [the mission for his foundation network] out here because it would interfere with my flexibility in carrying it out—there is a parallel here with the problem of making public pronouncements when I was actively engaged in making money—but I can state it in general terms: to foster the civil society component of the Open Society Alliance.

This is pure Soros: Soros writing a book about Soros and his secret plan to create a global open society. It befits the outsized ego of the man who in an interview for a 1995 *New Yorker* profile reflected on the parallels between himself and the God of the Old Testament and observed that as a child he thought of himself as superhuman.

Open Society, a revised edition of his earlier *The Crisis of Global Capitalism: Open Society Endangered,* is its own contradiction. After presenting a devastating critique of capitalism sure to beguile progres-

sives and infuriate market fundamentalists, it concludes that global capitalism is the best of all possible worlds and sets forth a programme of 'reforms' that on close reading are little more than a call to give yet more money and power to the stewards of global capitalism—the World Trade Organisation (WTO), the International Monetary Fund (IMF), and the World Bank.

There are three reasons to read *Open Society.* The first is for the penetrating Soros critique of capitalism. The second is for insights into the limited worldview of those who live in the world of high finance. The third is to understand why we must be sceptical of the public pretensions of persons of means who profess to serve two masters.

The critique Although the insights of the Soros critique of global capitalism are scarcely new, they are rarely articulated with such candour and accuracy by those who have so mastered its ways for personal gain. The following is a sampling of Soros' insights.

1 Unregulated financial markets are inherently unstable Soros observes that, contrary to conventional economic theory, financial markets are not driven toward a relatively stable and rational price by the objective value assessment of such things as the soundness of a company's management, products, or record of profitability. Rather they are constantly driven away from equilibrium by the momentum of self-fulfilling expectations—a rising stock price attracts buyers who

further raise the price—to the point of collapse. The recent massive inflation and subsequent collapse in the price of the shares of unprofitable dot-com companies illustrates Soros' point.

Bank lending also contributes to the instability, because the price of real and financial assets is set in part by their collateral value. The higher their market price rises the larger the loans banks are willing to make to their buyers to bid up prices. When the bubble bursts, the value of the assets plummets below the amount of the money borrowed against them. This forces banks to call their loans and cut back on the lending, which depresses asset prices and dries up the money supply. The economy then tanks—until credit worthiness is restored and a new boom phase begins

2 Financial markets render irrelevant the morality of their participants According to Soros there is no meaningful place for individual moral behaviour in the context of financial markets, because such behaviour has no consequence other than to reduce the financial return to the ethical actor.

When I bought shares in Lockheed and Northrop after the managements were indicted for bribery, I helped sustain the price of their stocks. When I sold sterling short in 1992, the Bank of England was on the other side of my transactions, and I was in effect taking money out of the pockets of

British taxpayers. But if I had tried to take social consequences into account, it would have thrown off my risk-reward calculation, and my profits would have been reduced.

Soros argues that if he had not bought Lockheed and Northrop, then somebody else would have, and Britain would have devalued sterling no matter what he did. 'Bringing my social conscience into the decision-making process would make no difference in the real world; but it may adversely affect my own results.' One can challenge the Soros claim that such behaviour is amoral rather than immoral, but his basic argument is accurate. His understanding that it is futile to look to individual morality as the solution to the excesses of financial markets is all too accurate.

3 Corporate employees are duty-bound to serve only corporate financial interests Soros writes:

Publicly owned companies are single-purpose organisations— their purpose is to make money. The tougher the competition, the less they can afford to deviate. Those in charge may be well-intentioned and upright citizens, but their room for manoeuvre is strictly circumscribed by the position they occupy. They are duty-bound to uphold the interests of the company. If they think that cigarettes are unhealthy or that fostering civil war to obtain mining concessions is unconscionable, they ought to quit their jobs. Their place will be taken by people who are willing to carry on.

Though not specifically mentioned by Soros, this is why corporations are properly excluded from the political processes by which societies define their goals and the rules of the marketplace. They are incapable of distinguishing between private corporate interests and broader public interests.

4 The fact that a strategy or policy produces economic returns in the short-term does not mean the long-term results will be beneficial The focus of financial markets is on short-term individual gain to the exclusion of both social and longer-term consequences. The fact that particular policies and strategies are effective in producing short-term financial returns does not mean they are more generally beneficial or desirable. Soros offers the example that running up a budget or trade deficit 'feels good while it lasts, but there can be hell to pay later.'

5 The relationship between the centre and the periphery of the capitalist system is profoundly unequal The powerful countries at the centre of the capitalist system are both wealthier and more stable than countries at the periphery because control of the financial system and ownership of productive assets allows them to shape economic and political affairs to their benefit. 'Foreign ownership of capital deprives peripheral countries of autonomy and often hinders the development of democratic institutions. The international flow of capital is subject to catastrophic interruptions.' In times of uncertainty financial capital tends to return to its country of origin, thus depriving countries at the periphery of the financial liquidity necessary to the function of monetised economies. 'The centre's most important feature is that it controls its own economic policies and holds in its hands the economic destinies of periphery countries.'

6. In the capitalist system financial values tend to displace social values in sectors where this is destructive of important public interests. Soros writes:

Monetary values have usurped the role of intrinsic values, and markets have come to dominate spheres of existence where they do not properly belong. Law and medicine, politics, education, science, the arts, even personal relations—achievements or qualities that ought to be valued for their own sake are converted into monetary terms; they are judged by the money they fetch rather than their intrinsic value.

Because financial 'capital is free to go where most rewarded,' countries vie to attract and retain capital, and if they are to succeed they must give precedence to the requirements of international capital over other social objectives.

The Limitations The Soros critique would seem to establish an iron-clad case for the conclusion—widely shared among the civil-society groups protesting the forces of corporate globalisation—that each nation must maintain its essential economic sovereignty by regulating the flow of goods and money across its borders and that market forces must be subordinated to the democratically determined rules of a strong public sector. Soros' world view and personal interests are, however, much too aligned with the status quo to accept the logical outcome of his own argument.

My critique of the global capitalist system falls under two main headings. One concerns the defects of the market mechanism, primarily the instabilities built into international financial markets. The other concerns the deficiencies of the non-market sector, primarily the failure of politics at the national and international levels. The deficiencies of the non-market sector far outweigh the defects of the market mechanism.

In his focus on financial markets, Soros scarcely mentions the real economy of goods and services, people and nature. Nor does he make more than passing reference to human rights, democracy, equity, and the environment—all of which are obvious victims of the corporate global economy. As to poverty and economic justice, Soros tells us, 'I am altogether leery of so-called social and economic freedoms and the corresponding human rights: freedom from hunger or the rights to a square meal' because rights must be enforced by the state and this 'would give the state too big a role in the economy.'

In a rare mention of the poor, Soros suggests their needs are best left to the charity of the rich: 'We must recognise that under global capitalism individual states have limited capacity to look after the welfare of their citizens, yet it behoves the rich to come to the aid of the poor.' His only mention of the possibility of a less extreme form of capitalism that might value a more equitable distribution of income and ownership is to categorically reject it.

> Social justice emphatically does not mean equality, because that would take us right back to communism. I prefer the Rawlsian concept of social justice, which holds that an increase in total wealth must also bring some benefit to the most disadvantaged. What 'some' means has to be defined by each society for itself, and the definition is liable to vary over time.

Soros has no great quarrel with democracy in moderation, but warns us to beware of the unruly masses. He fears, for example, that if the General Assembly of the United Nations were turned into an effective legislative body, 'we might just have an overdose of democracy, with every NGO breaking down the doors with legislative proposals. International civil society is capable of great achievements such as the ban on

land mines, but with the help of the Internet it could become too much of a good thing. We have all seen what happened at the WTO meeting in Seattle.' The self-appointed, self-righteous billionaire with a secret plan for the world goes on to tell us that he is 'rather leery of self-appointed, self-righteous NGOs.'

The limits of the Soros worldview were especially evident in his testimony of 13 April 1994 before the Banking Committee of the US House of Representatives. He explained to committee members that when a speculator bets that a price will rise and it falls instead, he is forced to protect himself by selling—which accelerates the price drop and increases market volatility. 'No great harm is done,' he told the Committee, 'except perhaps higher volatility,' unless everyone rushes to sell at the same time and a discontinuity is created, meaning that a speculator who has to sell can find no buyers and consequently may suffer 'catastrophic losses.'

When Soros says, 'No great harm is done,' he means there is no threat to the integrity of the system and the losses of the speculators who created the crisis fall within acceptable limits. The millions of people whose lives and livelihoods are disrupted by the machinations of the global financial casino in which they have no say simply aren't on his screen.

Soros takes no note of the fact that from an elite perspective, the genius of finance capitalism is its ability to manage the money system in a way that maintains a sharp distinction between those who live by their labour and those who live by money—keeping money scarce for the former while allowing the latter to create it in abundance through the interaction of debt pyramids and financial bubbles. The result is an inexorable transfer of control over the

real wealth of society from the many whose labour produces the goods and services by which we all live, to the financial elites who make only money. Enough money trickles down to the working classes in times of economic boom to create the illusion that new wealth is being enjoyed by all. Behind the illusion, however, there is a darker reality of growing inequality and the depletion of real wealth. Either Soros has not seen through to the reality behind the illusion or he chooses to ignore it.

The Contradictions Soros professes his allegiance to two masters: maximising private profit in his market dealings and the public good in his philanthropy. Indeed, he asserts as a guiding principle that, 'People should separate their role as market participant from their role as political participant. As market participants, people ought to pursue their individual self-interests; as participants in the political process, they ought to be guided by the public interest.' It's a tidy bifurcation, but begs the question of whether it is possible for either individuals or society to sustain such a division between private greed and public citizenship.

Consider what it means in the specific case of George Soros, who at one and the same time is investing hundreds of millions of dollars for his private profit in the countries of Eastern Europe and spending still more hundreds of millions through his foundations in those same countries to shape their economic and political policies in the public interest. One marvels at the discipline that would be required to compartmentalise these interests in one's daily dealings. When Soros meets with political leaders, including heads of state, how are they to know whether they are dealing with the private Soros or the public Soros? Can even Soros be clear which he is representing in any given encounter? When Soros The Beneficent finds himself pitted against Soros The Greedy, whose side is Soros the Arbiter most likely to favour?

The Soros reform agenda reveals the deep conflicts. Most of Chapter 10, 'A New Global Financial Architecture,' is devoted to spelling out the myriad reasons why governments of countries at the periphery of the global economy best serve their citizens by regulating financial markets, foreign investors, and economic borders. Yet Soros concludes that 'the instability of the international financial system has no architectural solution at present; it is more a challenge for day-to-day management' and declares capital controls, the obvious step to curtail instability, to be 'beggar-thy-neighbour policies that could disrupt the global capitalist system.'

Soros the Benevolent has confronted Soros the Greedy and Soros the Greedy wins hands down. Soros the Arbiter proceeds to settle for a no-reform strengthen-the-status-quo 'solution' that calls for the three stewards of global capitalism—the IMF, the World Bank, and the WTO—to keep markets open to foreign predators, keep the periphery in debt (but not too much debt), and step in when the system falters with generous bailouts for those who made bad bets.

The Soros treatment of democracy is similarly conflicted. He properly acknowledges that 'Open society cannot be designed from first principles: It must be created by the people who live in it.' Yet his proposal for creating open society centres on a proposed alliance of the world's most powerful states acting under the tutelage of the United States to impose on other states an unspecified set of open society principles. This sounds distressingly similar to the undemocratic, top-down process by which an alliance of the United States,

the European Union, Canada, and Japan under the leadership of the United States acts through the IMF, World Bank, and WTO to dictate the principles of open markets to the rest of the world. In the end, the main difference between the 'open society' of George Soros and the 'open markets' of the market fundamentalists who Soros criticises is that the former includes just enough space for self-criticism and error correction to prevent the self-destruction of capitalism's powerful mechanisms of wealth extraction and concentration.

Quoting the famous dictum of Cardinal Richelieu that 'states have no principles, only interests,' Soros concludes that his plan for open society can succeed only with the strong support of civil society. 'If citizens have principles, they can impose them on their governments. That is why I advocate an alliance of democratic states: It would have the active engagement of civil society to ensure that governments remain true to the principles of that alliance.' The Soros plan thus calls for civil society to impose the principles of open society on powerful states that will in turn impose them on weaker states.

It is here that Soros reveals the most fundamental contradiction of his plan—and the reason civil-society groups must be wary when the beguiling billionaire comes calling with chequebook in hand.

As the recent demonstrations in Seattle and Washington have shown, civil society can be mobilised in opposition to international institutions; a way must be found to mobilise it in their favour. While civil society is an important part of open society, the common good cannot be left solely in their care. We need public institutions to protect the public interests. The

WTO is such an institution; it would be a pity to destroy it.

The thrust of the secret plan for civil society Soros intends to implement through his network of foundations is thus revealed: to mobilise civil society in support of the institutions that to date it has valiantly opposed (even in the face of massive police violence and brutality) as elitist, undemocratic, and a threat to the health of people, community, and planet. Putting it bluntly, Soros plans to buy civil society. The chutzpah of this undertaking is exceeded only by its grand contradiction. Soros needs civil society because it is motivated by principle, not money. To buy civil society, Soros would first have to destroy the dedication to principle that makes it an essential element of his plan.

In his conclusion Soros tells us, 'I have learned a lot from other people's criticism, and I can continue to do so after the book is published.' I thus commend to him the biblical instruction that 'No man [nor woman] can serve two masters.' At any given point in our lifetime we each make our choice as to whether we will devote our life to the practice of public citizenship or the pursuit of private greed. George Soros now faces such a choice. If he proceeds with his plan to use his money and influence to realign civil society behind the institutions of greed and his personal financial interests he has made one choice. He could yet, however, make a choice for citizenship by heeding his own critique—which is consistent with that of civil society—and mobilise his foundations in support of civil society's self-defined mission to align the institutions and values of the economy with the interests of life.

This review was originally published in *Tikkun* magazine, a bimonthly Jewish critique of politics, culture and society. www.tikkun.org

LIST OF ABBREVIATIONS

AER	Alternative Energy Requirement
AO	Approved Organisation
C&C	Contraction and Convergence
CEO	Chief Executive Officer
CER	Commission for Electricity Regulation
CHP	Combined Heat and Power
CI	Citizen's Income
DSL	Development Studies Lecturer
DSP	Dominant Social Paradigm
DTQs	domestic tradeable quotas
ebcus	emissions-backed currency units
EPA	Environmental Protection Agency
EU	European Union
FDI	foreign direct investment
GATT	General Agreement on Tariffs and Trade
GDP	Gross Domestic Product
GNP	Gross National Product. The difference between GDP and GNP is that GDP measures the total incomes generated in a country, while GNP measures the incomes accruing to nationals of the country, whether people or firms.
IA	Issuing Agency
ICTU	Irish Congress of Trades Unions
IDA	Industrial Development Authority
IEA	International Energy Agency
IMF	International Monetary Fund
IPCC	Intergovernmental Panel on Climate Change
LETS	local exchange trading scheme

MAI	Multilateral Agreement on Investment
MEW	Measure of Economic Welfare
MIT	Massachusetts Institute of Technology
MW	majority world
MW	megawatts
NAFTA	North American Free Trade Agreement
NEP	New Environmental Paradigm
NGO	non-governmental organisation
OECD	Organisation for Economic Cooperation and Development. A body set up to promote economic growth and international trade made up of the 29 leading industrialised countries.
OPEC	Organisation of Petroleum Exporting Countries
PSRI	Pay Related Social Insurance
SERs	special emission rights
SIPTU	Services, Industrial and Professional Trades Union.
TNC	trans-national corporation
TUWF	Trades Union Women's Forum
UNDP	United Nations Development Programme
USAID	United States Agency for International Development.
USGS	United States Geological Survey
WTO	World Trade Organisation
WTR	work-time reduction
YPE	Yield per unit of energy. Often used to compare energy input with energy output.